UK Biodiversity Group

Tranche 2 Action Plans

Invertebrates

THE RT HON JOHN PRESCOTT MP
DEPUTY PRIME MINISTER AND SECRETARY OF STATE FOR THE ENVIRONMENT, TRANSPORT AND THE REGIONS

Dear Deputy Prime Minister,

BIODIVERSITY ACTION PLANS

I am writing to you in my capacity as Chairman of the United Kingdom Biodiversity Group (UKBG) about the latest group of biodiversity action plans which UKBG have completed and published in the present volume. The volume contains 103 species action plans (all for invertebrates) and a technical introduction by the Chairman of the editing group which drafted the plans, highlighting some of the conservation issues.

Also included are 28 species statements. For some of these species, monitoring is required to confirm whether there is any significant decline in their populations. For others, which have not been recorded for over 10 years, search is the only current action possible and action plans will need to be prepared if new populations are discovered.

This is the fourth volume in the Tranche 2 Action Plan series, and follows hard on the heels of the third which was published ten days ago. We expect to produce two more volumes this year, one containing the action plans for the remaining terrestrial priority habitats and species, including further invertebrates, the other covering coastal and marine priority habitats and species.

As ever, these action plans have been produced through the hard work of Government departments and agencies, voluntary conservation groups, land managers and academic institutions to set challenging but achievable targets to conserve and enhance these species. As in earlier volumes, these new species action plans are accompanied by a list of lead partners (often a NGO) who will take the lead in their implementation, supported by a contact point (always a Government agency or department). We are still looking for lead partners for some of the action plans.

The new action plans are accompanied by a table showing their indicative costings, so that those charged with implementation are clear about the scale of the financial consequences. As the phase of plan preparation draws to a close, UKBG will focus more sharply both on action plan implementation and the degree to which targets and objectives are actually being achieved.

I am confident that those most concerned with implementing the plans will work enthusiastically for their success. But, in many cases, such success requires reconsideration of wider policy, and consequent changes to programmes and practice too. A notable example is the Common Agricultural Policy which has not been helpful for wider biodiversity objectives. It is welcome to the Group that the Government's policy is to seek reform of the CAP and that its agri-environment schemes take account of biodiversity priorities.

But in the UK also, Government and its Agencies, and other sectors too, will need to take a hard look at their policies and practices to see how they might operate in a more biodiversity-friendly way. Often, this requires not that particular activities should cease but that they should be planned and undertaken in such a way as to take account of existing reservoirs of biodiversity, with a view to conserving and enhancing them. The growing number of local biodiversity action plans and the information they contain should make it rather easier for existing biodiversity resources to be identified and opportunities for their enhancement to be grasped.

On behalf of UKBG, I commend to you and your ministerial colleagues the action plans set out in this volume.

Sophia Lambert

SOPHIA LAMBERT

Contents

1. Introduction to the invertebrates

1.1 With more than 30,000 species of terrestrial and freshwater invertebrates in the UK there are inevitably exceptions to any generalisations regarding their life history. Nonetheless, many species share common factors in their life history that make them particularly vulnerable to the changes in land use that have prevailed in the latter half of the twentieth century. Four aspects are especially important:

1. most invertebrates have an annual life cycle and require their specific habitat conditions to be present each year;

2. the ecological niches occupied by invertebrates can be highly specialised;

3. many insect species require different conditions for each stage of their life cycle (egg, larva, pupa, adult); and

4. many species have limited powers of dispersal.

1.2 Changes in the physical structure of habitats, for example through an increase in grazing, can be catastrophic to invertebrate populations, leading to local extinctions if nearby refugia are not available. Invertebrates are dependent on continuity of management within range of colonisation if they are to sustain populations in the medium to long term. These detrimental changes may even be more subtle, such as the loss of flowerheads through untimely cutting, and may affect relatively small areas of a particular habitat that may be of crucial importance to certain species. As semi-natural habitats, especially in the lowlands, become more and more fragmented the possibility of species colonising adjacent patches becomes increasingly less likely. For our more specialised species the result is a steady loss of populations at a national scale, heralding concerns about eventual extinction.

1.3 The greatest threats to invertebrate populations in the UK come from habitat mis-management or loss and increasing fragmentation of habitats. Often these threats arise from ignorance of the significance of particular features (or combinations of features) within habitats. Nature conservation can address these problems by (1) sympathetic habitat management, (2) a greater awareness of the vulnerability of invertebrate populations, and (3) by sharing knowledge on the locations of vulnerable species and their ecological requirements.

1.4 These three elements are at the heart of practically all of the Species Action Plans contained within this volume and their instigation would go a long way towards ensuring that the biological objectives are achieved. However, it is also true that knowledge about the status, distribution and ecology of many species is imperfect. This is inevitable given the vast number of invertebrate species and the relative paucity of specialists and enthusiasts. Very few invertebrate species have been the subject of detailed studies in the UK and the starting point for most plans is to undertake surveys to establish status and to carry out research to identify ecological requirements. In some cases, particularly with regard to species considered to be endemic, there is uncertainty over taxonomic status. This is an area of research that must be given greater attention if we are to be fully aware of the contribution the UK can make to global biodiversity.

1.5 For many species it was considered that it was premature to be dogmatic about specific actions before survey and research has been completed. In these cases actions have been proposed that are commensurate with our level of knowledge of the species. It is proposed that lead partners/steering groups will refine (by agreement with all key agencies involved) individual actions necessary to achieve the plan objectives once sufficient information is available. However, where species have been subjected to autecological research (especially in the case of Species Recovery programmes, etc), more detailed and specific actions have been included. Of course, action should not be deferred indefinitely until autecological studies have been completed. In most cases habitat management can be implemented using basic principles that address the four key aspects of life history discussed above. To account for this, target dates assigned to actions have frequently been staggered to reflect stages of implementation in line with the accumulation of knowledge.

1.6 For a proportion of species, reintroductions are proposed as a possible means of increasing the number of UK populations or of restoring historic range. Few invertebrate species have been the subject of reintroduction attempts and hence there is little experience to build on for restoration of former populations. Without autecological research to inform establishment projects, failure rates are likely to be high and therefore reintroductions have only been proposed for species where there would appear to be a reasonable chance of success. In such cases reintroduction attempts should follow the IUCN (1995) guidelines on translocations of species, particularly with respect to preparatory studies, the selection of donor stock of suitable genetic and ecological characteristics, screening for pathogens and parasites, post-release habitat management and monitoring, and the publication of results. All translocations should be approved and co-ordinated at national level by the relevant lead partner/steering group to maximise the chances of success.

1.7 As a final point, it should be made clear that to improve our understanding of population dynamics, of species' distributions and their ecological requirements, the collecting of all but a handful of conspicuous and readily-identified invertebrates is a necessary and important activity. Collecting is perceived to be a threat to a very small number of species, most of which are already covered by inclusion on Schedule 5 of the Wildlife & Countryside Act 1981. Therefore, actions to consider legal protection for species rarely feature in these plans.

Priority Species Action Plans and Species Statements

Coleoptera

Agabus brunneus (a diving beetle) Action Plan

1. Current status

1.1 *Agabus brunneus* is a beetle of shallow, sometimes intermittent, lowland streams, often occurring deep in the gravel. Last instar larvae have been noted in Britain in January and March, indicating that eggs are laid in the autumn, with the larvae overwintering. Early spring breeding of adults is, however, possible in the climatically favoured, southern coastal sites. Extensive tests using specimens from the Pyrenees have demonstrated that this species is unable to fly.

1.2 In the UK this species is confined to two areas, one in west Cornwall and one centred on the New Forest, but extending to south Wiltshire. Since 1970 *Agabus brunneus* has been recorded from 3 ten km squares in west Cornwall and in four squares in the New Forest and Dorset heath area. Most recent records are for the Charnon River in 1991 and Portreath in 1997 (west Cornwall), Linford Brook in 1997 and Widden Bottom in 1998 (the New Forest), and a stream near Wool (Dorset) in 1998. Thus it continues to occupy the two areas of its British distribution, but in both it is confined to a small number of sites. A recent survey of 26 streams in the New Forest revealed its presence in only one site. *Agabus brunneus* is centred on the Mediterranean, reaching northern Europe in southern England and Belgium. The type form, which occurs in Britain, has recently been recognised as part of a species complex, the other member (or members) coexisting with it in the Mediterranean area.

1.3 In Great Britain this species is classified as *Vulnerable*.

2. Current factors causing loss or decline

2.1 Water abstraction.

2.2 Damage to headwater drainage systems, particularly associated with tourist development and road improvement.

2.3 Agricultural improvement in occupied catchments, resulting in altered run-off and eutrophication.

2.4 Reduced grazing resulting in scrub encroachment and shading of streams.

3. Current action

3.1 A survey of the status of *Agabus brunneus*, commissioned by EN, has recently been completed.

3.2 An unpublished action plan has been written for EN.

3.3 Genetic studies are being undertaken by the University of Plymouth.

3.4 The New Forest is a candidate SAC.

4. Action plan objectives and targets

4.1 Maintain viable populations within each of the catchments currently occupied.

4.2 Ensure that viable populations are maintained at a minimum of five sites by 2010.

5. Proposed action with lead agencies

A survey of all known and extant historic sites has recently been undertaken, supported by EN and the Balfour-Browne Club. This survey should be followed up by monitoring of key sites in order to evaluate year-on-year variation in populations and in order to confirm the life-cycle strategy of this species in England.

5.1 Policy and legislation

5.1.1 Where appropriate, include the requirements of the species when preparing or revising prescriptions for agri-environment schemes. (ACTION: EN, MAFF)

5.1.2 Undertake a review of water abstraction policies within areas where the species occurs. (ACTION: EA)

5.1.3 Address the requirements of this species in the LEAP process and in relevant WLMPs. (ACTION: EA, IDBs, LAs, MAFF)

5.2 Site safeguard and management

5.2.1 Where possible, ensure that all occupied habitat is appropriately managed by 2008. (ACTION: EA, EN, FE)

5.2.2 Ensure that the habitat requirements of *A. brunneus* are taken into account in any development policies, plans and proposals likely to affect headwater drainage systems. (ACTION: EN, Heritage Department, Highways Agency, LAs)

5.2.3 Ensure that the species is included in site management documents for all relevant SSSIs. (ACTION: EN)

5.2.4 Consider notifying as SSSIs sites holding key populations of the species where this is necessary to secure their long-term protection and appropriate management. (ACTION: EN)

5.3 Species management and protection

5.3.1 Consider the need for reintroductions/ reinforcements to ensure the maintenance of five viable populations, with at least one in each of the catchments currently occupied. Undertake through translocations of native stock, if considered appropriate and feasible. (ACTION: EN)

5.4 Advisory

5.4.1 Advise landowners and managers of the presence of this species and the importance of beneficial management for its conservation. (ACTION: EN)

5.5 Future research and monitoring

5.5.1 Establish a regular monitoring programme at key sites. (ACTION: EN)

5.5.2 Conduct targeted autecological research to inform habitat management. (ACTION: EN)

5.5.3 If necessary, undertake genetic studies to inform a reintroduction programme. (ACTION: EN)

5.5.4 Pass information gathered during survey and monitoring of this species to a central database for incorporation in national and international databases. (ACTION: EN)

5.6 Communications and publicity

5.6.1 Promote opportunities for the appreciation of the species, and the conservation issues associated with its habitat. This should be achieved through articles within appropriate journals, as well as by a publicity leaflet. (ACTION: EN)

5.6.2 Encourage research on the ecology and conservation of this species on an international level, and use the experience gained towards its conservation in the UK. (ACTION: EN, JNCC)

5.7 Links with other action plans

5.7.1 Implementation of this action plan could benefit other species of lowland streams, including the freshwater crayfish *Austropotamobius pallipes*.

5.7.2 This plan should be considered in conjunction with that for lowland heathland.

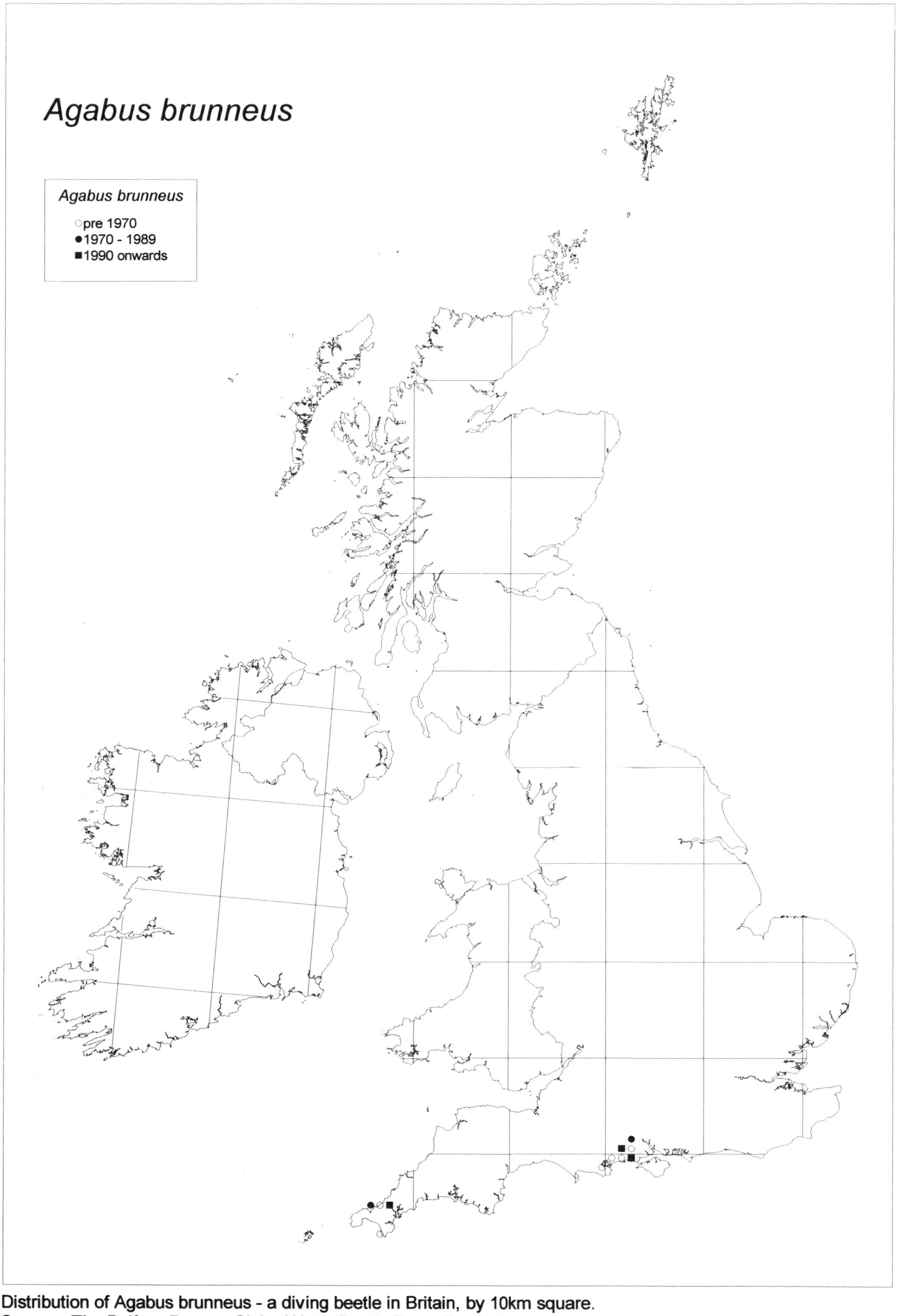

Distribution of Agabus brunneus - a diving beetle in Britain, by 10km square.
Source: The Balfour-Browne Club - Water Beetle Recording Scheme.

Amara famelica (a ground beetle) Action Plan

1. Current status

1.1 *Amara famelica* is found on open sandy or gravelly heaths. It usually lives near water in such habitats, on open, flat, partly vegetated sites. *Amara famelica* has an annual life cycle. It breeds in the spring, with summer larvae, and pupates before overwintering as an adult, probably in tussocks and litter. It is probably carnivorous as an adult, but seed-feeding in the larval stage. It is fully winged, but flight has not actually been observed. Species of the genus *Amara* can be difficult to identify; *A. famelica* is most likely to be confused with *A. aenea*, *A. spreta* and *A. lunicollis*.

1.2 *Amara famelica* has occurred widely in southern and eastern England from Yorkshire to Cornwall, but since 1970 has been found only on Strensall Common in Yorkshire and Ashdown Forest in Sussex, where single examples have been found at both sites. It is at the western limit of its range in Britain. In Europe it extends east through Russia to Siberia.

1.3 In Great Britain this species is now classified as *Rare*.

2. Current factors causing loss or decline

2.1 Loss of heathland.

2.2 Inappropriate heathland management.

2.3 Scrub encroachment

3. Current action

3.1 Both extant sites are SSSIs.

4. Action plan objectives and targets

4.1 Maintain populations at all known sites.

4.2 Enhance population size at known sites by 2010.

4.3 Ensure the establishment and maintenance of five viable populations in suitable sites within the historic range by 2010.

5. Proposed action with lead agencies

The processes required to deliver the above objectives involve maintaining or increasing the amount of suitably managed wet heathland habitat within the species' historic range, possibly with reintroduction of the species to sites within this range. These actions should be accompanied by surveys, population monitoring and autecological studies.

5.1 Policy and legislation

5.1.1 Where appropriate, include the requirements of the species when preparing or revising agri-environment schemes. (ACTION: EN, MAFF)

5.2 Site safeguard and management

5.2.1 Where possible, ensure that all occupied habitat is appropriately managed by 2008, including the provision of south-facing patches of bare ground and damp hollows. (ACTION: EN, LAs, MoD)

5.2.2 Where possible, increase the available habitat at known sites and adjacent areas. (ACTION: EN, LAs, MoD)

5.3 Species management and protection

5.3.1 Consider reintroducing *Amara famelica* to a series of sites within the former range, if necessary to establish five viable populations by 2010. (ACTION: EN)

5.4 Advisory

5.4.1 Advise landowners and managers of the presence of this species and the importance of beneficial management for its conservation. (ACTION: EN)

5.5 Future research and monitoring

5.5.1 Undertake surveys to determine the status of the species. (ACTION: EN, LAs, MoD)

5.5.2 Conduct targeted autecological research to inform habitat management. (ACTION: EN)

5.5.3 Establish a regular monitoring programme for the species. (ACTION: EN, MoD, LAs)

5.5.4 Pass information gathered during survey and monitoring of this species to a central database for incorporation into national and international databases. (ACTION: EN, LAs, MoD)

5.6 Communications and publicity

5.6.1 Promote opportunities for the appreciation of the species and the conservation issues associated with wet heathland. This should be achieved through articles within appropriate journals, as well as by a publicity leaflet. (ACTION: EN).

5.7 Links with other action plans

5.7.1 Implementation of this action plan could benefit other species of lowland heaths, including *Bombylius minor, Chrysotoxum octomaculatum, Thyridanthrax fenestratus, Cicindela sylvatica, Pterostichus kugelanni,* and *Harpalus froelichi.*

5.7.2 This plan should be considered in conjunction with that for lowland heathland.

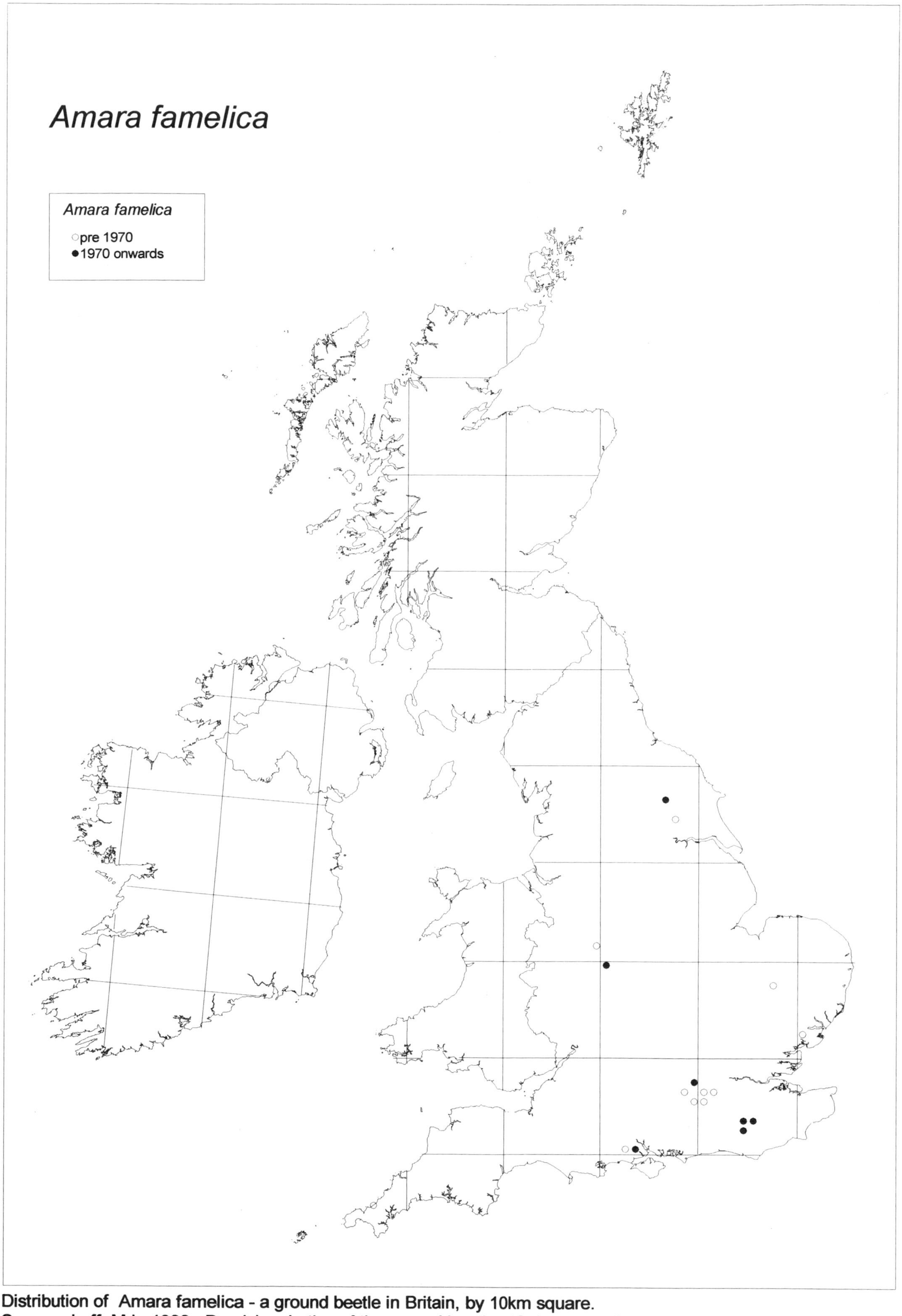

Distribution of Amara famelica - a ground beetle in Britain, by 10km square.
Source: Luff, M.L. 1998. Provisional atlas of the ground beetles (Coleoptera: Carabidae) of Britain, Biological Records Centre (ITE), English Nature - Invertebrate Site Register and R. Key - Coloepterist, March 1999.

Anisodactylus poeciloides (a ground beetle) Action Plan

1. Current status

1.1 *Anisodactylus poeciloides* is found in coastal saltmarshes, saltpans and at the edge of brackish ditches in coastal grazing marsh. It has an annual life cycle and breeds in the spring, with summer larvae, and pupates before overwintering as an adult, probably in tussocks and other locally slightly elevated shelter. Both larvae and adults are probably mainly seed feeders. *Anisodactylus poeciloides* is winged and is presumably able to disperse by flight.

1.2 During this century, *Anisodactylus poeciloides* has occurred along the southern English coast from Cornwall to Essex, but since 1970 it has been recorded from only four sites in Kent (Higham Marshes, Murston, Kingsferry, Sheerness) and one in Sussex (near Camber). In Europe it is found on the coasts of western Europe from Germany to northern Spain, as well as at inland saline localities in south-east Europe.

1.3 In Great Britain this species is classified as *Rare*.

2. Current factors causing loss or decline

2.1 Loss of coastal saltmarshes to urban, industrial or recreational developments.

2.2 Coastal erosion, or construction of sea walls to prevent erosion.

2.3 Intensive grazing of coastal brackish grasslands.

3. Current action

3.1 All extant Kent sites, except Sheerness, are SSSIs within a Ramsar and SPA site.

4. Action plan objectives and targets

4.1 Maintain populations at all known sites.

4.2 Enhance populations at known sites by 2010.

4.3 Restore populations to five suitable sites within the historic range by 2010.

5. Proposed action with lead agencies

The priorities for this species are appropriate management and restoration of saltmarsh habitat within the its historic range, together with reintroduction of the species to sites within this range. These actions will need to be underpinned by surveys, population monitoring and autecological studies.

5.1 Policy and legislation

5.1.1 Where appropriate, include the requirements of the species when preparing or revising prescriptions for agri-environment schemes. (ACTION: EN, MAFF)

5.1.2 Address the requirements of this species in the LEAP process and in relevant Shoreline Management Plans. (ACTION: EA, EN, LAs, MAFF)

5.2 Site safeguard and management

5.2.1 Where possible, ensure that all occupied habitat is appropriately managed by 2008, including the reduction of grazing levels on saltmarshes. This may be through SSSI or agri-environment scheme management agreements. (ACTION: EN, MAFF)

5.2.2 Ensure that the habitat requirements of *Anisodactylus poeciloides* are taken into account in relevant development policies, plans and proposals. (ACTION: EN, LAs)

5.2.3 Encourage the creation of suitable saltmarsh habitat by managed retreat where possible. (ACTION: EA, EN, MAFF)

5.2.4 Ensure that the species is included in site management documents for all relevant SSSIs. (ACTION: EN)

5.3 Species management and protection

5.3.1 Reintroduce *Anisodactylus poeciloides* to a series of sites within the former range in order to establish five new viable populations. (ACTION: EN)

5.4 Advisory

5.4.1 Advise landowners and managers of the presence of the species and the importance of beneficial management for its conservation. (ACTION: EN)

5.5 Future research and monitoring

5.5.1 Undertake surveys to determine the status of the species. (ACTION: EN)

5.5.2 Conduct targeted autecological research to inform habitat management. (ACTION: EN)

5.5.3 Establish a regular monitoring programme for the species. (ACTION: EN)

5.5.4 Pass information gathered during survey and monitoring of this species to a central database

for incorporation into national and international databases. (ACTION: EN)

5.6 Communications and publicity

5.6.1 Promote opportunities for the appreciation of the species, and the conservation issues associated with saltmarsh. This should be achieved through articles within appropriate journals, as well as by a publicity leaflet. (ACTION: EN)

5.7 Links with other action plans

5.7.1 This action plan should be considered in conjunction with those for coastal saltmarsh, coastal sand dunes, and coastal and floodplain grazing marsh.

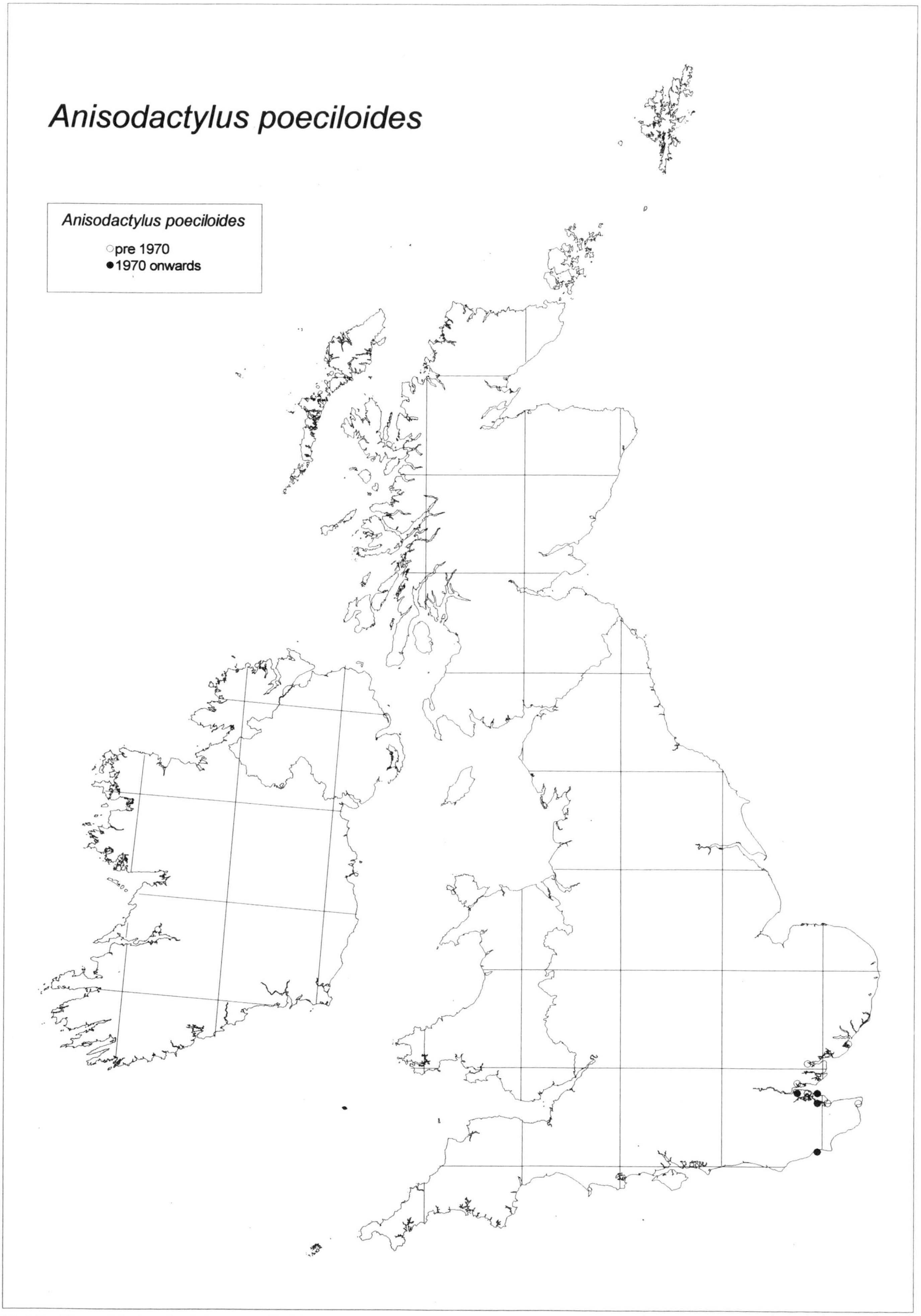

Distribution of Anisodactylus poeciloides - a ground beetle in Britain, by 10km square.
Source: Luff, M.L. 1998. Provisional atlas of the ground beetles (Coleoptera, Carabidae) of Britain, Biological Records Centre (ITE).

Anostirus castaneus (a click beetle) Action Plan

1. Current status

1.1 *Anostirus castaneus* is a click beetle characteristically occurring on expanses of open ground, often maintained by disturbance, with a sheltered, sunny situation and free-draining, usually sandy soils. Larvae live in the soil and are largely predatory, although they also eat the roots of various plants. Pupation is normally in late summer, with the adults developing in autumn but remaining within the pupal cell over the winter. Adults emerge in warm weather in the following spring, usually in late April or in May. Males fly freely in the sunshine, but females are more often found under clods of earth or crawling over the ground.

1.2 *Anostirus castaneus* used to be widely distributed but very local in Britain, with 19th century records from the Isle of Wight, Wye Valley/Forest of Dean, Norfolk, mid-west Yorkshire and Northumberland. There is a single old record from Wales. Over the past 15 years it has been recorded from just two localities, Luccombe Chine on the Isle of Wight and Birk Crag, near Harrogate in Yorkshire. The main period of decline appears to have been during the first half of this century, probably due to loss of habitat to forestry or development. *Anostirus castaneus* is found widely in central and northern Europe (eg France, northern Italy, Germany, Denmark, Norway), east to Siberia, but is usually very localised.

1.3 In Great Britain this species is classified as *Endangered*.

2. Current factors causing loss or decline

2.1 Not known.

3. Current action

3.1 None known.

4. Action plan objectives and targets

4.1 Maintain populations at all known sites.

4.2 Enhance populations at all known sites by 2010.

4.3 Ensure the establishment and maintenance of a minimum of six viable populations within the historic range by 2010.

5. Proposed action with lead agencies

Meeting the objectives of this plan depend at first on implementing beneficial habitat management at the known sites. A survey of all historic sites for the species, to determine current distribution and status and to identify suitable habitat for possible reintroductions, is a priority, combined with autecological studies and population monitoring.

5.1 Policy and legislation

5.1.1 None proposed.

5.2 Site safeguard and management

5.2.1 Where possible, ensure that all occupied habitat is appropriately managed, including the creation of areas of bare ground, by 2008. This may be through site management agreements. (ACTION: EN, Harrogate Borough Council)

5.2.2 Ensure that the habitat requirements of the species are taken into account in relevant development policies, plans and proposals. (ACTION: EN, LAs)

5.2.3 Consider notifying as SSSIs sites holding key populations of the species where this is necessary to secure their long-term protection and appropriate management. (ACTION: EN)

5.3 Species management and protection

5.3.1 Consider the need for reintroductions/ reinforcements to ensure the establishment and maintenance of six viable populations. Undertake through translocations of native stock, if considered appropriate and feasible. (ACTION: CCW, EN)

5.4 Advisory

5.4.1 Advise landowners and managers of the presence of this species and the importance of beneficial management for its conservation. (ACTION: EN)

5.5 Future research and monitoring

5.5.1 Undertake surveys to determine the status of this species. (ACTION: CCW, EN)

5.5.2 Conduct targeted autecological research to elucidate the causes of decline and inform habitat management. (ACTION: EN)

5.5.3 Establish a regular monitoring programme for the species. (ACTION: EN)

5.5.4 Pass information gathered during survey and monitoring of this species to a central database

for incorporation in national and international databases. (ACTION: CCW, EN)

5.6 Communications and publicity

5.6.1 Promote opportunities for the appreciation of the species and the conservation issues associated with its habitat. This should be achieved through articles within appropriate journals, as well as by a publicity leaflet. (ACTION: EN)

5.7 Links with other action plans

5.7.1 This action plan should be considered in conjunction with that for maritime cliffs and slopes.

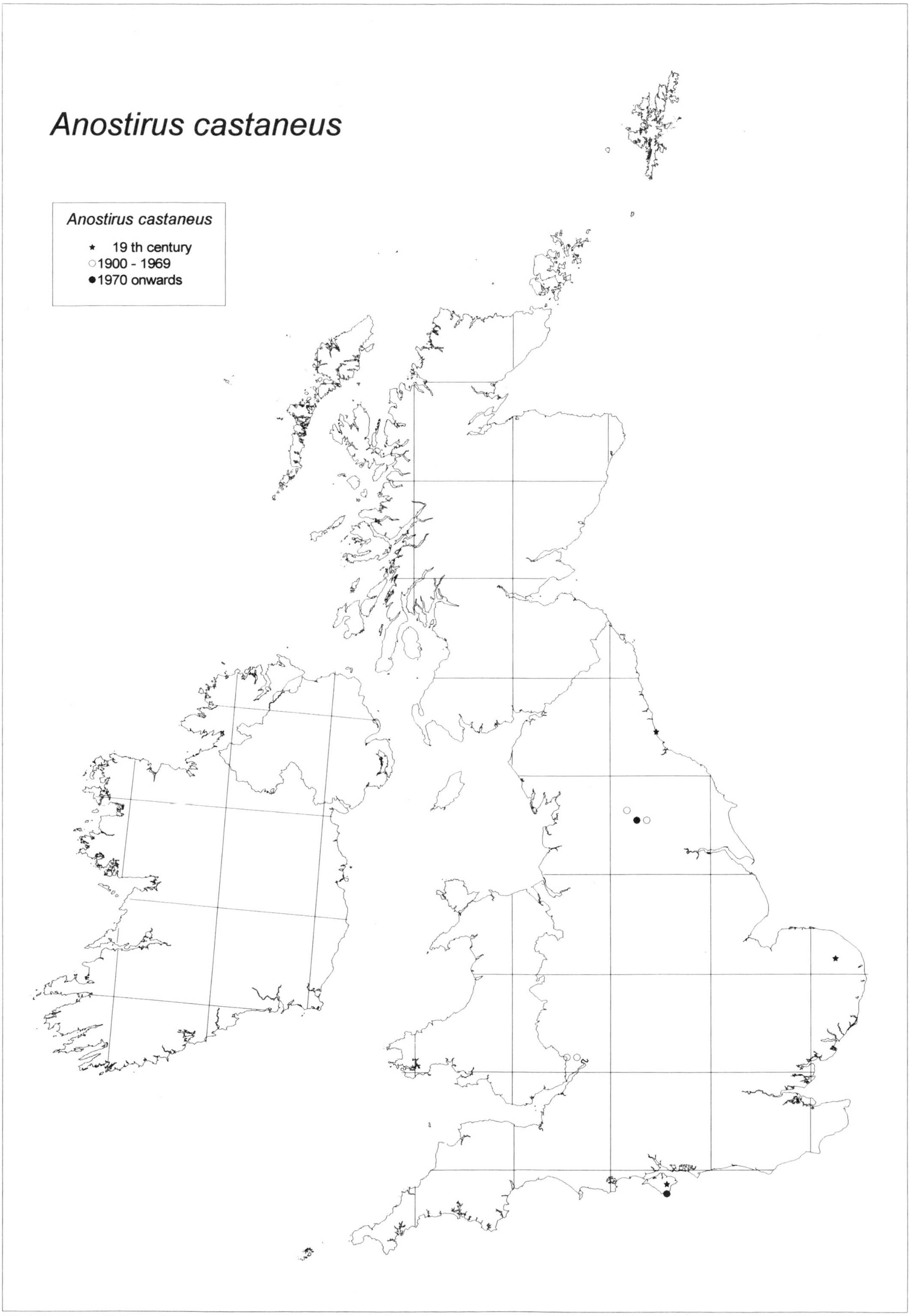

Distribution of Anostirus castaneus - a click beetle in Britain, by 10km square.
Source: H.Mendel, 1988. Provisional atlas of the click beetles (Coleoptera: Elateroidea) of the British Isles, Biological Records Centre (ITE) and English Nature - Invertebrate Site Register.

Bidessus unistriatus (a diving beetle) Action Plan

1. Current status

1.1 *Bidessus unistriatus* is confined to lowland, stagnant water bodies and slow drains. Typical habitats include the extreme edge of sparsely vegetated pools of moderate depth, such as the fluctuating meres of the Brecks, and old drainage ditches full of reed litter. *B. unistriatus* has not been found in brackish water despite its occasional association with coastal areas. There is evidence of flight ability in south-west France.

1.2 This is a widespread species in Europe, being rare in the northern and southern extremes, and possibly found in Mongolia and China. In the UK, there are recent records for east and west Norfolk, from a Broadland drain, and from fluctuating meres. There is also an unconfirmed record for the Pevensey Levels, East Sussex. *B. unistriatus* has been recorded from 4 ten km squares in England since 1970. It appears to have become extinct at former sites in the New Forest, Studland, Camber and south Cambridgeshire. Post-glacial subfossil records for this species are widespread within England, but some may refer to another species of *Bidessus*, presumed to be extinct in Britain.

1.3 In Great Britain this species is currently classified as *Endangered*.

2. Current factors causing loss or decline

2.1 Water abstraction for agricultural and domestic use.

2.2 Agricultural improvement resulting in drainage and enrichment.

2.3 Cessation of traditional management techniques for reed fen in the Broads.

3. Current action

3.1 Surveys were undertaken in the Catfield area of Broadland by the Balfour-Browne Club in 1997/98.

3.2 The species is present on the MoD Stanford Training Area SSSI, which is within the Breckland candidate SAC.

4. Action plan objectives and targets

4.1 Maintain populations at all known sites.

4.2 Enhance populations at known sites by 2010.

4.3 Re-establish populations at one former site by 2010.

5. Proposed action with lead agencies

The objectives of this plan will be achieved by implementing beneficial habitat management at known sites, surveys to determine the status of the species, and by autecological research. Populations should be reintroduced to a former site with suitable habitat conditions.

5.1 Policy and legislation

5.1.1 Address the requirements of this species in the LEAP process and in relevant WLMPs. (ACTION: EA, IDBs, LAs, MAFF)

5.1.2 Take account of the species' requirement in response to applications for water abstraction licenses. (ACTION: EA)

5.1.3 Where appropriate, include the requirements of the species when preparing or revising prescriptions for agri-environment schemes. (ACTION: EN, MAFF)

5.2 Site safeguard and management

5.2.1 Where possible, ensure that all occupied habitat is appropriately managed, including the maintenance of traditional reed-harvesting practices, by 2008. This may be through SSSI or agri-environment scheme management agreements. (ACTION: Broads Authority, EN, MoD)

5.2.2 Ensure that the species is included in site management documents for all relevant SSSIs. (ACTION: EN)

5.2.3 Consider notifying as SSSIs sites holding key populations of the species, where this is necessary to secure their long-term protection and appropriate management. (ACTION: EN)

5.3 Species management and protection

5.3.1 Reintroduce a series of populations at a suitably managed former site by 2010. (ACTION: EN)

5.4 Advisory

5.4.1 Advise landowners and managers of the presence of this species and the importance of beneficial management for its conservation. (ACTION: EN, MAFF)

5.4.2 As far as possible, ensure that all relevant agri-environment project officers, and members of regional agri-environment consultation groups, are advised of locations of this species, its importance, and the management needed for its conservation. (ACTION: EN, MAFF)

5.5 Future research and monitoring

5.5.1 Undertake further surveys to determine the status of the species. (ACTION: EN)

5.5.2 Conduct targeted autecological research to inform habitat management. (ACTION: EN)

5.5.3 Establish a regular monitoring programme for the species. (ACTION: EN)

5.5.4 Consider undertaking genetic studies to inform the reintroduction programme. (ACTION: EN)

5.5.5 Pass information gathered during survey and monitoring of this species to a central database for incorporation in national and international databases. (ACTION: EN)

5.5.6 Encourage research on the ecology and conservation of this species on an international level, and use the experience gained towards its conservation in the UK. (ACTION: EN, JNCC)

5.6 Communications and publicity

5.6.1 Promote opportunities for the appreciation of tne species and the conservation issues associated with its habitat. This should be achieved through articles within appropriate journals, as well as by a publicity leaflet. (ACTION: EN)

5.7 Links with other action plans

5.7.1 This action plan should be considered in conjunction with those for lowland heathland, reedbeds, fens and aquifer-fed naturally fluctuating water bodies.

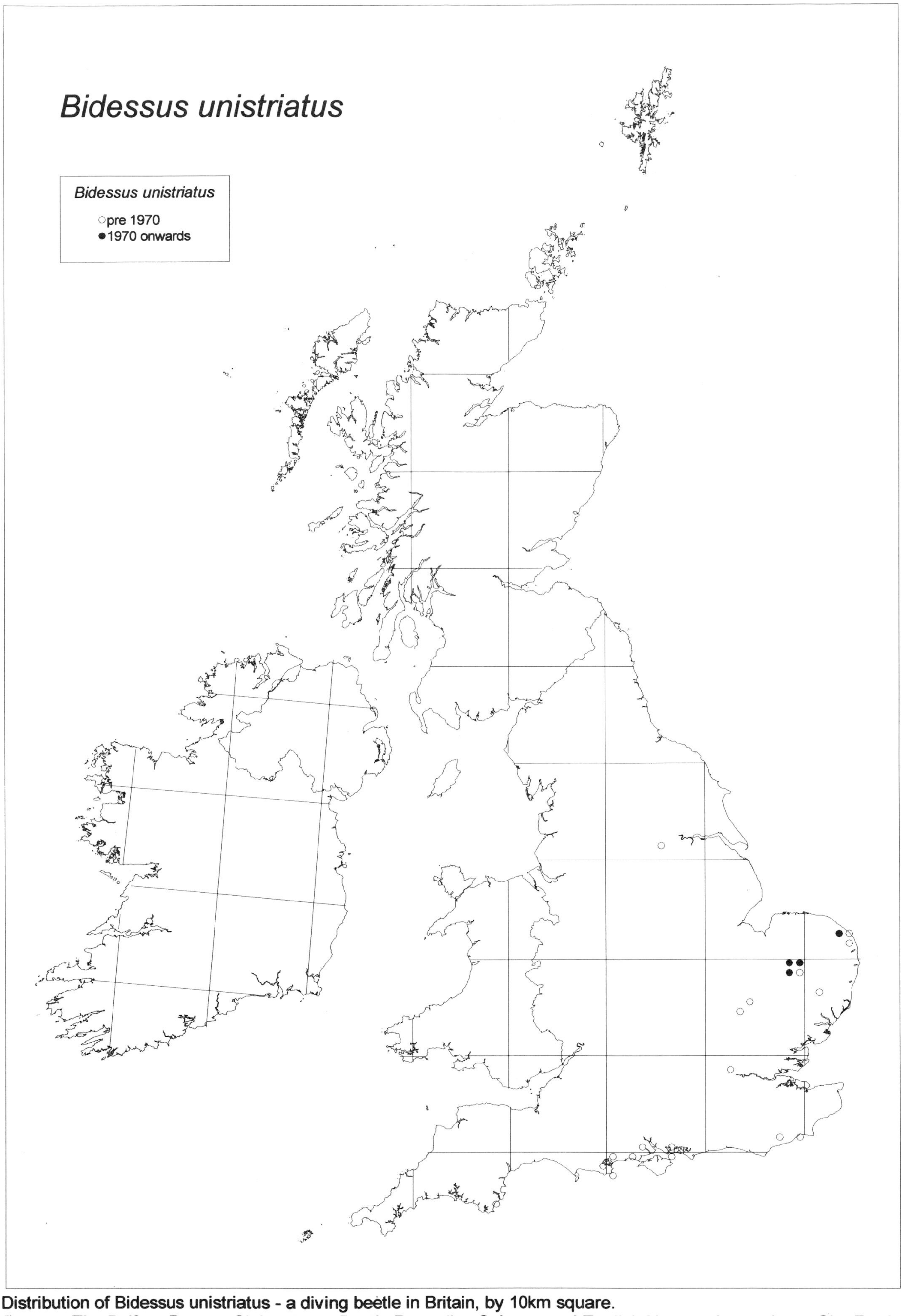

Distribution of Bidessus unistriatus - a diving beetle in Britain, by 10km square.
Source: The Balfour-Browne Club - Water Beetle Recording Scheme and English Nature - Invertebrate Site Register.

Byctiscus populi (a leaf-rolling weevil) Action Plan

1. Current status

1.1 *Byctiscus populi* is associated with aspen and white poplar in woodland and thickets where these trees are common. A reported association with black poplar appears to be exceptional. The ovipositing female constructs a leaf-roll ('cradle'), usually from a single leaf, and the developing larva feeds on the leaf tissue. There is anecdotal evidence that the weevil prefers young growth of suckering and regenerating trees to large, mature individuals, though adults certainly occur on the latter.

1.2 There are post-1970 records from East Sussex, east Kent and Surrey, but historically it was more widely distributed, being recorded from much of southern England northwards to east Norfolk, east Gloucestershire and Worcestershire. *Byctiscus populi* is widely distributed and fairly common over most of central-western Europe, and is found in the Nordic countries and the Mediterranean region. Its range includes Asia Minor, central Asia and Siberia, and extends to Mongolia and northern China.

1.3 In Great Britain this species is now classified as *Rare*.

2. Current factors causing loss and decline

2.1 Loss of broadleaved woodland through conversion to exotic conifer plantations.

2.2 Inappropriate woodland management.

2.3 Decline of coppice management.

3. Current action

3.1 A number of the more recent sites on which it occurs are SSSIs.

4. Action plan objectives and targets

4.1 Maintain populations at all known sites.

4.2 Enhance populations at all known sites by 2010.

4.3 Ensure that viable populations are established and maintained at a minimum of five well-separated sites, distributed across the former range, by 2010.

5. Proposed action with lead agencies

The priority action of this plan is to instigate beneficial management at known sites in order to maintain and enhance populations. Following surveys and autecological research, reintroductions may be required to reinstate populations across its former range.

5.1 Policy and legislation

5.1.1 Where appropriate, include the requirements of the species in the preparation or revision of prescriptions for agri-environment (farm woodland) or woodland grant schemes. (ACTION: EN, FC, MAFF)

5.1.2 Take full account of the requirements of the species when considering felling and restocking proposals in its current and former range. (ACTION: FC)

5.2 Site safeguard and management

5.2.1 Where possible, ensure that all occupied habitat is appropriately managed by 2008, for example through SSSI or woodland grant scheme management agreements. (ACTION: EN, FC)

5.2.2 Ensure that *Byctiscus populi* is included in management documents for all relevant SSSIs. (ACTION: EN)

5.2.3 Consider notifying as SSSIs sites holding key populations of the weevil, where this is necessary to secure their long-term protection and appropriate management. (ACTION: EN)

5.3 Species management and protection

5.3.1 Consider reintroducing *Byctiscus populi* to a series of sites within the former range, if necessary to ensure that five viable populations are established and maintained by 2010. (ACTION: EN)

5.4 Advisory

5.4.1 Advise landowners and managers of the presence of this species and the importance of beneficial management for its conservation. (ACTION: EN)

5.4.2 Develop and disseminate guidelines to protect *Byctiscus populi* for use with landowners, FA, FE, LA, and EN area staff. (ACTION: EN, FC)

5.5 Future research and monitoring

5.5.1 Undertake surveys to determine the status of the species. (ACTION: EN)

5.5.2 Conduct targeted autecological research to inform habitat management. (ACTION: EN)

5.5.3 Establish a regular monitoring programme for the species. (ACTION: EN)

5.5.4 Pass information gathered during survey and monitoring of this species to a central database for incorporation into national and international databases. (ACTION: EN)

5.6 Communications and publicity

5.6.1 Promote opportunities for the appreciation of the species and the conservation issues associated with coppice woodland. This should be achieved through articles within appropriate journals, as well as by a publicity leaflet. (ACTION: EN).

5.7 Links with other action plans

5.7.1 Implementation of this action plan could benefit other species of wet woodland, including the lesser belle moth *Colobochyla salicalis*.

5.7.2 This plan should be considered in conjunction with that for wet woodlands.

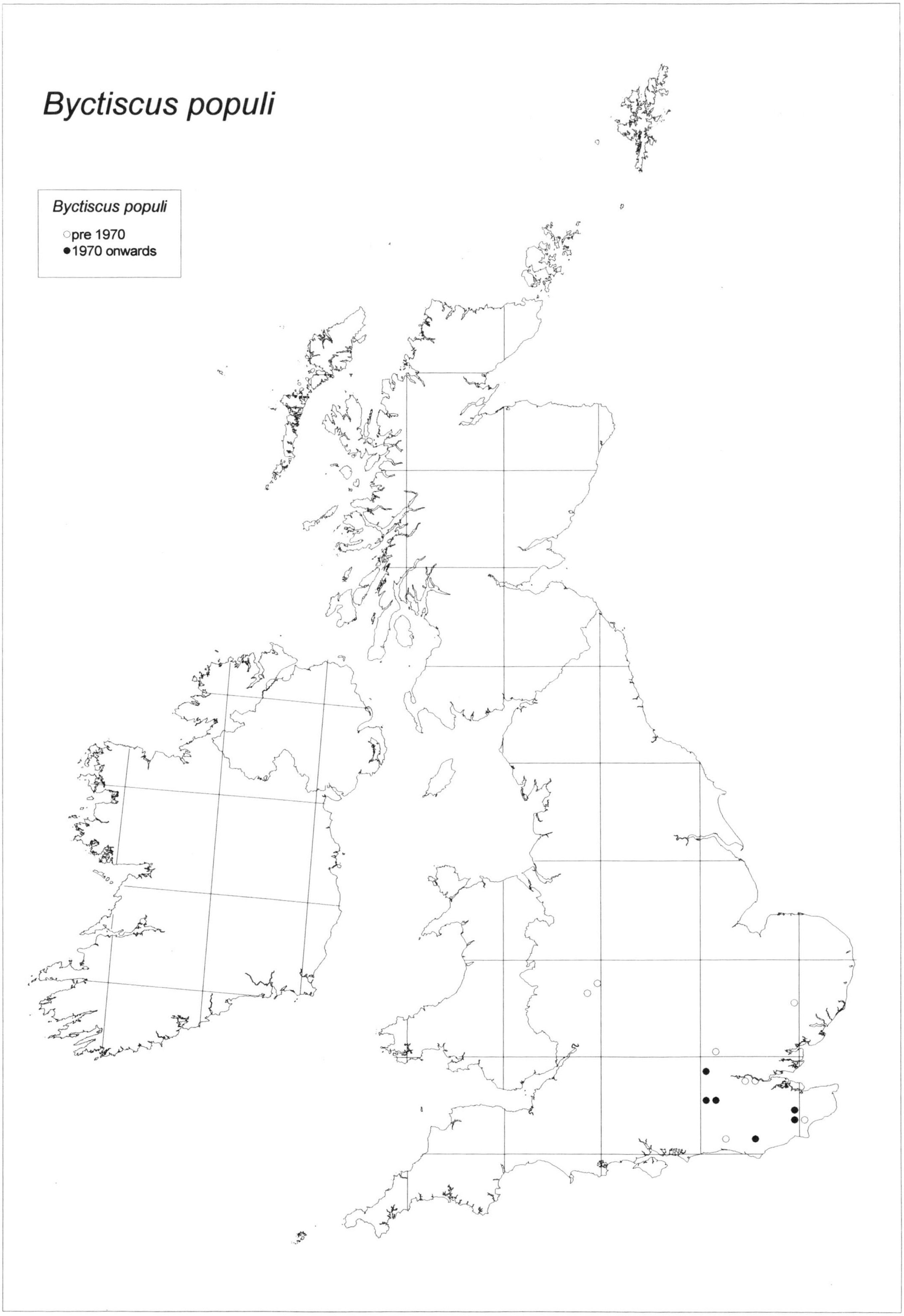

Distribution of Byctiscus populi - a leaf-rolling weevil in Britain, by 10km square.
Source: English Nature - Invertebrate Site Register.

Cicindela germanica (a tiger beetle) Action Plan

1. Current status

1.1 *Cicindela germanica* occurs on, or near the base of, coastal cliffs or steep slopes, on bare or little-vegetated sand or silt near to freshwater seepages. It has, however, also been found on dry, gravelly but open situations. *Cicindela germanica* has an annual life cycle. It breeds in the summer and overwinters as larvae, sometimes at localised high densities, in vertical burrows in damp, open sand or silt. Both larvae and adults are predatory on surface-active invertebrates, possibly chiefly on ants. Adults disperse by running rather than by flight.

1.2 This species used to occur along the English south coast from Hampshire to Devon, as well as in South Wales, and there are unconfirmed pre-1900 inland records from Berkshire and Kent. Since 1970 it has been found only on the coasts of Dorset and the Isle of Wight. Its wider distribution covers much of the Palearctic, from western Europe to eastern China, but it is generally local.

1.3 In Great Britain this species is now classified as *Rare*.

2. Current factors causing loss or decline

2.1 Cliff stabilisation schemes.

2.2 Rapid coastal erosion exacerbated by coastal protection works.

2.3 Scrub encroachment on stabilised cliffs.

3. Current action

3.1 The Axmouth to Lyme Regis landslip is an NNR; Chideock and Eype's Mouth are part of an SSSI and a proposed SAC. Totland Bay is an SSSI; the Isle of Wight chines are all in an SSSI and a proposed SAC.

4. Action plan objectives and targets

4.1 Maintain populations at all known sites.

4.2 Restore populations to five suitable sites within the historic range by 2010.

5. Proposed action with lead agencies

The processes required to deliver the above objectives involve appropriate management of known habitats for the species, followed by reintroductions to potential sites within its historic range. Surveys to determine its status, population monitoring and autecological studies will also need to be undertaken.

5.1 Policy and legislation

5.1.1 Address the requirements of this species in the LEAP process and in relevant WLMPs and Shoreline Management Plans. (ACTION: EA, IDBs, LAs, MAFF)

5.2 Site safeguard and management

5.2.1 Ensure that the species requirements are included in site objective and site management statements for all relevant SSSIs. (ACTION: EN)

5.2.2 Where possible, ensure that all occupied habitat is appropriately managed by 2008, including the maintenance of groundwater systems that supply natural freshwater seepages. (ACTION: EA, EN, IDBs)

5.2.3 Ensure that the habitat requirements of this species are taken onto account in relevant coastal protection and development policies, plans and proposals. (ACTION: EN, LAs, MAFF)

5.2.4 Consider notifying as SSSIs sites holding key populations of the species, where this is necessary to secure their long-term protection and appropriate management. (ACTION: EN)

5.3 Species management and protection

5.3.1 Consider reintroducing *Cicindela germanica* to a series of sites within the former range, if necessary to establish five new viable populations. (ACTION: CCW, EN)

5.4 Advisory

5.4.1 Advise landowners and managers of the presence of the species and the importance of beneficial management for its conservation. (ACTION: EN)

5.5 Future research and monitoring

5.5.1 Undertake surveys to determine the status of the species. (ACTION: CCW, EN)

5.5.2 Conduct targeted autecological research to inform habitat management. (ACTION: EN)

5.5.3 Establish an appropriate monitoring programme for this species. (ACTION: EN)

5.5.4 Pass information gathered during survey and monitoring of this species to a central database

for incorporation into national and international databases. (ACTION: CCW, EN)

5.6 Communications and publicity

5.6.1 Promote opportunities for the appreciation of the species and the conservation issues associated with soft-rock cliffs and coastal seepages. This should be achieved through articles within appropriate journals, as well as by a publicity leaflet. (ACTION: EN)

5.7 Links with other action plans

5.7.1 This action plan should be considered in conjunction with that for maritime cliffs and slopes.

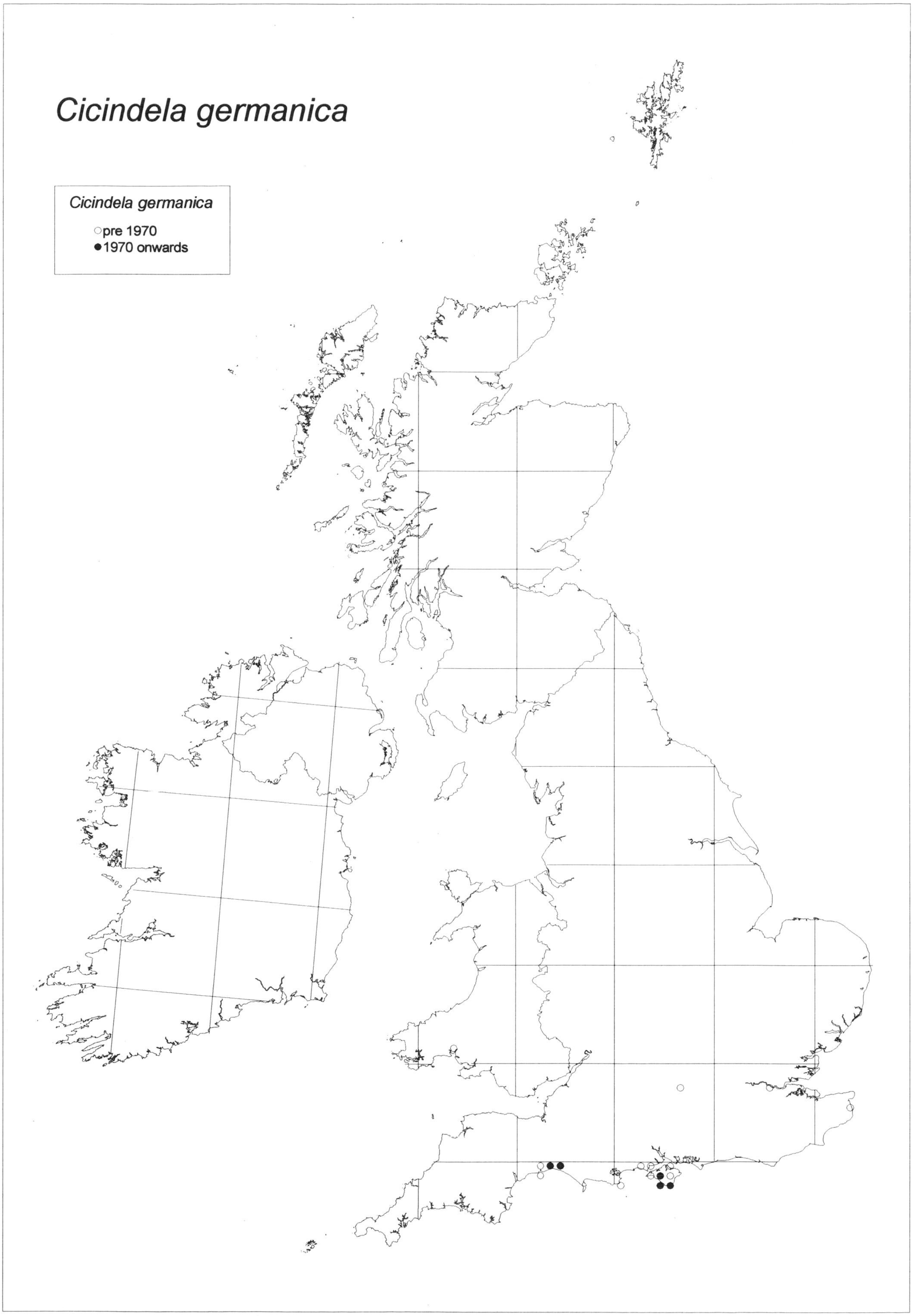

Distribution of Cicindela germanica - a tiger beetle in Britain, by 10km square.
Source: Luff, M.L. 1998. Provisional atlas of the ground beetles (Coleoptera, Carabidae) of Britain, Biological Records Centre (ITE) and English Nature - Invertebrate Site Register.

Cicindela hybrida (a tiger beetle) Action Plan

1. Current status

1.1 *Cicindela hybrida* is found on sand dunes and warm, sandy open sites near the coast, occurring on sun-exposed bare substrates some way from water. Breeding occurs in early summer, but larvae may overwinter half-grown before the adults emerge in mid-late summer and overwinter again before breeding. The species may therefore be biennial. Adults and larvae are predatory, the larvae living in burrows in the substrate. This species flies readily.

1.2 The current UK distribution is restricted to coastal sites in Lancashire and Cumbria, but it used to extend into North Wales at the beginning of this century. Old records from Lincolnshire and Norfolk were probably *C. maritima*, as the two species were not differentiated in the past. It is found throughout Europe, except the extreme north, and is not restricted to the coast.

1.3 In Great Britain this species is now classified as *Vulnerable*.

2. Current factors causing loss or decline

2.1 Dune stabilisation schemes.

2.2 Increased recreational use of coastal dunes.

3. Current action

3.1 All known sites are SSSIs. Formby/Ainsdale Dunes are an NNR, Drigg/Eskmeal Dunes are LNRs, Eskmeals and Altcar Ranges are owned by the MoD. Ainsdale is a candidate SAC.

4. Action plan objectives and targets

4.1 Maintain populations at all known sites.

4.2 Restore populations to five suitable sites within the historic range by 2010.

5. Proposed action with lead agencies

The processes required to deliver the above objectives involve appropriate management of known habitats for the species, followed possibly by reintroductions to potential sites within its historic range. Surveys to determine status, population monitoring and autecological studies will also need to be undertaken.

5.1 Policy and legislation

5.1.1 Ensure that the requirements of the species are taken into account in relevant Shoreline Management Plans. (ACTION : LAs, MAFF)

5.2 Site safeguard and management

5.2.1 Where possible, ensure that all occupied habitat is appropriately managed by 2008, including the provision of natural mosaics of vegetated and bare sand on dune habitats. This may be through site management agreements. (ACTION: EN, MoD)

5.2.2 Where possible, ensure that recreational pressure is minimised on sites supporting populations of this species. (ACTION: LAs)

5.2.3 Ensure that the habitat requirements of *Cicindela hybrida* are taken into account in any relevant development policies, plans and proposals. (ACTION: EN, Department of Culture, Media and Sport, LAs)

5.2.4 Ensure that the species is included in site management documents for all relevant SSSIs. (ACTION: EN)

5.3 Species management and protection

5.3.1 Consider reintroducing *Cicindela hybrida* to a series of sites within the former range, if necessary to establish five new viable populations. (ACTION: CCW, EN)

5.4 Advisory

5.4.1 Advise landowners and managers of the presence of this species and the importance of beneficial management for its conservation. (ACTION: EN)

5.5 Future research and monitoring

5.5.1 Undertake surveys to determine the status of the species. (ACTION: CCW, EN)

5.5.2 Conduct targeted autecological research to inform habitat management. (ACTION: EN)

5.5.3 Establish a regular monitoring programme for this species. (ACTION: EN)

5.5.4 Pass information gathered during survey and monitoring of this species to a central database for incorporation into national and international databases. (ACTION: CCW, EN)

5.6 Communications and publicity

5.6.1 Promote opportunities for the appreciation of the species and the conservation issues associated with coastal sand dunes. This should be achieved through articles within appropriate journals, as well as by a publicity leaflet. (ACTION: EN)

5.7 Links with other action plans

5.7.1 This plan should be considered in conjunction with that for coastal sand dunes.

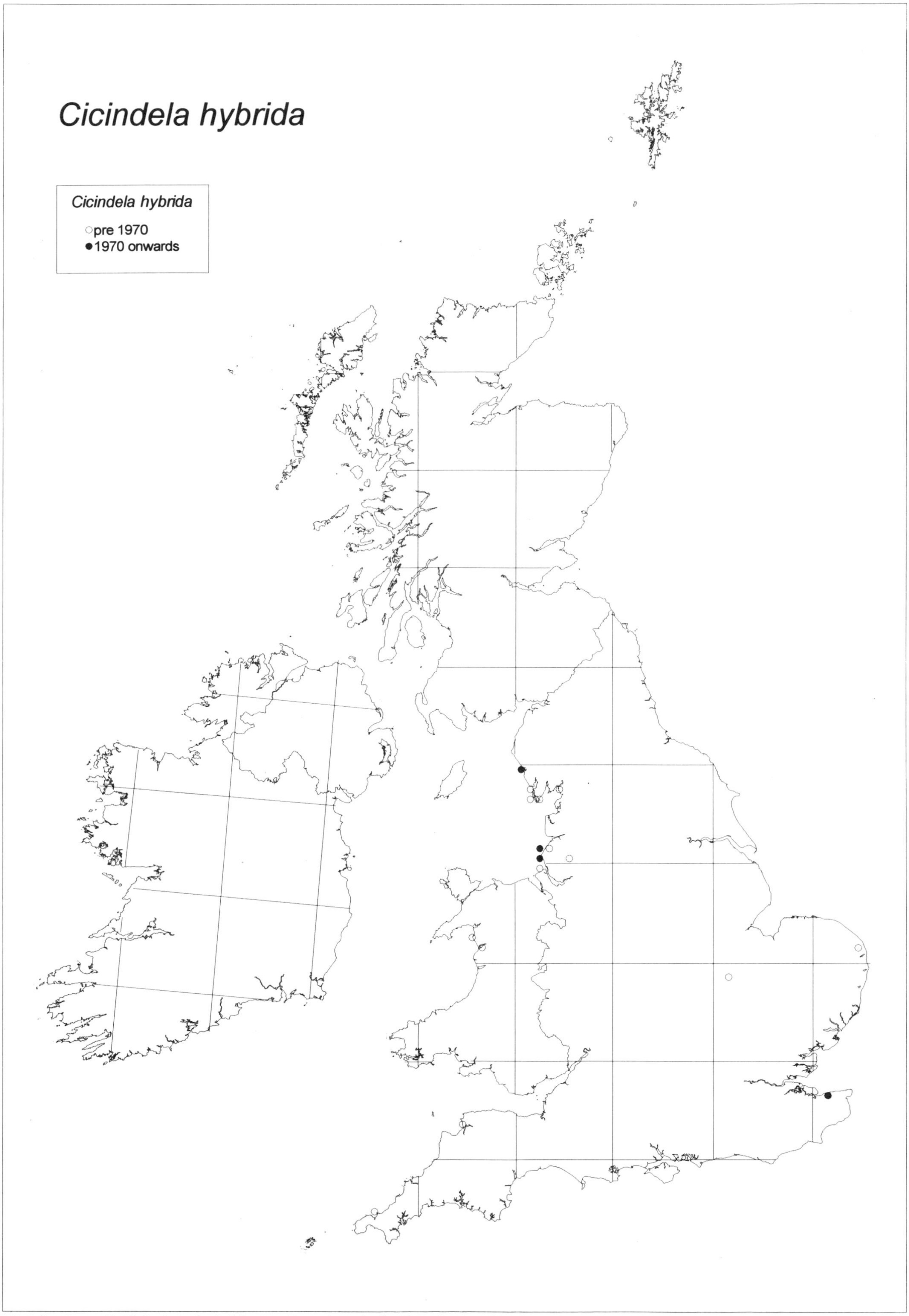

Distribution of Cicindela hybrida - a tiger beetle in Britain, by 10km square.
Source: Luff, M.L. 1998. Provisional atlas of the ground beetles (Coleoptera, Carabidae) of Britain, Biological Records Centre (ITE) and English Nature - Invertebrate Site Register.

Heath tiger beetle (*Cicindela sylvatica*) Action Plan

1. Current status

1.1 The heath tiger beetle occurs on open, dry and sandy soils with heather, sometimes among open coniferous woodland. Adults are active in bright sunshine and fly readily, although it is not clear whether flight ever leads to long-range dispersal rather than to movement within the suitable habitat. The beetle has an annual life cycle. It breeds in spring and summer. The larvae occur in vertical burrows in the soil. Both larvae and adults are predatory on surface-active invertebrates, including ants and lepidopteran larvae.

1.2 At the beginning of this century the heath tiger beetle occurred widely on southern English heaths from Dorset to Kent, as well as at one site in Lincolnshire, but since 1970 it has been very localised in Surrey, Sussex, Hampshire and Dorset. It occurs throughout Europe, except the extreme north and the Mediterranean regions.

1.3 In Great Britain this species is classified as *Nationally Scarce*.

2. Current factors causing loss or decline

2.1 Loss of heathland.

2.2 Inappropriate heathland management, especially neglect leading to loss of open sand, and scrub invasion.

3. Current action

3.1 This species occurs on Studland Heath NNR and several SSSIs.

4. Action plan objectives and targets

4.1 Maintain populations at all known sites.

4.2 Enhance the populations at all known sites by 2010.

4.3 Ensure the establishment and maintenance of five new viable populations at suitable sites within the historic range by 2010.

5. Proposed action with lead agencies

The priority for the heath tiger beetle is appropriate management of known habitats for the species, followed by reintroductions to suitable sites within its historic range. Surveys, population monitoring and autecological studies will also need to be undertaken.

5.1 Policy and legislation

5.1.1 Where appropriate, include the requirements of the species when preparing or revising prescriptions for agri-environment schemes. (ACTION: EN, MAFF)

5.2 Site safeguard and management

5.2.1 Where possible, ensure that all occupied habitat is appropriately managed by 2008, including the provision of south-facing patches of bare ground. This may be through SSSI or agri-environment scheme management agreements. (ACTION: EN, MAFF)

5.2.2 Ensure that the species is included in site management documents for all relevant SSSIs. (ACTION: EN)

5.3 Species management and protection

5.3.1 Consider reintroducing the heath tiger beetle to a series of sites within the former range, if necessary to establish five new viable populations by 2010. (ACTION: EN)

5.4 Advisory

5.4.1 Advise landowners and managers of the presence of this species and the importance of beneficial management for its conservation. (ACTION: EN)

5.5 Future research and monitoring

5.5.1 Undertake surveys to determine the status of the species. (ACTION: EN)

5.5.2 Conduct targeted autecological research to inform habitat management. (ACTION: EN)

5.5.3 Establish a regular monitoring programme for this species. (ACTION: EN)

5.5.4 Pass information gathered during survey and monitoring of this species to a central database for incorporation into national and international databases. (ACTION: EN)

5.6 Communications and publicity

5.6.1 Promote opportunities for the appreciation of the species and the conservation issues associated with sandy heathland. This should be achieved through articles within appropriate journals, as well as by a publicity leaflet. (ACTION: EN)

5.7 Links with other action plans

5.7.1 Implementation of this action plan could benefit other species of lowland heathland, including the ground beetles *Pterostichus kugelanni* and *Amara famelica*, woodlark *Lullula arborea*, and the sand lizard *Lacerta agilis*.

5.7.2 This plan should be considered in conjunction with that for lowland heathland.

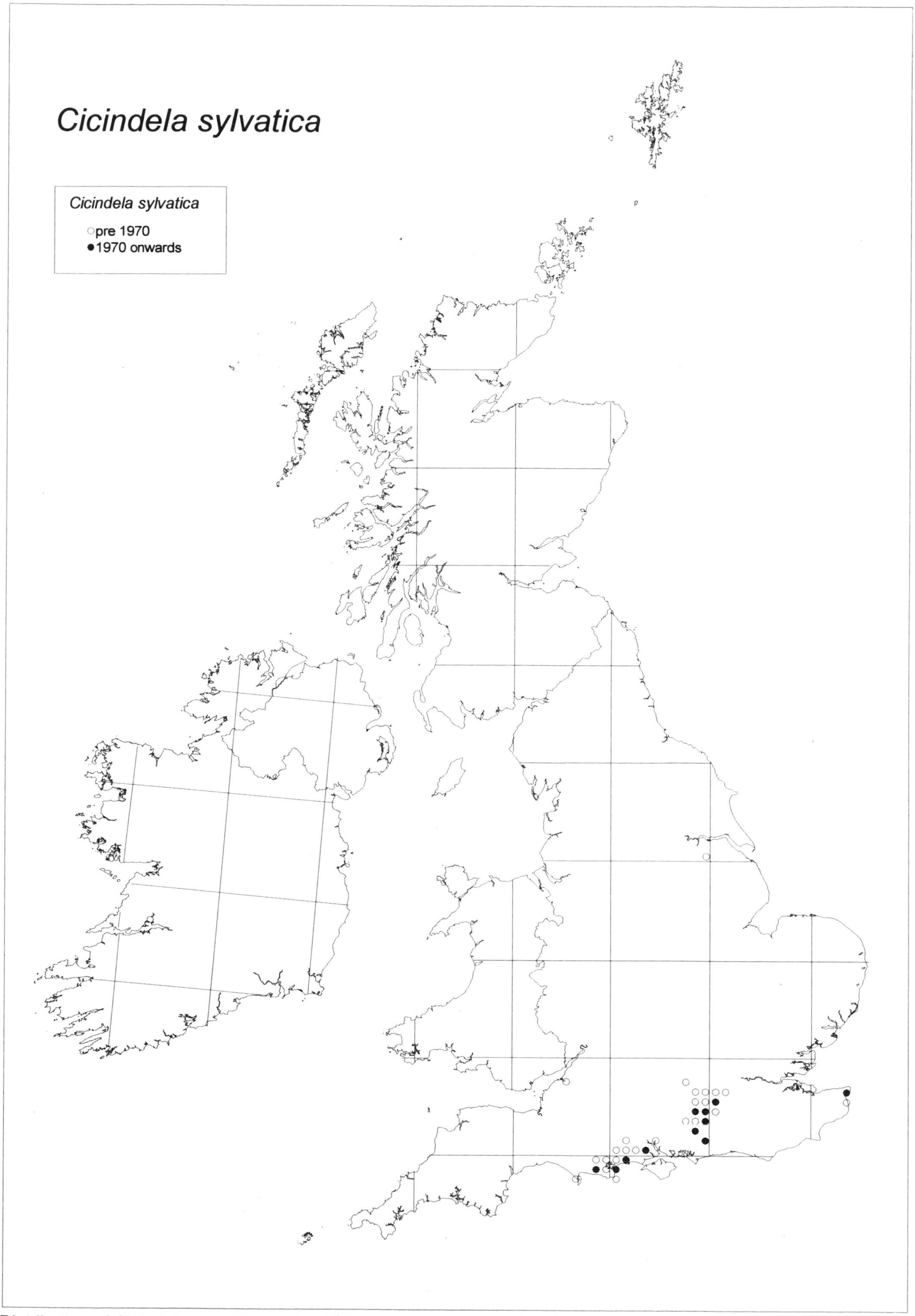

Distribution of Cicindela sylvatica - a heath tiger beetle in Britain, by 10km square.
Source: Luff, M.L. 1998. Provisional atlas of the ground beetles (Coleoptera, Carabidae) of Britain, Biological Records Centre (ITE) and English Nature - Invertebrate Site Register.

Cryptocephalus nitidulus (a leaf beetle) Action Plan

1. Current status

1.1 *Cryptocephalus nitidulus* usually occurs on young birch and hazel in broadleaved woodland and downland scrub. Adults also occur on flowering hawthorn and privet. The larval ecology is unknown.

1.2 Old records suggest that *Cryptocephalus nitidulus* had a widely scattered distribution in southern England and the Midlands as far north as Nottinghamshire. Pre-1970 records include the following vice-counties: south Hampshire (New Forest, Bournemouth), west Kent (Cobham, Darenth Wood), Surrey (Box Hill), Oxfordshire (Wychwood Forest), east Gloucestershire (Colesbourne), west Gloucestershire and Nottinghamshire (Sherwood Forest). Records suggest that adults only occurred in low numbers in these historic localities. It appears to have declined since the middle of this century, and has recently been recorded only from Surrey (several records since 1970). It occurred on White Down from 1988-1990 and on Hackhurst Down in 1989. *Cryptocephalus nitidulus* occurs in northern and central Europe.

1.3 In Great Britain this species is classified as *Endangered*.

2. Current factors causing loss or decline

2.1 Elimination of scrub from chalk downland.

2.2 Cessation of coppicing in woodland.

3. Current action

3.1 Many of the localities where this species has been recorded are SSSIs.

4. Action plan objectives and targets

4.1 Maintain populations at all known sites.

4.2 Ensure the establishment and maintenance of four new viable populations at suitable sites within the historic range by 2010.

5. Proposed action with lead agencies

A survey of extant colonies and historic sites should be undertaken for this species. This will establish its current status and provide information to allow targeting of the other measures recommended. Priorities will include appropriate management of all extant sites, based on a better understanding of the beetles' ecological requirements, and protection for each colony from damaging forestry activities. Experimental work should also be undertaken to assess the feasibility of reintroducing viable populations to other sites.

5.1 Policy and legislation

5.1.1 Where appropriate, include the requirements of the species when preparing or revising prescriptions for agri-environment or woodland grant schemes. (ACTION: EN, FC, MAFF)

5.2 Site safeguard and management

5.2.1 Where possible, ensure that all occupied habitat is appropriately managed by 2008, for example through SSSI or agri-environment/woodland grant scheme management agreements. (ACTION: EN, MAFF)

5.2.2 Ensure that the species is included in site management documents for all relevant SSSIs. (ACTION: EN)

5.2.3 Consider notifying as SSSIs sites holding key populations of the species, where this is necessary to secure their long-term protection and appropriate management. (ACTION: EN)

5.3 Species management and protection

5.3.1 Consider reintroducing *Cryptocephalus nitidulus* to a series of sites within the former range, if necessary to establish four new viable populations by 2010. (ACTION: EN)

5.4 Advisory

5.4.1 Advise landowners and managers of the presence of this species and the importance of beneficial management for its conservation. (ACTION: EN)

5.5 Future research and monitoring

5.5.1 Undertake surveys to determine the status of this species. (ACTION: EN)

5.5.2 Conduct targeted autecological research to inform habitat management and reintroduction proposals. (ACTION: EN)

5.5.3 Establish a regular monitoring programme for the species. (ACTION: EN)

5.5.3 Pass information gathered during survey and monitoring of this species to a central database for incorporation in national and international databases. (ACTION: EN)

5.6 Communications and publicity

5.6.1 Promote opportunities for the appreciation of the species and the conservation issues associated with its habitat. This should be achieved through articles within appropriate journals, as well as by a publicity leaflet. (ACTION: EN)

5.7 Links with other action plans

5.7.1 This action plan should be considered in conjunction that for lowland calcareous grassland.

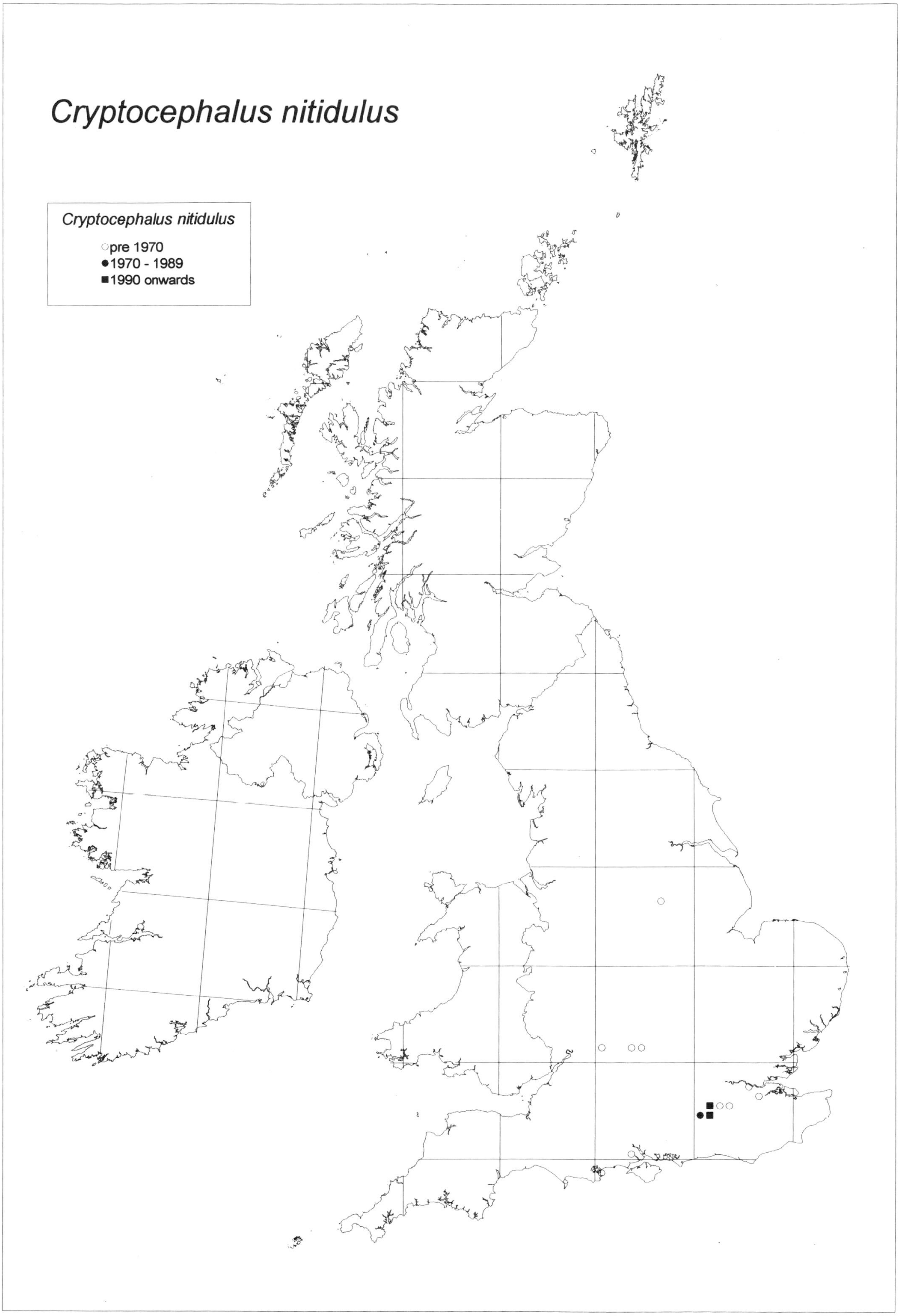

Distribution of Cryptocephalus nitidulus - a leaf beetle in Britain, by 10km square.
Source: M.Cox - Natural History Museum and English Nature - Invertebrate Site Register.

Cryptocephalus primarius (a leaf beetle) Action Plan

1. Current status

1.1 *Cryptocephalus primarius* adults are associated with common rock-rose in calcareous grassland, particularly on dry, warm, sheltered hillsides. The larval ecology is unknown.

1.2 The species was recorded from the following five widely scattered vice-counties in England and Scotland before 1970: Dorset (Ballard Down), Berkshire (Cholsey), Cambridgeshire (Gogmagog Hills), west Gloucestershire (Rodborough Hill) and mid Perthshire. This species has declined since the mid 1950s and, during 1990 and 1991, it was recorded only in two areas on the edge of the Cotswolds near Dursley, west Gloucestershire. *Cryptocephalus primarius* usually occurs in small isolated populations, although it was not uncommon in one localised area on Rodborough Hill in 1944. This is chiefly a central and south European species.

1.3 In Great Britain this species is classified as *Endangered*.

2. Current factors causing loss or decline

2.1 Loss of calcareous grassland.

2.2 Inappropriate grazing regimes.

3. Current action

3.1 Rodborough Hill is an SSSI.

4. Action plan objectives and targets

4.1 Maintain populations at all known sites.

4.2 Ensure the establishment and maintenance of three new viable populations within the historic range by 2010.

5. Proposed action with lead agencies

A survey of extant colonies and historic sites should be undertaken for this species. This will establish its current status and provide information to allow targeting of the other measures recommended. Priorities will include appropriate management of all extant sites, based on a better understanding of the beetles' ecological requirements, and protection for each colony from damaging agricultural activities. Experimental work should also be undertaken to assess the feasibility of reintroducing viable populations to other sites.

5.1 Policy and legislation

5.1.1 Where appropriate, include the requirements of the species when preparing or revising prescriptions for agri-environment schemes. (ACTION: EN, FC, MAFF)

5.2 Site safeguard and management

5.2.1 Where possible, ensure that all occupied habitat is appropriately managed by 2008. This may be through SSSI or agri-environment scheme management agreements. (ACTION: EN, MAFF)

5.2.2 Ensure that the species is included in site management documents for all relevant SSSIs. (ACTION: EN)

5.2.3 Consider notifying as SSSIs sites holding key populations of the species, where this is necessary to secure their long-term protection and appropriate management. (ACTION: EN)

5.3 Species management and protection

5.3.1 Consider reintroducing *Cryptocephalus primarius* to a series of sites within the former range, if necessary to establish three new viable populations by 2010. (ACTION: EN)

5.4 Advisory

5.4.1 Advise landowners and managers of the presence of this species and the importance of beneficial management for its conservation. (ACTION: EN)

5.5 Future research and monitoring

5.5.1 Undertake surveys to determine the status of this species. (ACTION: EN)

5.5.2 Conduct targeted autecological research to inform habitat management. (ACTION: EN)

5.5.3 Establish a regular monitoring programme for the species. (ACTION: EN)

5.5.4 Pass information gathered during survey and monitoring of this species to a central database for incorporation in national and international databases. (ACTION: EN)

5.6 Communications and publicity

5.6.1 Promote opportunities for the appreciation of the species and the conservation issues associated with calcareous grassland. This should be achieved through articles within appropriate journals, as well as by a publicity leaflet. (ACTION: EN)

5.7 Links with other action plans

5.7.1 This action plan should be considered in conjunction with that for lowland calcareous grassland.

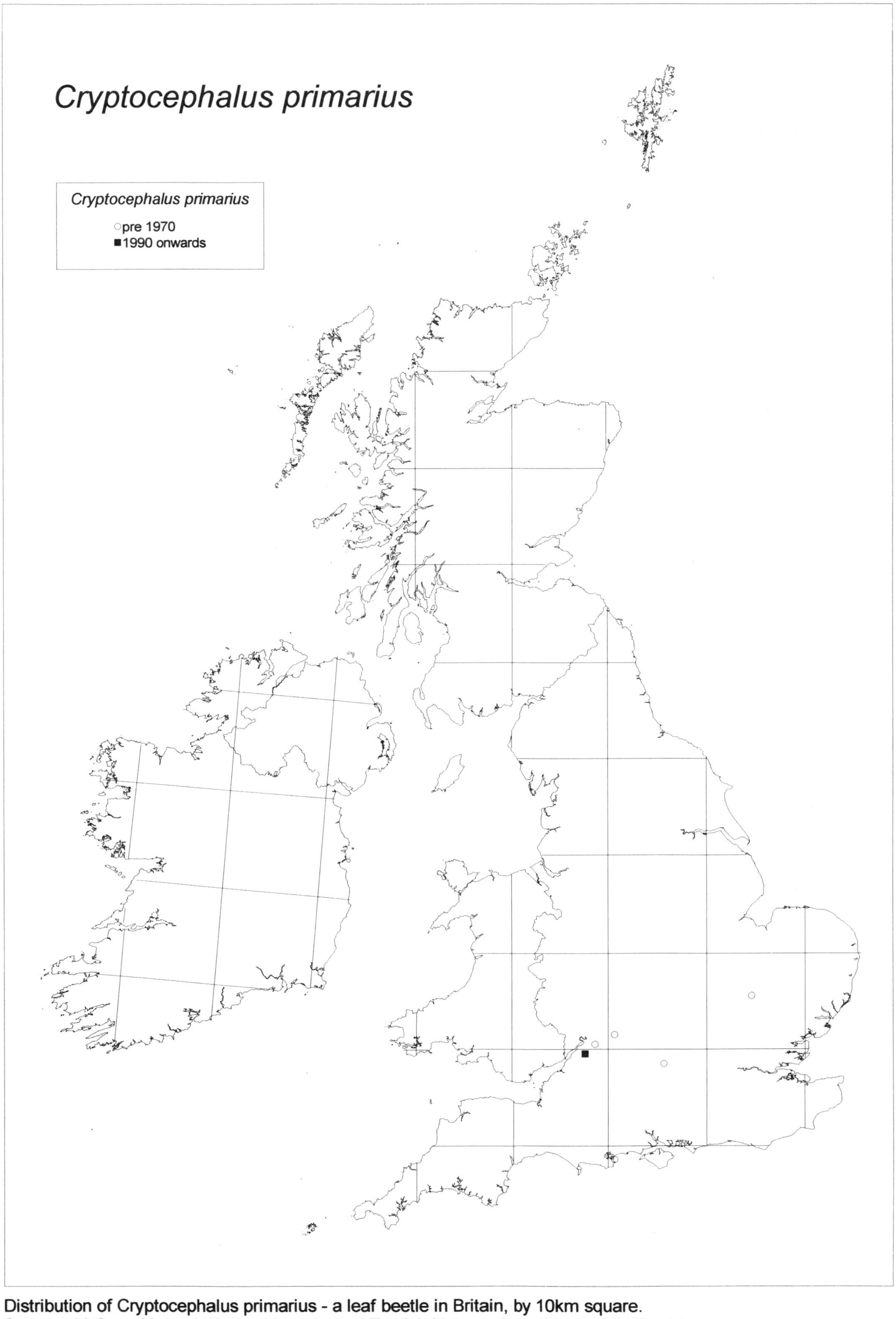

Distribution of Cryptocephalus primarius - a leaf beetle in Britain, by 10km square.
Source: M.Cox - Natural History Museum and English Nature - Invertebrate Site Register.

Cryptocephalus sexpunctatus (a leaf beetle) Action Plan

1. Current status

1.1 *Cryptocephalus sexpunctatus* occurs on hazel, birch, aspen, crack willow, hawthorn and young oak in broadleaved woodland. Adults have also been collected from the flowers of wood spurge. Complete development from egg to adult occurs within a faecal case which is enlarged as growth proceeds. Oviposition probably occurs in late June or early July, the females dropping the eggs, encapsulated with faeces to the ground. Captive rearing on hazel leaves suggests that eggs hatch in three to four weeks and larval development is completed in 12 to 21 months. Fully grown larvae anchor their cases to withered leaves, sealing the opening and turning to face the opposite end of the case. The adults emerge, from April onwards, by cutting a circular hinged flap at the end of the case.

1.2 Old records indicate that this species was widely distributed in southern England, with scattered records north to Ayrshire in Scotland. There are pre-1970 records for south Wiltshire, Dorset, south Hampshire, East and West Sussex, east and west Kent, Surrey, south and north Essex, east Suffolk, east Gloucestershire, Worcestershire, Warwickshire, north Lincolnshire, Dumfriesshire, Ayrshire and Midlothian. However from 1970 onwards, it was recorded only from Grays, south Essex (1978) and West Sussex and, more recently, from near Stockbridge, Hampshire (1993) and at Kirkconnell Flow NNR, Kirkcudbrightshire (1996). At each of these recent sites it was found in low numbers. This species occurs throughout northern, central and southern Europe.

1.3 In Great Britain this species is classified as *Vulnerable*.

2. Current factors causing loss or decline

2.1 Loss of broadleaved woodland.

2.2 Inappropriate woodland management.

3. Current action

3.1 Kirkconnell Flow is an NNR and the south Essex site is an Essex Wildlife Trust Reserve.

4. Action plan objectives and targets

4.1 Maintain populations at all known sites.

4.2 Ensure the establishment and maintenance of five new viable populations within the historic range by 2010.

5. Proposed action with lead agencies

A survey of extant populations and historic sites should be undertaken for this species. This will establish its current status, and provide information to allow targeting of the other measures recommended. Priorities will include appropriate management of all extant sites, based on a better understanding of the species' ecological requirements, and protection for each population from damaging forestry activities. Experimental work should also be undertaken to assess the feasibility of reintroducing viable populations on other sites.

5.1 Policy and legislation

5.1.1 Where appropriate, include the requirements of the species when preparing or revising prescriptions for agri-environment (farm woodland) or woodland grant schemes. (ACTION: EN, FC, MAFF, SNH, SOAEFD)

5.2 Site safeguard and management

5.2.1 Where possible, ensure that all occupied habitat is appropriately managed, including rotational management of glades and ride margins, by 2008. This may be through SSSI or woodland grant scheme management agreements. (ACTION: EN, FC, SNH)

5.2.2 Ensure that the species is included in site management documents for all relevant SSSIs. (ACTION: EN, SNH)

5.2.3 Consider notifying as SSSIs sites holding key populations of the species, where this is necessary to secure their long-term protection and appropriate management. (ACTION: EN, SNH)

5.3 Species management and protection

5.3.1 Consider reintroducing *Cryptocephalus sexpunctatus* to a series of sites within the former range, if necessary to establish five new viable populations. (ACTION: EN, SNH)

5.4 Advisory

5.4.1 Advise landowners and managers of the presence of this species and the importance of beneficial management for its conservation. (ACTION: EN, SNH)

5.4.2 Develop and disseminate guidelines to protect *C. sexpunctatus* for use with landowners; FC, LA, and EN/SNH area staff. (ACTION: LAs, EN, FC, SNH)

5.5 Future research and monitoring

5.5.1 Undertake surveys to determine the status of this species. (ACTION: EN, SNH)

5.5.2 Conduct targeted autecological research to inform habitat management. (ACTION: EN, SNH)

5.5.3 Establish an appropriate regular monitoring programme for the species. (ACTION: EN, SNH)

5.5.4 Pass information gathered during survey and monitoring of this species to a central database for incorporation in national and international databases. (ACTION: EN, SNH)

5.6 Communications and publicity

5.6.1 Promote opportunities for the appreciation of the species and the conservation issues associated with its habitat. This should be achieved through articles within appropriate journals, as well as by a publicity leaflet. (ACTION: EN, SNH)

5.7 Links with other action plans

5.7.1 This action plan should be considered in conjunction with that for upland oak wood.

Cryptocephalus sexpunctatus

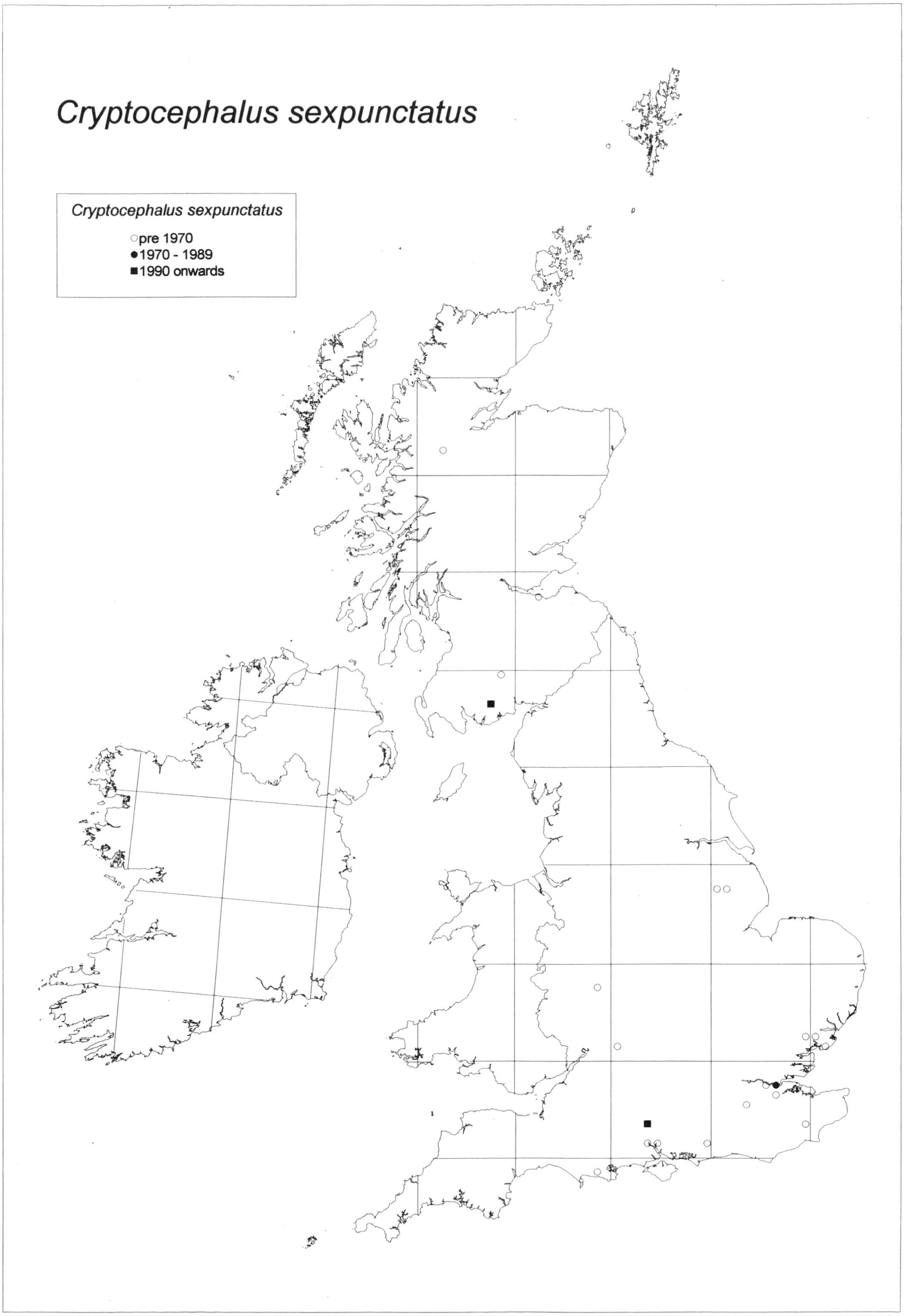

Distribution of Cryptocephalus sexpunctatus - a leaf beetle in Britain, by 10km square.
Source: M.Cox - Natural History Museum and English Nature - Invertebrate Site Register.

Mire pill-beetle (*Curimopsis nigrita*)
Action Plan

1. Current status

1.1 Mire pill-beetle is confined to lowland floodplain raised mires. Bronze Age subfossils have been found at two of its current sites. It has thus survived during periods of flooding, rapid mire growth and drought, so it is likely to be able to find pockets of suitable habitat within a range of future mire-surface conditions. It prefers open damp, rather than dry or wet, peat, with abundant low-growing acrocarpous mosses, especially *Dicranella cerviculata, D. heteromalla* and *Campylopus pyriformis*.

1.2 The species was first found alive in Britain in 1977 and three sites are now known, all in the Humberhead Levels of South Yorkshire and north Lincolnshire. The two large sites, Thorne and Hatfield Moors, each support numerous small and fragmented populations. Removal or destruction of habitat for peat extraction has reduced the potential area of habitat for the species by 80% on Hatfield Moors and around 30% on Thorne Moors since 1970. A very small, isolated population was found at Haxey Grange Fen, about 5 km south of Hatfield Moors, but the area of suitable habitat is only a few square metres.

1.3 In Great Britain this species is classified as *Endangered*. It is protected under Schedule 5 of the Wildlife and Countryside Act 1981, with respect to disturbance or destruction of its habitat.

2. Current factors causing loss or decline

2.1 Drainage for peat extraction.

2.2 Drought and fire.

2.3 Shading by encroaching birch scrub and bracken.

2.4 Falling groundwater levels, due to land drainage and excessive water abstraction.

3. Current action

3.1 Populations on all three sites are contained within SSSIs. Thorne and Hatfield Moors are proposed SPAs, and *c*50% of Thorne Moors is a candidate SAC.

3.2 The majority of Thorne and Hatfield Moors is owned by EN. Part of these sites are managed as an NNR. The eastern part of Thorne Moors (Crowle Moors) is a Lincolnshire Wildlife Trust reserve and a small area of Hatfield Moors is managed under a Section 39 agreement between Doncaster Metropolitan Borough Council, EN and the owners.

4. Action plan objectives and targets

4.1 Maintain populations on all known sites.

4.2 Enhance the population size at all known sites by 2010.

4.3 Restore populations to areas lost since 1970 by 2020.

5. Proposed action with lead agencies

A survey of other acidic peatland sites in eastern England should be undertaken. A better understanding of population processes and structures will assist in determining the precise requirements to achieve the above targets. Reintroductions may be necessary to ensure populations are restored to areas where they have been lost in recent years.

5.1 Policy and legislation

5.1.3 Take account of the species' requirement in response to applications for water abstraction licences. (ACTION: EA)

5.2 Site safeguard and management

5.2.1 Where possible, ensure that all occupied habitat is appropriately managed by 2010. (ACTION: EN)

5.2.2 Ensure that the habitat requirements of the species are taken into account in relevant development policies, plans and proposals, including peat extraction. (ACTION: EN, LAs)

5.2.3 Ensure that the species is included in site management documents for all relevant SSSIs. (ACTION: EN)

5.3 Species management and protection

5.3.1 If necessary to restore populations lost since 1970, undertake habitat restoration and/or re-introductions at suitable former or potential sites. (ACTION: EN)

5.4 Advisory

5.4.1 Advise landowners and managers of the presence of the species and the importance of beneficial management for its conservation. (ACTION: EN)

5.5 **Future research and monitoring**

5.5.1 Undertake surveys to determine the status of this species. (ACTION: EN)

5.5.2 Conduct targeted autecological research to inform habitat management. (ACTION: EN)

5.5.3 Establish a regular monitoring programme for the species. (ACTION: EN)

5.5.4 Pass information gathered during survey and monitoring of this species to a central database for incorporation in national and international databases. (ACTION: EN)

5.5.5 Encourage research on the ecology and conservation of this species on an international level, and use the experience gained towards its conservation in the UK. (ACTION: EN, JNCC)

5.6 **Communications and publicity**

5.6.1 Promote opportunities for the appreciation of mire pill-beetle and the conservation issues associated with its. This should be achieved through articles within appropriate journals, as well as by a publicity leaflet. (ACTION: EN)

5.7 **Links with other action plans**

5.7.1 This action plan should be considered in conjunction with that for lowland raised bog.

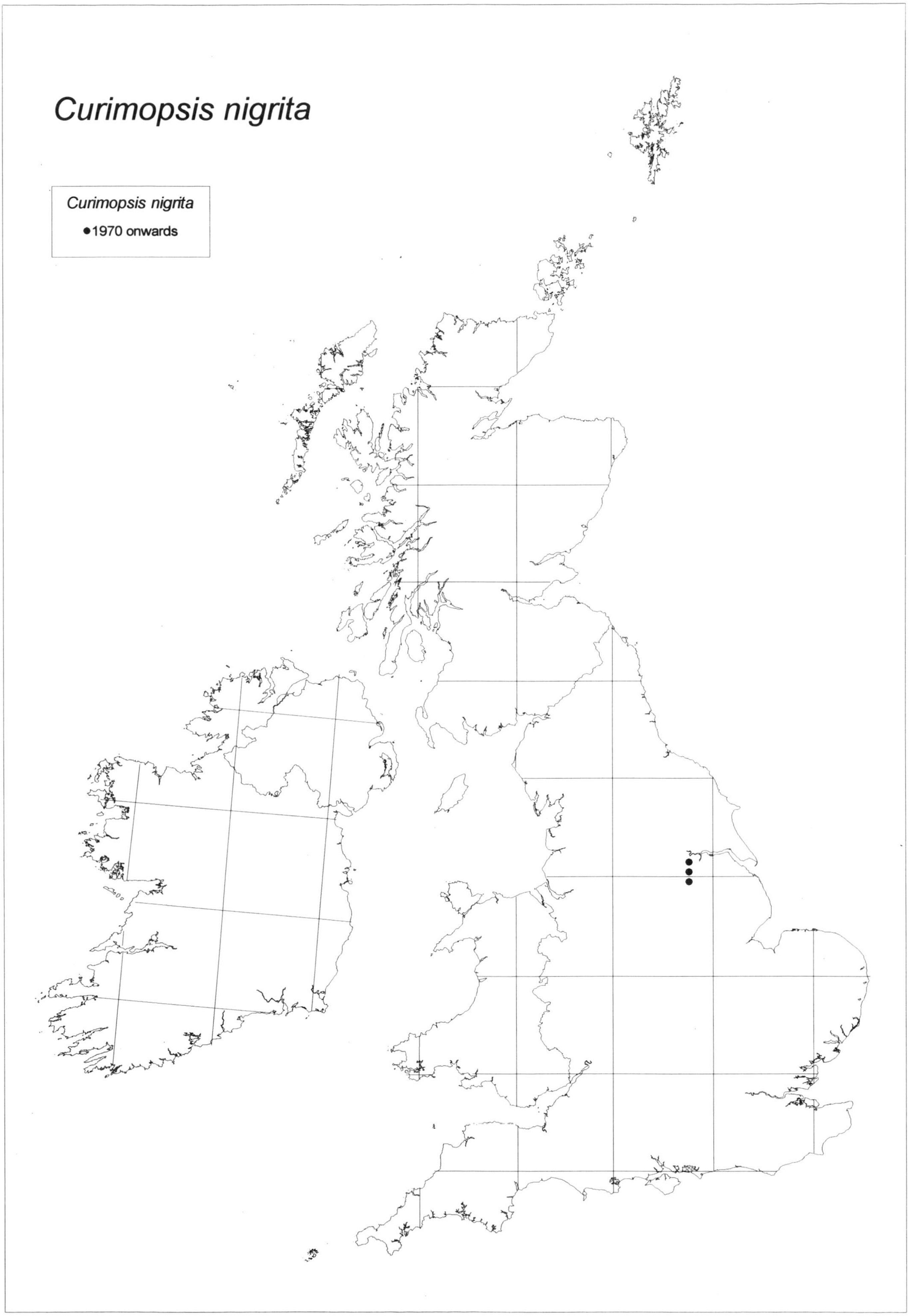

Distribution of Curimopsis nigrita - mire pill-beetle in Britain, by 10km square.
Source: English Nature - Invertebrate Site Register.

Donacia aquatica (a reed beetle)
Action Plan

1. Current status

1.1 *Donacia aquatica* usually occurs in small numbers on aquatic vegetation dominated by sedges, such as *Carex acutiformis*, at the margins of open water (lakes and fens). Adults are active during May and June. The larvae are aquatic, feeding below the surface on the submerged parts of emergent vegetation.

1.2 This was formerly a widespread but local species with pre-1970 records from much of southern and eastern England as far north as Northumberland and Cumberland. In Scotland there are old records from Dumfries-shire, east Inverness and Nairn, and Argyll mainland, and there is a single old record from Merionethshire in Wales. Post-1970 records show a considerable decline, with records restricted to West Sussex, Westmorland and north Lancashire, Roxburghshire and east Inverness and Nairn. It was also collected in County Fermanagh, Northern Ireland in 1992. This species is widespread in Europe.

1.3 In Great Britain this species is now classified as *Rare*.

2. Current factors causing loss or decline

2.1 Water abstraction.

2.2 Disturbance to marginal vegetation.

2.3 Infilling of lakes and ponds.

2.4 Eutrophication.

3. Current action

3.1 This species occurs on several SSSIs. The Northern Ireland site is an ASSI which is included within the Upper Lough Erne proposed SAC.

3.2 One site is a Sussex Wildlife Trust Reserve, and another (Insh Marshes) is an RSPB reserve.

4. Action plan objectives and targets

4.1 Maintain populations at all known sites.

4.2 Ensure the maintenance of a minimum of six viable populations across the historic range by 2010.

5. Proposed action with lead agencies

A survey of extant colonies and historic sites should be undertaken for this species. This will establish its current status and provide information to allow implementation of the other measures. Priorities include appropriate management of all extant sites, but this must be based on a better understanding of the beetle's ecological requirements. Each colony needs to be protected from water pollution, damaging agricultural practices and excessive water abstraction.

5.1 Policy and legislation

5.1.1 Take account of the species' requirements in response to applications for water abstraction licences. (ACTION: EA, EHS, SEPA)

5.1.2 Where appropriate, include the requirements of the species when preparing or revising prescriptions for agri-environment schemes. (ACTION: DANI, EHS, EN, MAFF, SNH, SOEAFD)

5.1.3 Address the requirements of this species through the LEAP process and in relevant WLMPs. (ACTION: EA, IDBs, LAs, MAFF)

5.2 Site safeguard and management

5.2.1 Where possible, ensure that all occupied habitat is appropriately managed, including the maintenance of water quality and water levels, by 2008. This may be through SSSI/ASSI or agri-environment scheme management agreements. (ACTION: DANI, DoE(NI), EA, EHS, EN, MAFF, SEPA, SNH, SOAEFD)

5.2.2 Ensure that the habitat requirements of *Donacia aquatica* are taken into account in any development policies, plans and proposals, particularly in respect to the infilling of ponds and lakes in which it occurs. (ACTION: EN, EHS, LAs, SNH)

5.2.3 Ensure that the species is included in site management documents for all relevant ASSIs and SSSIs. (ACTION: EN, EHS, SNH)

5.2.4 Consider notifying as SSSI/ASSIs sites supporting viable populations, where this is necessary to secure their long-term protection and appropriate management. (ACTION: EHS, EN, SNH)

5.3 **Species management and protection**

5.3.1 Consider reintroducing *Donacia aquatica* to a series of sites within the former range, if necessary to maintain six viable populations. (ACTION: CCW, EHS, EN, SNH)

5.4 **Advisory**

5.4.1 Advise landowners and managers of the presence of the species and the importance of beneficial management for its conservation. (ACTION: EA, EHS, EN, SNH)

5.4.2 As far as possible, ensure that all relevant agri-environment project officers, members of regional agri-environment consultation groups, relevant drainage engineers and waterways managers are advised of locations for this species, its importance, and management needed for its conservation. (ACTION: DANI, EA, EHS, EN, IDBs, MAFF, SEPA, SNH, SOAEFD)

5.5 **Future research and monitoring**

5.5.1 Undertake surveys to determine the status of this species. (ACTION: CCW, EHS, EN, SNH)

5.5.2 Conduct targeted autecological research to inform habitat management. (ACTION: EHS, EN, SNH)

5.5.3 Establish a regular monitoring programme for the species and its habitat. (ACTION: EHS, EN, SNH)

5.5.4 Pass information gathered during survey and monitoring of this species to a central database for incorporation in national and international databases. (ACTION: CCW, EHS, EN, SNH)

5.6 **Communications and publicity**

5.6.1 Promote opportunities for the appreciation of the species and the conservation issues associated with its habitat. This should be achieved through articles within appropriate journals, as well as by a publicity leaflet. (ACTION: EHS, EN, SNH)

5.7 **Links with other action plans**

5.7.1 This action plan should be considered in conjunction with those for eutrophic standing waters, fens, and mesotrophic lakes.

Donacia aquatica

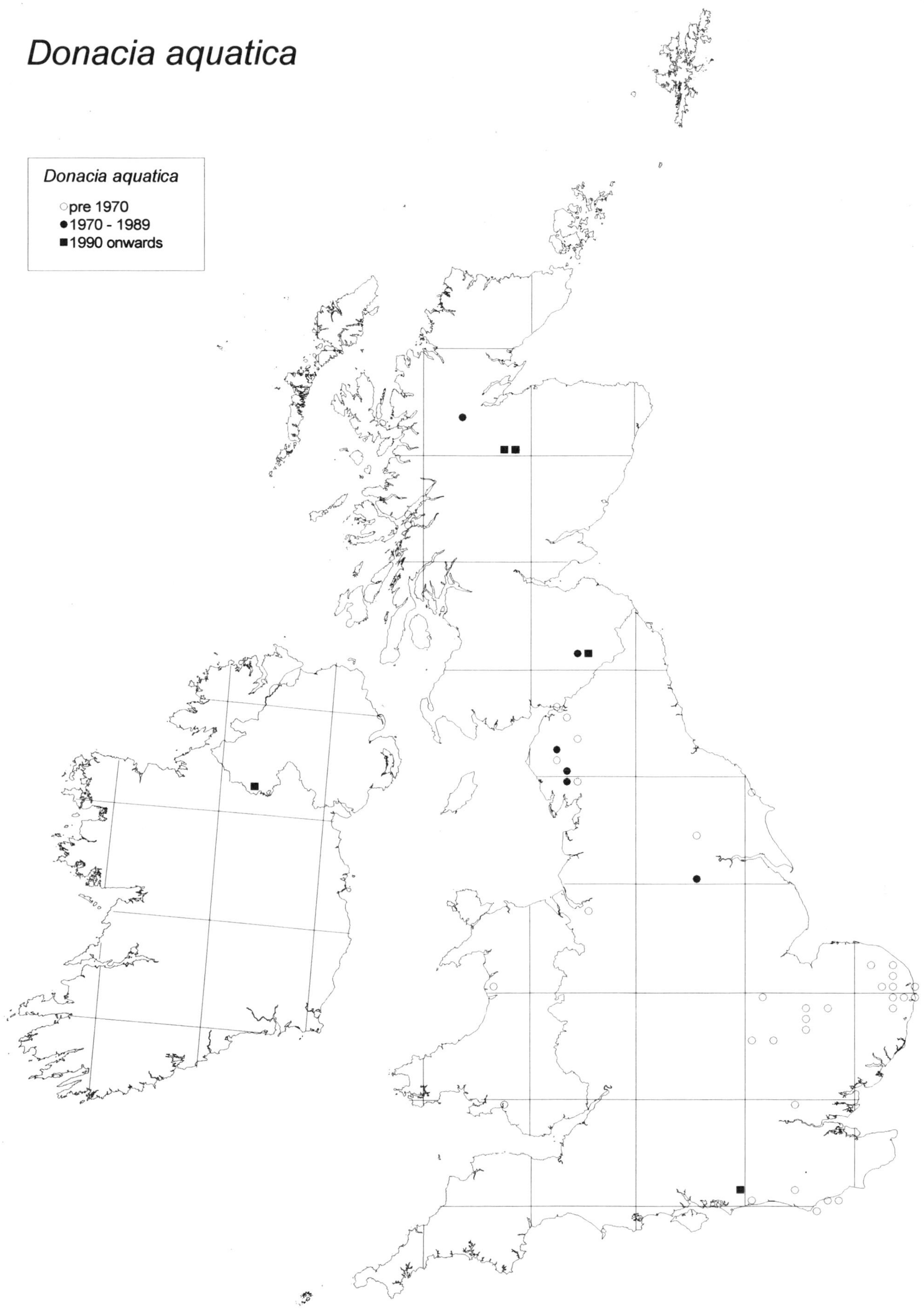

Distribution of Donacia aquatica - a reed beetle in Britain and Northern Ireland, by 10km square.
Source: M.Cox - Natural History Museum, English Nature - Invertebrate Site Register, Ulster Museum - CEDaR, Scottish Natural Heritage and Countryside Council for Wales records.

Donacia bicolora (a reed beetle) Action Plan

1. Current status

1.1 *Donacia bicolora* is associated with branched bur-reed growing along the margins of rivers, and sometimes ponds, lakes and canals; proximity to flowing water seems to be preferred. The biology has not been studied in the UK. The adults probably feed on the foliage of the host plant, or possibly on the pollen of other aquatic plants, such as yellow flag (*Iris pseudacora*). The larvae are aquatic and feed at the roots/rhizomes of the host plant. Adults occur from mid April until August, with most records in June. The larvae probably have a one or two year developmental period.

1.2 This species has declined dramatically since 1970, before which it was widespread throughout southern England, with scattered records north to Northumberland, and in Wales and Ireland. In Britain this species is now restricted to three sites: in Dorset, Surrey and south Hampshire. In Northern Ireland it has been recorded from six sites in County Fermanagh since 1988 and was also collected at Kiltubbrid Lough, County Armagh in 1997. Although rare, it may be quite plentiful in favoured localities. The reasons for the decline of this species are unknown, but possible causes are listed below. Its congener *D. simplex*, which also occurs on branched bur-reed, has not declined. *Donacia bicolora* is widespread in northern, central and southern Europe, the Mediterranean region, Middle East and Siberia.

1.3 In Great Britain this species is now classified as *Vulnerable*.

2. Current factors causing loss or decline

2.1 Water abstraction.

2.2 Disturbance of marginal vegetation.

2.3 Infilling of lakes and ponds.

2.4 Eutrophication.

3. Current action

3.1 Three of the Northern Ireland sites are ASSIs, two of which are within the Upper Lough Erne candidate SAC. At least two of the three recent records for England fall within SSSIs.

4. Action plan objectives and targets

4.1 Maintain populations at all known sites.

4.2 Ensure the establishment and maintenance of six viable populations across the historic range by 2010.

5. Proposed action with lead agencies

A survey of extant colonies and historic sites should be undertaken for this species. This will establish its current status and provide information to allow targeting of the other measures recommended. Priorities will include appropriate management of all extant sites, based on a better understanding of the beetles' ecological requirements, and protection for each colony from water pollution, damaging agricultural practices and excessive water abstraction activities.

5.1 Policy and legislation

5.1.1 Take account of the species' requirements in response to applications for water abstraction licences. (ACTION: EA, EHS)

5.1.2 Where appropriate, include the requirements of the species when preparing or revising prescriptions for agri-environment schemes. (ACTION: DANI, EHS, EN, MAFF)

5.1.3 Address the requirements of this species in the LEAP process and in relevant WLMPs. (ACTION: EA, IDBs, LAs, MAFF)

5.2 Site safeguard and management

5.2.1 Ensure that all occupied habitat is appropriately managed, including the maintenance of water quality and water levels, by 2008. This may be through SSSI/ASSI or agri-environment scheme management agreements. (ACTION: DANI, EA, EHS, EN, MAFF)

5.2.2 Ensure that the habitat requirements of *Donacia bicolor* are taken into account in any development policies, plans and proposals, particularly those involving the infilling of ponds and lakes in which it occurs. (ACTION: EHS, EN, LAs)

5.2.3 Ensure that the species is included in site management documents for all relevant SSSIs/ASSIs. (ACTION: EHS, EN)

5.2.4 Consider notifying as SSSIs/ASSIs sites holding key populations of the species, where this is necessary to secure their long-term protection and appropriate management. (ACTION: EHS, EN)

5.3 **Species management and protection**

5.3.1 Consider reintroducing *Donacia bicolora* to a series of sites within the former range, if necessary to maintain six viable populations. (ACTION: CCW, EHS, EN)

5.4 **Advisory**

5.4.1 Advise land owners and managers of the presence of the species and the importance of beneficial management for its conservation. (ACTION: EHS, EN)

5.4.2 As far as possible, ensure that all relevant agri-environment project officers, members of regional agri-environment consultation groups, relevant drainage engineers and waterways managers are advised of locations for this species, its importance, and the management needed for its conservation. (ACTION: DANI, EA, EHS, EN, IDBs, MAFF)

5.5 **Future research and monitoring**

5.5.1 Undertake surveys to determine the status of this species. (ACTION: CCW, EHS, EN)

5.5.2 Conduct targeted autecological research to inform habitat management. (ACTION: EHS, EN)

5.5.3 Establish a regular monitoring programme for the species. (ACTION: EHS, EN)

5.5.4 Pass information gathered during survey and monitoring of this species to a central database for incorporation in national and international databases. (ACTION: CCW, EHS, EN)

5.6 **Communications and publicity**

5.6.1 Promote opportunities for the appreciation of the species and the conservation issues associated with its habitat. This should be achieved through articles within appropriate journals, as well as by a publicity leaflet. (ACTION: EHS, EN)

5.7 **Links with other action plans**

5.7.1 This action plan should be considered in conjunction with those for coastal and floodplain grazing marsh, chalk rivers, fens, eutrophic standing waters, and mesotrophic lakes.

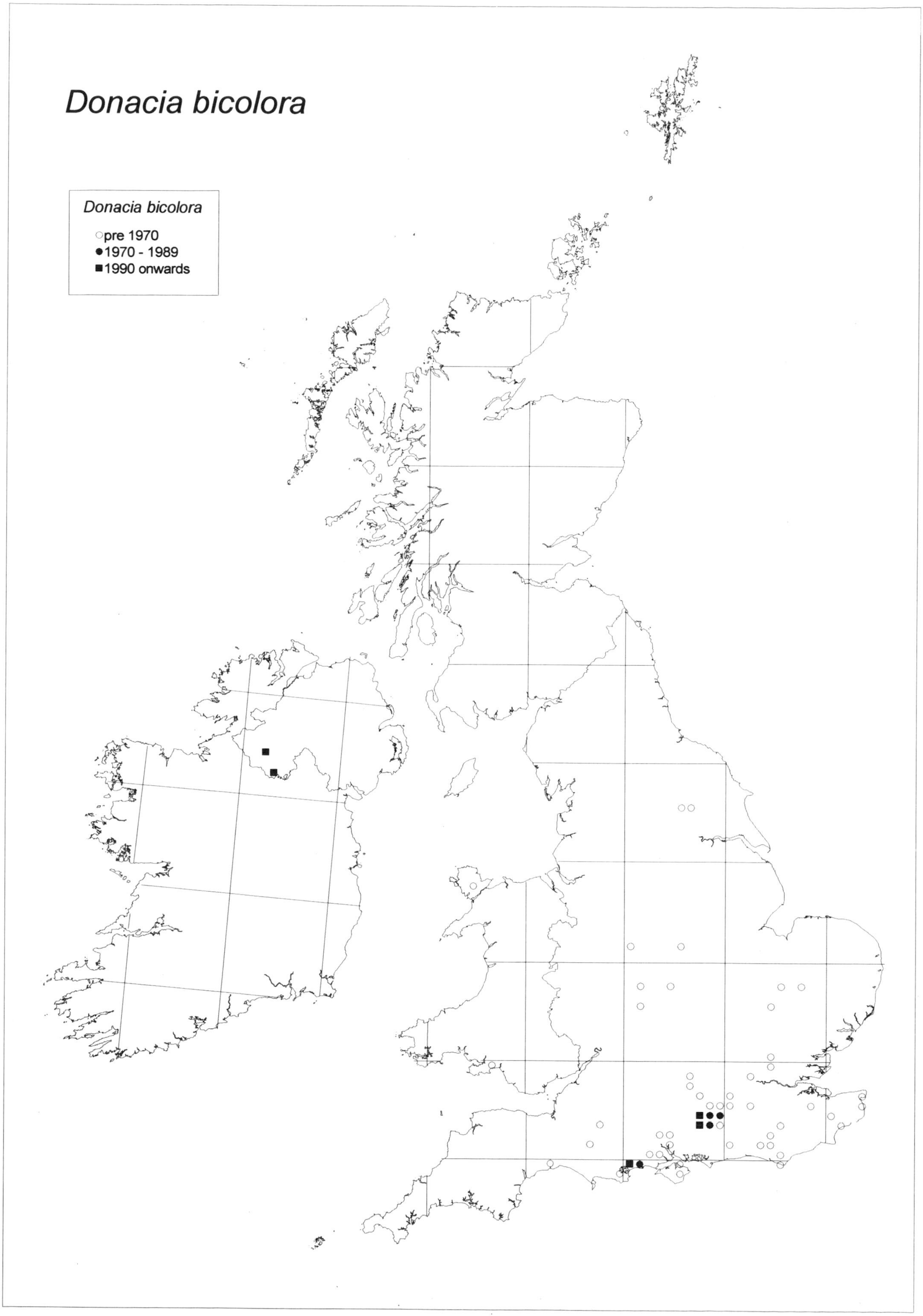

Distribution of Donacia bicolora - a reed beetle in Britain and Northern Ireland, by 10km square.
Source: M.Cox - Natural History Museum, English Nature - Invertebrate Site Register, Ulster Museum - CEDaR, and Countryside Council for Wales records.

Ernoporus tiliae (a bark beetle) Action Plan

1. Current status

1.1 *Ernoporus tiliae* is a small brown beetle specific to lime and preferring small-leafed lime. It seems to favour old coppiced woodlands with a continuity of lime, and requires branches or coppice poles up to 12 cm thick that still have some sap left in the cambium and which have relatively thick bark (1-2 mm). Large populations develop where brashings are left *in situ,* and old poles are not removed from coppice stools. Appropriately-sized branches of mature parkland trees are also suitable, although most modern records are from coppiced woods.

1.2 *E. tiliae* has become increasingly scarce in Britain in the last 50 years with few post-1970 records, though this may result from under-recording. Old records indicate a western distribution centred on Gloucestershire, Shropshire and Worcestershire, but there have also been records from Durham, Yorkshire, Lincolnshire, Leicestershire, Hertfordshire and Surrey. Since 1970 it has been recorded from just five areas: Yorkshire (Rudding Park), Gloucestershire (Forest of Dean), Lincolnshire (Central Limewoods), Northamptonshire (Easton Hornstocks) and Norfolk (Hockering Wood). *E. tiliae* is widespread but often localised throughout the Palearctic, from Scandinavia, through the Caucasus and across to western Siberia.

1.3 In Great Britain this species is classified as *Endangered*.

2. Current factors causing loss or decline

2.1 Decline in coppice as a regular management regime.

2.2 Loss of old lime woodlands.

2.3 Removal of fallen and dying timber.

3. Current action

3.1 A number of existing sites are SSSIs, and Collyweston Great Wood and the Central Lincolnshire Limewoods are NNRs.

3.2 Coppicing regimes at Collyweston Great Wood and the Central Lincolnshire Limewoods are favouring the maintenance and expansion of this species.

3.3 FE has restored conifer plantations on limewood sites in Lincolnshire to broadleaved woodland.

4. Action plan objectives and targets

4.1 Maintain and enhance the populations at all known sites.

5. Proposed action with lead agencies

The measures required to achieve the objectives of this plan are to identify all sites which contain populations of *Ernoporus tiliae,* ensure their protection, and apply management regimes which are conducive to the enhancement of populations of this species.

5.1 Policy and legislation

5.1.1 Where appropriate, include the requirements of the species when preparing or revising prescriptions for agri-environment or woodland grant schemes. (ACTION: EN, FE, MAFF)

5.2 Site safeguard and management

5.2.1 Where possible, ensure that all occupied habitat is appropriately managed, including the retention of dead wood, by 2008. This may be achieved through SSSI or agri-environment/ woodland grant scheme management agreements. (ACTION: EN, FE, MAFF)

5.2.2 Increase the area of lime coppice by conversion of plantation conifers in areas where this would benefit this species. (ACTION: FE)

5.2.3 Ensure that the species is included in site management documents for all relevant SSSIs. (ACTION: EN)

5.2.4 Consider notifying as SSSIs sites holding key populations of the species. (ACTION: EN)

5.3 Species management and protection

5.3.1 None proposed.

5.4 Advisory

5.4.1 Advise landowners and managers of the presence of this species and the importance of beneficial management for its conservation. (ACTION: EN, FC)

5.5 Future research and monitoring

5.5.1 Undertake surveys to determine the status of this species. (ACTION: EN)

5.5.2 Conduct targeted autecological research to inform habitat management. (ACTION: EN)

5.5.2 Establish a regular monitoring programme for the species. (ACTION: EN)

5.5.4 Pass information gathered during survey and monitoring of this species to a central database for incorporation in national and international databases. (ACTION: EN)

5.6 Communications and publicity

5.6.1 Promote opportunities for the appreciation of this beetle and the conservation issues associated with its habitat. This should be achieved through articles within appropriate journals, as well as by publicity leaflets. (ACTION: EN)

5.7 Links with other action plans

5.7.1 The requirements of this species should be taken into account in the delivery of the action plan for lowland wood pastures and parklands.

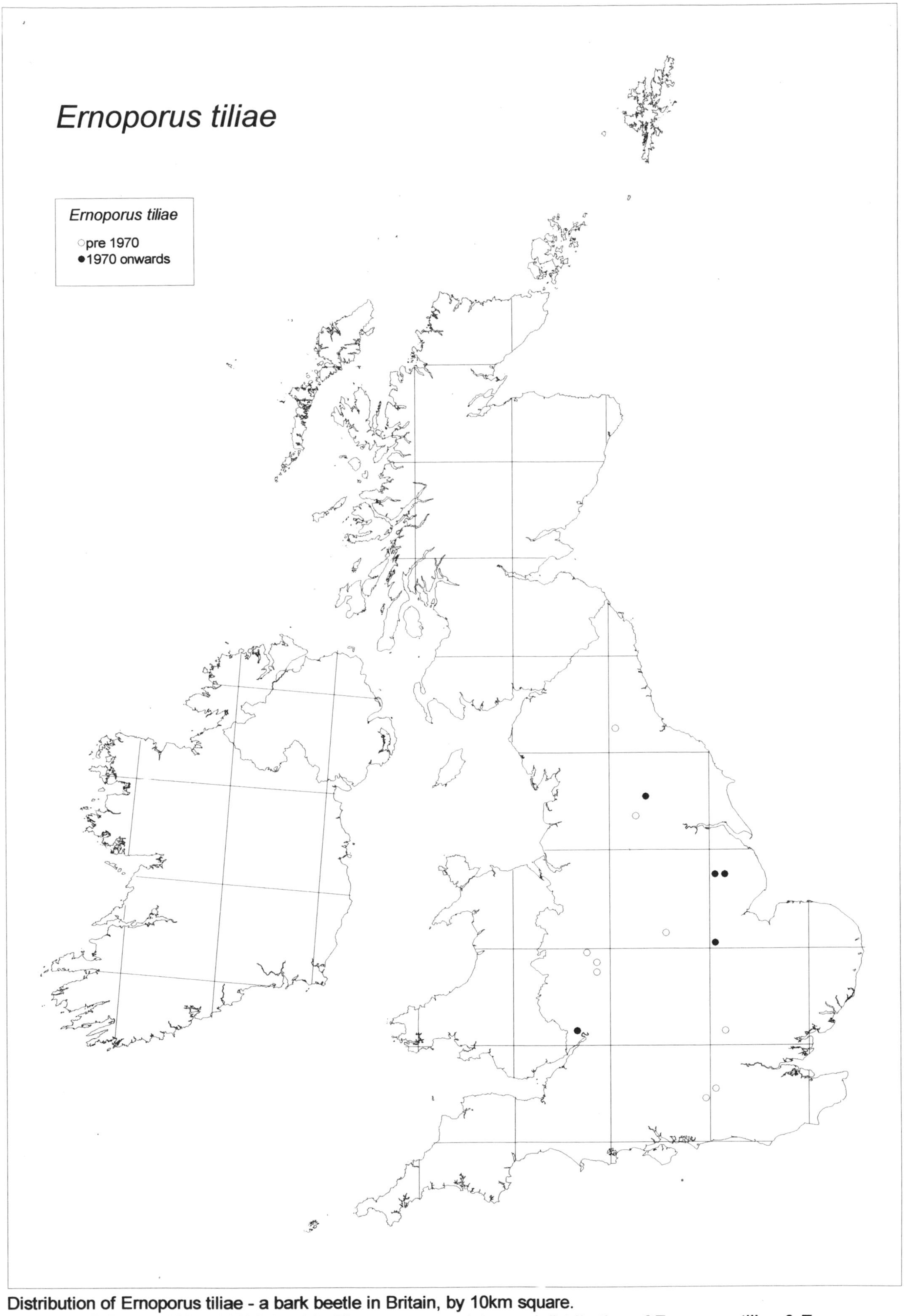

Distribution of Ernoporus tiliae - a bark beetle in Britain, by 10km square.
Source: A.B.Drane, 1997, (MPhil thesis). The taxonomy, status and distribution of Ernoporus tiliae & Ernoporus caucasicus, with reference to their occurence in Northamptonshire, Leicestershire & Lincolnshire, Leicester University.

Spangled diving beetle (*Graphoderus zonatus*) Action Plan

1. Current status

1.1 The spangled diving beetle is known to occur naturally in Britain only in Woolmer Forest, north Hampshire. Within the Woolmer Forest area, adults occur in a wide range of pools, most of which are relatively recent in origin and which vary considerably in vegetation, pH, depth and degree of permanence. These include a deep, permanently flooded pond, with its bottom covered by *Sphagnum*, created by peat cutting in 1895; pools resulting from military activities; and pools dug as breeding sites for natterjack toads. Several of the pools receive inflow and are less acidic, and one has been limed. These pools have in common the absence of fish. Teneral adults of the beetle have been found in four of these ponds, indicating successful breeding. Woolmer Pond was excavated in 1986 and 1993 to recreate its mere structure. In the following years larvae were present in the pond from April to July, with third instars into August. Newly emerged adults occurred at the end of June, having pupated at the bases of rush tussocks. Adults may overwinter out of the water. In captivity young larvae fed on Cladocera, and older larvae fed on water boatmen and *Notonecta* nymphs; they showed a preference for open water.

1.2 In Europe the spangled diving beetle has two subspecies. The nominate form extends from south and central Europe to Mongolia, whilst *G. z. verrucifer* is boreo-alpine, extending from Scandinavia to northern Siberia and Italy. In mainland Europe the beetle occurs in the exposed edges of wave-washed sandy lakes, amongst submerged vegetation with some peat substratum, usually in moorland. The British form is probably the nominate form; this is consistent with the confinement of the spangled diving beetle to southern England, despite the abundance of apparently suitable habitats in Scotland.

1.3 In Great Britain the spangled diving beetle is currently classified as *Endangered*. It is given special protection under Schedule 5 of the Wildlife and Countryside Act 1981.

2. Current factors causing loss or decline

2.1 Dessication of ponds, caused by low winter rainfall and, possibly, water abstraction.

2.2 Pollution by increased run-off from neighbouring roads, and leakage of effluent from a nearby pig farm.

2.3 Hydrological succession, leading to the loss of open water and eventually scrub encroachment.

2.4 Increases in pH, allowing colonisation by fish.

3. Current action

3.1 All of the occupied ponds at Woolmer are within an SSSI.

3.2 The species has been the subject of an English Nature Species Recovery Programme since 1993.

3.3 Woolmer Pond has been excavated by the MoD in 1986 and 1993.

3.4 Surveys have been undertaken of the water beetle fauna of Woolmer Forest and neighbouring areas.

3.5 Annual monitoring has been undertaken since 1993.

3.6 The identity and some aspects of the ecology of the previously undescribed larvae have been elucidated.

3.7 Material from Woolmer has been introduced into neighbouring sites, the survey of which had previously demonstrated the absence of this species. The translocations appear to have been unsuccessful.

4. Action plan objectives and targets

4.1 Ensure that at least four sub-populations are maintained within the Woolmer Forest area by 2010.

5. Proposed action with lead agencies

The priorities under this action plan are to refine knowledge of the ecology of the spangled diving beetle, to maintain constantly high water levels in occupied ponds, and to maintain the number of self-sustaining populations.

5.1 Policy and legislation

5.1.1 Undertake a review of water abstraction policies within the area where the species occurs. (ACTION: EA)

5.1.2 Address the requirements of this species in the LEAP process and in relevant WLMPs. (ACTION: EA, IDBs, LAs, MAFF)

5.2 **Site safeguard and management**

5.2.1 Ensure that the species is included in site management documents for the Woolmer SSSI. (ACTION: EN)

5.2.2 Ensure that the habitat requirements of this species are taken into account in any development policies, plans and proposals that might affect the Woolmer area. (ACTION: EA, EN, LAs)

5.2.3 Where possible, ensure that all occupied habitat is appropriately managed, including prevention of pollution, by 2008. (ACTION: EN, MoD)

5.2.4 If practicable, excavate four new pools in the Woolmer area. (ACTION: EN, MoD)

5.3 **Species management and protection**

5.3.1 If necessary, introduce the spangled diving beetle to newly-created pools to ensure that four sub-populations are maintained in the area. (ACTION: EN)

5.4 **Advisory**

5.4.1 Advise all landowners, land managers and planning authorities associated with the Woolmer Forest catchment of appropriate management, including the risks associated with contaminated run-off. (ACTION: EA, EN)

5.5 **Future research and monitoring**

5.5.1 Continue annual monitoring of adults and larvae. (ACTION: EN)

5.5.2 Conduct targeted autecological research to inform habitat management, in particular the overwintering preferences and feeding habits of the adults. (ACTION: EN)

5.5.3 Pass information gathered during survey and monitoring of this species to a central database for incorporation in national and international databases. (ACTION: EN)

5.6 **Communications and publicity**

5.6.1 Promote opportunities for the appreciation of the species and the conservation issues associated with its habitat. This should be achieved through articles within appropriate journals, as well as by a publicity leaflet. (ACTION: EN)

5.7 **Links with other action plans**

5.7.1 Implementation of this plan could benefit other species of shallow heathland pools, including natterjack toad *Bufo calamita*.

5.7.2 This plan should be considered in conjunction with that for lowland heathland.

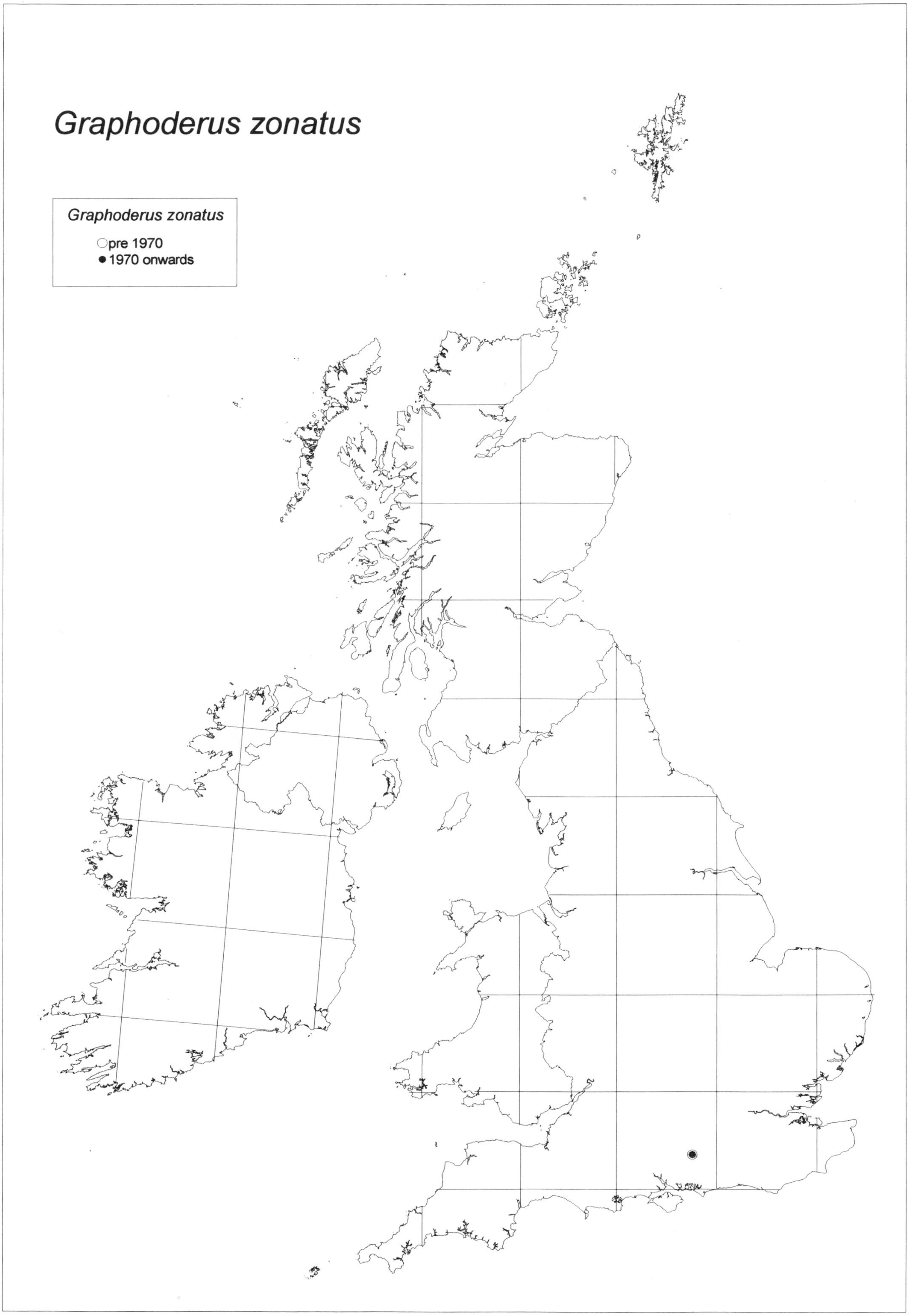

Distribution of Graphoderus zonatus - spangled diving beetle in Britain, by 10km square.
Source: The Balfour-Browne Club - Water Beetle Recording Scheme.

Helophorus laticollis (a water beetle) Action Plan

1. Current status

1.1 *Helophorus laticollis* is found in shallow, exposed, grassy pools on heathland. Unlike other British species of the genus which place their egg cocoons in mud beside water, *H. laticollis* places its cocoons among vegetation in the water.

1.2 Although originally found on heathland in Dorset, south Hampshire and Surrey, *Helophorus laticollis* has been recorded only from the New Forest since the 1960s. This species is centred on northern Europe, from Scandinavia south-west to The Netherlands and east to Moscow, with other outlying populations in the central French mountains, southern Germany and Iceland.

1.3 In Great Britain this species is now classified as *Vulnerable*.

2. Current factors causing loss or decline

2.1 Water abstraction.

2.2 Damage to headwater drainage systems, in particular associated with tourist development and road improvement.

2.3 Reduction in grazing, resulting in scrub encroachment.

3. Current action

3.1 Recent records are from within the New Forest SSSI/candidate SAC.

4. Action plan objectives and targets

4.1 Maintain populations at all known sites.

4.2 Ensure populations at known sites have long-term viability.

4.3 Restore populations to two suitable sites within the historic range by 2010.

5. Proposed action with lead agencies

The priority for action is to ensure the continuation of suitable grazing practice in the New Forest so that the habitat is maintained. Reintroductions to sites within the former range must be undertaken. In addition, surveys are required to establish the distribution of the beetle.

5.1 Policy and legislation

5.1.1 Take account of the species' requirements in response to water abstraction licences. (ACTION: EA)

5.1.2 Address the requirements of this species in the LEAP process and in relevant WLMPs. (ACTION: EA, IDBs, LAs, MAFF)

5.2 Site safeguard and management

5.2.1 Where possible, ensure that all occupied habitat is appropriately managed by 2008. (ACTION: EN, FE)

5.2.2 Ensure that the species is included in site management documents for all relevant SSSIs. (ACTION: EN)

5.2.3 Ensure that the habitat requirements of *Helophorus laticollis* are taken into account in any relevant development policies, plans and proposals. (ACTION: EN, LAs)

5.2.4 Consider notifying as SSSIs sites holding key populations of the species, where this is necessary to secure their long-term protection and appropriate management. (ACTION: EN)

5.3 Species management and protection

5.3.1 Reintroduce this species to two heathland sites, one in Surrey and one in north Hampshire, to establish two new viable populations. (ACTION: EN)

5.4 Advisory

5.4.1 Advise landowners and managers of the presence of this species and the importance of beneficial management for its conservation. (ACTION: EA, EN)

5.5 Future research and monitoring

5.5.1 Undertake surveys of New Forest and Dorset heathland to identify the extent of the present distribution of this species. (ACTION: EN)

5.5.2 Conduct targeted autecological research to inform habitat management. (ACTION: EN)

5.5.3 Establish a regular monitoring programme for the species. (ACTION: EN)

5.5.4 Pass information gathered during survey and monitoring of this species to a central database for incorporation in national and international databases. (ACTION: EN)

5.6 Communications and publicity

5.6.1 Promote opportunities for the appreciation of the species and the conservation issues associated with heathland pools. This should be achieved through articles within appropriate journals, as well as by a publicity leaflet. (ACTION: EN)

5.7 Links with other action plans

5.7.1 Implementation of this action plan could benefit other species associated with wet heathland, including the water beetle *Agabus brunneus*.

5.7.2 This plan should be considered in conjunction with that for lowland heathland.

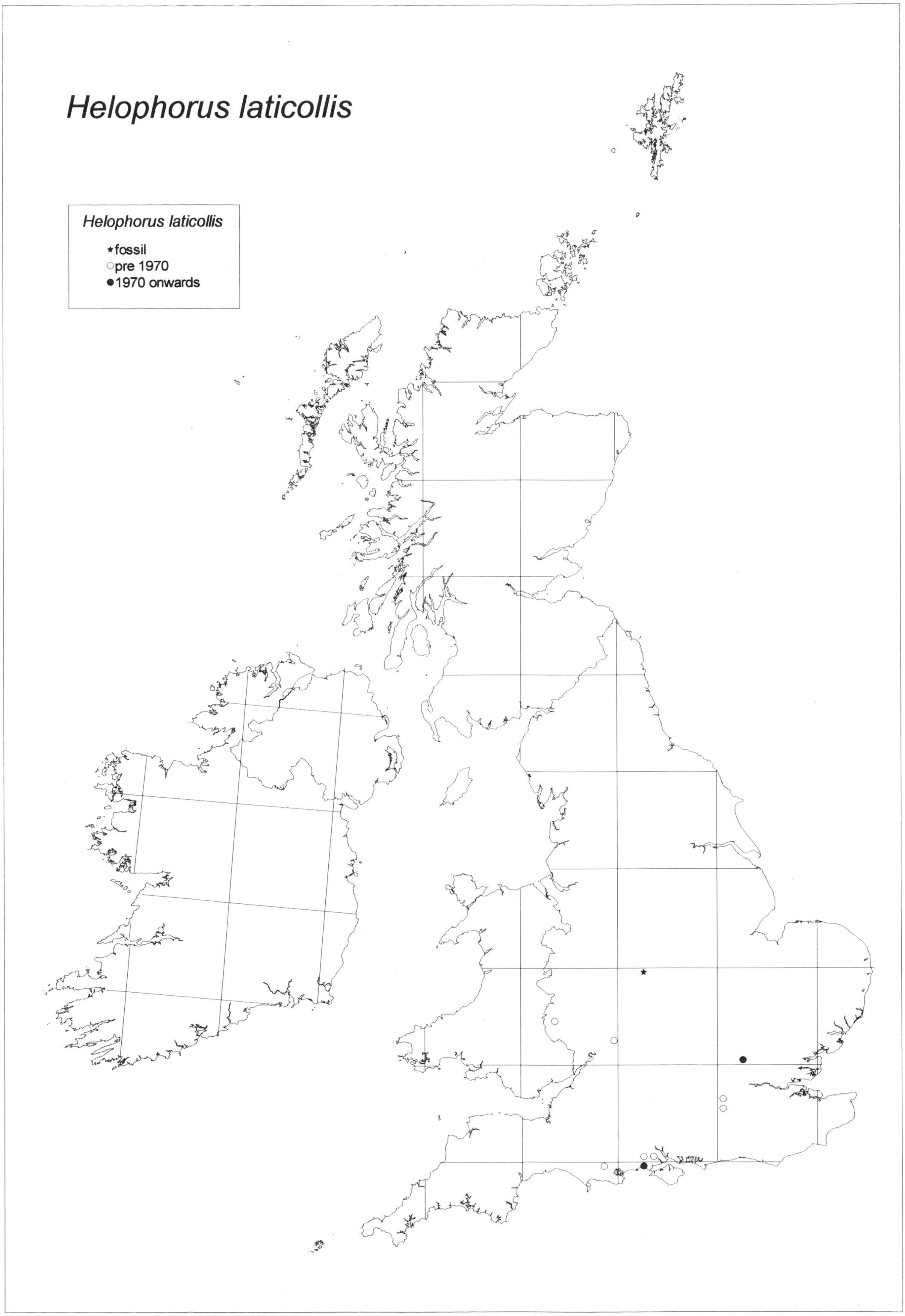

Distribution of Helophorus laticollis - a water beetle in Britain, 10km square.
Source: Balfour-Browne Club - Water Beetle Recording Scheme.

Lesser silver water beetle (*Hydrochara caraboides*) Action Plan

1. Current status

1.1 The lesser silver water beetle is found in exposed, richly vegetated ditches and ponds. In the Somerset Moors, this species is confined to peat areas and is frequent only on the turbary peats of Tadham and Westhay Moors. The species benefits from piecemeal, periodic ditch cleaning and high water levels that reduce peat wastage on the Somerset Moors. The Cheshire sites include some relatively undisturbed ponds. The egg cocoon's construction necessitates the use of floating debris and, therefore, large floating plants, such as frogbit and flote-grass, are thought to be beneficial. However, access to ponds and ditches by grazing animals may be required in order to maintain an open structure. Eggs are laid in spring or early summer, and larvae occur, often floating just below the surface, from May to July. The larvae are predators of water snails. Adults emerge during the summer and overwinter, though it is not clear whether this occurs in the water or on the bank. Adults are occasionally found attracted to light or to glass, and fly readily at dusk if kept in captivity.

1.2 In Britain this species is known from 11 ten km squares since 1970. It was much more widely distributed in the 19th century, being particularly well recorded from the Hammersmith Marshes, the Cambridgeshire Fens and Askham Bog. Until recently it was thought to have become confined to ditches on the deeper turbary peats of the Somerset Moors, but the discovery in 1990 of an adult in a pond on the Cheshire Plain has been followed by the discovery of more colonies, some with egg cocoons and larvae. By 1997, it had been recorded from 7 ten km squares here.

1.3 In Great Britain this species is classified as *Endangered*. It is given full protection under Schedule 5 of the Wildlife and Countryside Act 1981.

2. Current factors causing loss or decline

2.1 Inappropriate ditch management.

2.2 Conversion of grazing marsh to arable land, resulting in steeper ditch profiles and overgrowth of ditches in the absence of grazing.

2.3 Infilling of ponds.

2.4 Agricultural improvement.

2.5 Loss of ponds to urban development.

3. Current action

3.1 Ponds on the Cheshire Plain have been the subject of the Pond Life Survey since 1995.

3.2 Through EN's Species Recovery Programme, additional survey has been undertaken and some ponds have been managed to improve them for this species.

3.3 Surveys for this species were undertaken in 1993 and 1994 on the Somerset Moors.

3.4 The species is present in the Somerset Levels and Moors SPA.

4. Action plan objectives and targets

4.1 Maintain viable populations within the Somerset Moors and the Cheshire Plain.

5. Proposed action with lead agencies

The priorities for the lesser silver water beetle are to implement appropriate habitat management at existing sites, and to undertake research to elucidate relevant aspects of the species' ecology. In addition, further surveys should be carried out to establish the distribution of the beetle.

5.1 Policy and legislation

5.1.1 Where appropriate, include the requirements of the species when preparing or revising prescriptions for agri-environment schemes. (ACTION: EN, MAFF)

5.1.2 Take account of this species' requirements in response to applications for water abstraction licences. (ACTION: EA)

5.1.3 Address the requirements of this species in the LEAP process and in relevant WLMPs. (ACTION: EA, IDBs, LAs, MAFF)

5.2 Site safeguard and management

5.2.1 Where possible, ensure that all occupied habitat is appropriately managed, including periodic ditch cleaning on the Somerset Moors, by 2008. This may be through SSSI or agri-environment scheme management agreements. (ACTION: EA, EN, IDBs, MAFF)

5.2.2 Ensure that the habitat requirements of *Hydrochara caraboides* are taken into account in any relevant development policies, plans and proposals. (ACTION: EN, LAs)

5.2.3 Ensure that the species is included in site management documents for all relevant SSSIs. (ACTION: EN)

5.2.4 Consider notifying as SSSIs sites holding key populations of the species, where this is necessary to secure their long-term protection and appropriate management. (ACTION: EN)

5.3 **Species management and protection**

5.3.1 None proposed.

5.4 **Advisory**

5.4.1 Advise landowners and managers of the presence of this species and the importance of beneficial management for its conservation. (ACTION: EA, EN, MAFF)

5.4.2 As far as possible, ensure that all relevant agri-environment project officers, and members of regional agri-environment consultation groups, are advised of locations of this species, its importance, and the management needed for its conservation. (ACTION: EN, MAFF)

5.5 **Future research and monitoring**

5.5.1 Undertake further surveys to determine the status of this species. (ACTION: EN)

5.5.2 Establish a regular monitoring programme for this species. (ACTION: EN)

5.5.3 Conduct targeted autecological research to inform habitat management. (ACTION: EN)

5.5.4 Pass information gathered during survey and monitoring of this species to a central database for incorporation in national and international databases. (ACTION: EN)

5.6 **Communications and publicity**

5.6.1 Promote opportunities for the appreciation of the species and the conservation issues associated with its habitat. This should be achieved through articles within appropriate journals, as well as by a publicity leaflet. (ACTION: EN)

5.7 **Links with other action plans**

5.7.1 Implementation of this action plan could benefit other species of grazing marsh, including the shining ramshorn snail *Segmentina nitida*.

5.7.2 This plan should be considered in conjunction with that for coastal and floodplain grazing marsh.

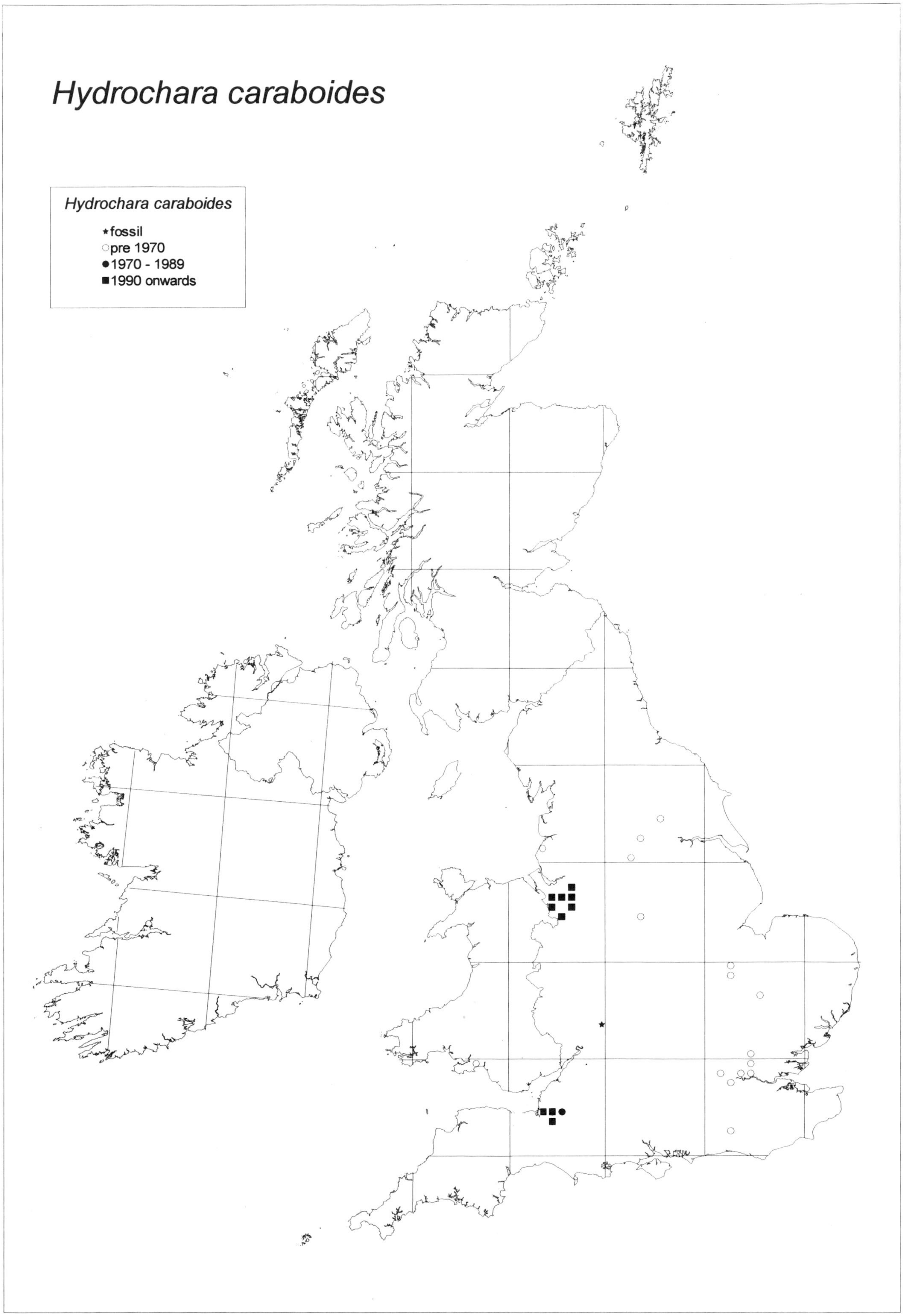

Distribution of Hydrochara caraboides - lesser silver water beetle in Britain, by 10km square.
Source: Balfour-Browne Club - Water Beetle Recording Scheme.

Hydroporus rufifrons (a diving beetle)
Action Plan

1. Current status

1.1 *Hydroporus rufifrons* occurs in extremely shallow, temporary pools in unimproved pasture, often in old oxbow systems. Its elusiveness is probably, in part, the result of the brief period of adult activity in the autumn and spring. Flight tests have proved negative.

1.2 *Hydroporus rufifrons* is generally regarded as a rare species, scattered through north and central Europe from France to western Siberia. In the UK, recent published records are for Cardiganshire, north Lincolnshire, mid-west Yorkshire, Westmorland, south Northumberland, Dumfries-shire, and Stirlingshire. An earlier record for Raasay is considered unlikely. It has been recorded at seven sites in the 1980s and three in the 1990s. This species has apparently become extinct in many former habitats on the east side of England from Boldon Flats, County Durham, to west Norfolk, where it was formerly found near to the fluctuating meres of Wretham Heath. The species has also been lost from some northern sites, for example Thurstonfield Lough, but appears to have a stronghold in Galloway and in the southern part of the Lake District.

1.3 In Great Britain this species is classified as *Vulnerable*.

2. Current factors causing loss or decline

2.1 Loss of unimproved pasture.

2.2 Damage to lakeside marginal pool complexes.

2.3 Inundation through impoundment for reservoirs.

3. Current action

3.1 This species occurs on several SSSIs, NNRs and other nature reserves.

4. Action plan objectives and targets

4.1 Ensure that viable populations are maintained within each of the areas currently occupied.

4.2 Reintroduce two populations of this species in East Anglia, and one population in South Wales, by 2010, if not refound in these former parts of its range.

5. Proposed action with lead agencies

The actions in this plan focus on maintaining or establishing appropriate management on sites where *Hydroporus rufifrons* is present. This requires research to supplement existing knowledge of the beetle and its habitat. This beetle is flightless and unlikely to recolonise sites, so a reintroduction programme is needed to recover former sites.

5.1 Policy and legislation

5.1.1 Where appropriate, include the requirements of the species when preparing or revising prescriptions for agri-environment schemes. (ACTION: CCW, EN, MAFF, SNH, SOAEFD, WOAD)

5.1.2 Address the requirements of this species in the LEAP process and in relevant WLMPs. (ACTION: EA, IDBs, LAs, MAFF)

5.2 Site safeguard and management

5.2.1 Where possible, ensure that all occupied habitat is appropriately managed by 2010, for example through SSSI or agri-environment scheme management agreements. (ACTION: CCW, EN, MAFF, SNH, SOAEFD, WOAD)

5.2.2 Ensure that the species is included in site management documents for all relevant SSSIs. (ACTION: CCW, EN, SNH)

5.2.3 Consider notifying as SSSIs sites holding key populations, where this is necessary to secure their long-term protection and appropriate management. (ACTION: CCW, EN, SNH)

5.3 Species management and protection

5.3.1 Consider reintroducing the beetle to a series of sites within the former range to establish three new viable populations, two in East Anglia and one in South Wales. (ACTION: CCW, EN)

5.4 Advisory

5.4.1 Advise landowners and managers of the presence of the species and the importance of beneficial management for its conservation. (ACTION: CCW, EN, MAFF, SNH, SOAEFD, WOAD)

5.4.2 As far as possible, ensure that all relevant agri-environment project officers, and members of regional agri-environment consultation groups, are advised of locations of this species, its importance, and the management needed for its conservation. (ACTION: CCW, EN, MAFF, SNH, SOAEFD, WOAD)

5.5 Future research and monitoring

5.5.1 Undertake surveys to determine the status of the species. (ACTION: CCW, EN, SNH)

5.5.2 Conduct targeted autecological research to inform habitat management. (ACTION: CCW, EN, SNH)

5.5.3 Pass information gathered during survey and monitoring of this species to a central database for incorporation in national and international databases. (ACTION: CCW, EN, SNH)

5.5.4 Encourage studies of the genetics of the beetle to inform any reintroduction programme. (ACTION: CCW, EN, SNH)

5.5.5 Encourage research on the ecology and conservation of this species on an international level, and use the experience to inform habitat management in the UK. (ACTION: CCW, EN, JNCC, SNH)

5.6 Communications and publicity

5.6.1 Promote opportunities for the appreciation of this species and the conservation issues associated with its habitat. This should be achieved through articles within appropriate journals, as well as by a publicity leaflet. (ACTION: CCW, EN, SNH)

5.7 Links with other action plans

5.7.1 This plan should be considered in conjunction with those for fens, and coastal and floodplain grazing marsh.

Hydroporus rufifrons

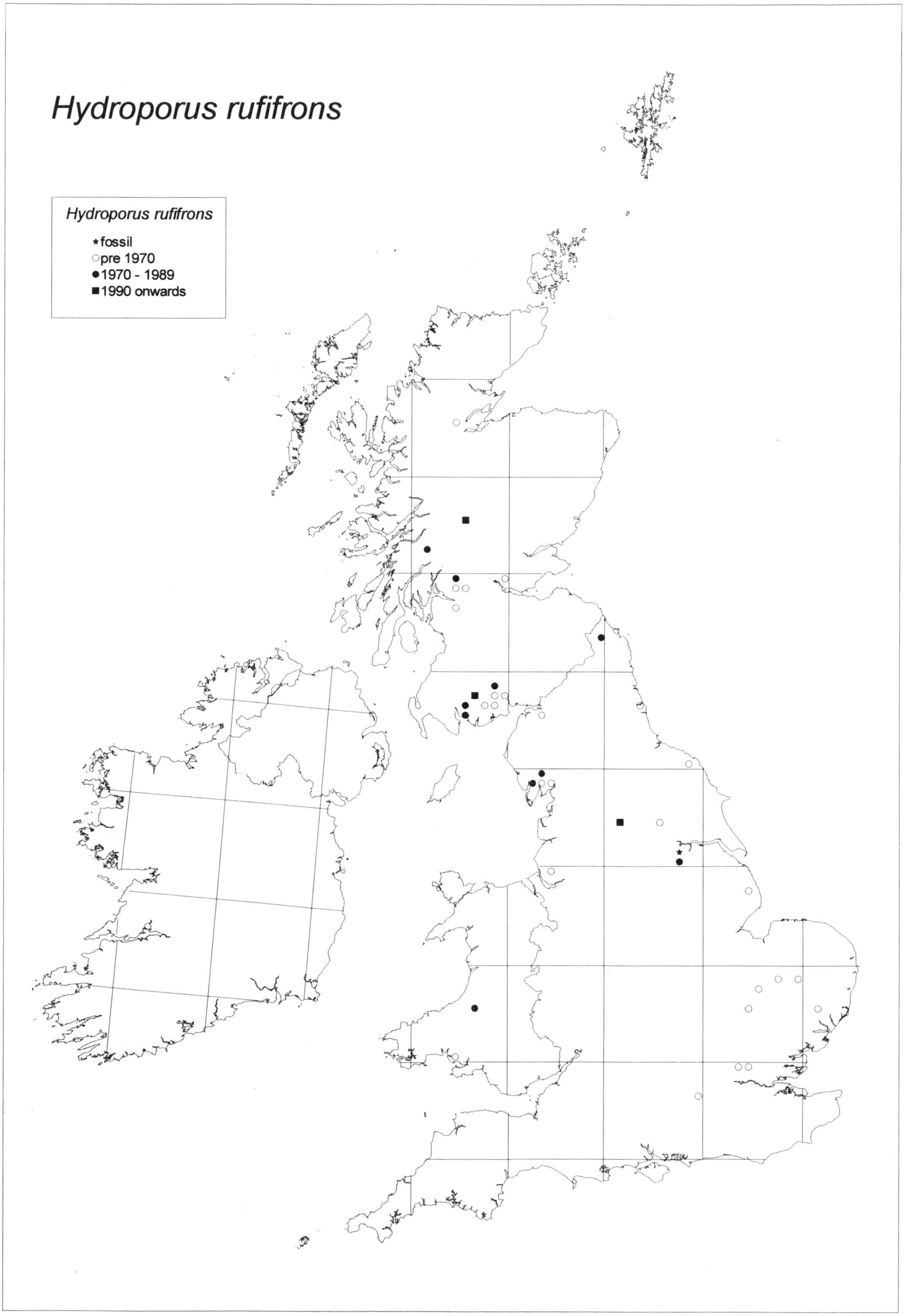

Distribution of Hydroporus rufifrons - a water beetle in Britain, by 10km square.
Source: Balfour-Browne Club - Water Beetle Recording Scheme.

Laccophilus poecilus (=obsoletus) (a diving beetle) Action Plan

1. Current status

1.1 *Laccophilus poecilus* occupies lowland fen and grazing marsh, near the coast but not in brackish water. Typically, it is associated with richly vegetated margins of ditches and lakes, often with dense ivy-leaved duckweed and aquatic liverwort, but also in dense wet litter in beds of reeds and sedges. There is evidence of flight ability from south-west France.

1.2 There are recent published records for East Sussex and older records for south Hampshire, West Sussex, east Kent and south-west Yorkshire. The species was not found during recent survey work on Thorne Waste, from where it was last reported in 1954. The most recent record for Kent is based on a specimen taken at Canterbury in 1958. *Laccophilus poecilus* appears to have become extinct everywhere in its British range except the Lewes Levels, where it was rediscovered in July 1996. It used to be common in parts of the Pevensey Levels, from where it has been lost after water quality deteriorated. *Laccophilus poecilus* is a widely distributed Palearctic species, probably commonest around the Mediterranean; it ranges north to southern Norway and Sweden, extending to Asia Minor, Syria, Egypt and the Caspian.

1.3 In Great Britain this species is currently classified as *Vulnerable*.

2. Current factors causing loss or decline

2.1 Water abstraction.

2.2 Declining water quality.

2.3 Conversion of grazing marsh to arable land.

2.4 Inappropriate ditch management.

3. Current action

3.1 A survey, funded by EN, has recently been undertaken of the area of the Lewes Levels formerly occupied by *L.poecilus*.

3.2 The only proven extant site is on the Lewes Brooks SSSI.

4. Action plan objectives and targets

4.1 Maintain a viable population on the Lewes Levels.

4.2 Ensure the establishment and maintenance of viable populations in each of the Pevensey Levels and Deal Marshes by 2010, if not refound in these former parts of its range.

5. Proposed action with lead agencies

The actions in this plan focus on maintaining or establishing appropriate management on sites where *Laccophilus poecilus* is present. This requires research to supplement existing knowledge of the beetle and its habitat. A reintroduction programme may be needed to recover former sites.

5.1 Policy and legislation

5.1.1 Where appropriate, include the requirements of the species when preparing or revising prescriptions for agri-environment schemes. (ACTION: EN, MAFF)

5.1.2 Take account of the species' requirement in response to applications for water abstraction licences. (ACTION: EA)

5.1.3 Address the requirements of this species in the LEAP process and in relevant WLMPs. (ACTION: EA, IDBs, LAs, MAFF)

5.2 Site safeguard and management

5.2.1 Where possible, ensure that occupied habitat is appropriately managed, including rotational management of ditch systems, by 2008. This may be achieved through SSSI or agri-environment scheme management agreements. (ACTION: EA, EN, IDBs, MAFF)

5.2.2 Ensure that the species is included in site management documents for the Lewes Brooks SSSI. (ACTION: EN)

5.2.3 Consider notifying as SSSIs any newly-discovered sites holding viable populations of the species. (ACTION: EN)

5.3 Species management and protection

5.3.1 If surveys show that no populations exist outside the Lewes Levels, reintroduce populations of this species to a series of sites within the former range by 2010. (ACTION: EN)

5.4 Advisory

5.4.1 Advise landowners and managers of the presence of this species and the importance of beneficial management for its conservation. (ACTION: EA, EN)

5.5 Future research and monitoring

5.5.1 Undertake surveys to determine the status of this species. (ACTION: EN)

5.5.2 Conduct targeted autecological research to inform habitat management. (ACTION: EN)

5.5.3 Establish a regular monitoring programme at Lewes Levels and any newly-discovered sites. (ACTION: EN)

5.5.4 Pass information gathered during survey and monitoring of this species to a central database for incorporation in national and international databases. (ACTION: EN)

5.6 Communication and publicity

5.6.1 Promote opportunities for the appreciation of the species and the conservation issues associated with its habitat. This should be achieved through articles within appropriate journals, as well as by a publicity leaflet. (ACTION: EN)

5.7 Links with other action plans

5.7.1 Implementation of this action plan could benefit other species of grazing marsh, including the aquatic molluscs *Segmentina nitida* and *Anisus vorticulus*.

5.7.2 This plan should be considered in conjunction with those for fens, and coastal and floodplain grazing marsh.

Laccophilus poecilus

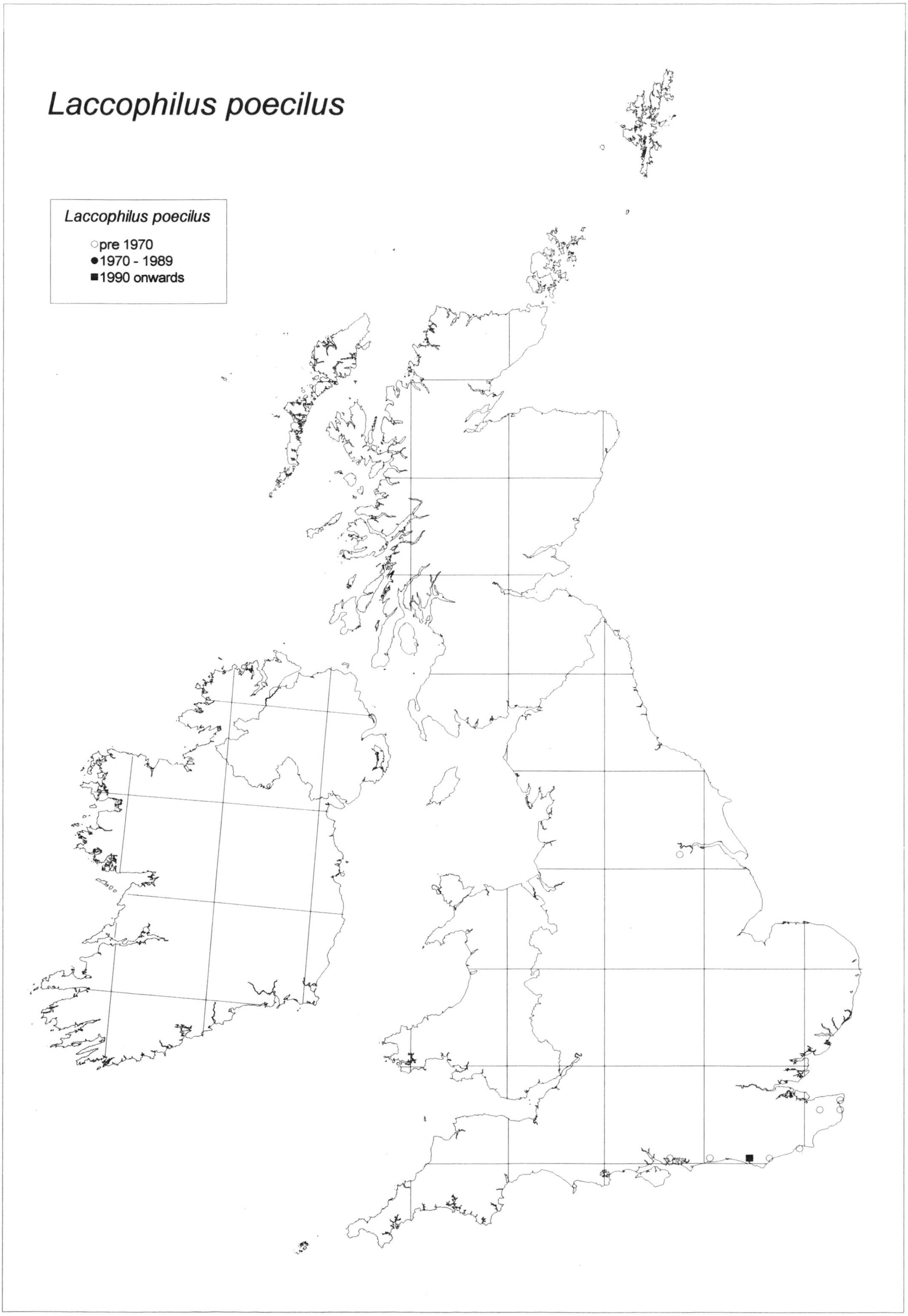

Distribution of Laccophilus poecilus - a diving beetle in Britain, by 10km square.
Source: Balfour-Browne Club - Water Beetle Recording Scheme.

Malachius aeneus (a false soldier beetle) Action Plan

1. Current status

1.1 *Malachius aeneus* adults frequent flowers, especially buttercups, and have been swept from vegetation, in grassland and grassy areas in woodland, during May and June. They are known to feed on the pollen of various grasses, including cock's-foot and meadow foxtail. The larvae are ground-frequenting predators and feed on insect larvae, including those of the pollen beetle *Meligethes aeneus*, in grass and stubble.

1.2 This species was formerly local but widespread throughout England, with records from the following vice-counties: north and south Devon, north Somerset, Dorset, Isle of Wight, south Hampshire, East Sussex, east and west Kent, Surrey, south Essex, Hertfordshire, Berkshire, east Gloucestershire, Warwickshire, Derbyshire, Cheshire, south-east Yorkshire, Durham and south Northumberland. *Malachius aeneus* was also recorded from Glamorgan. Most post-1970 records are from north Somerset, south Hampshire, west Kent and Hertfordshire. It has recently been recorded from very few sites in southern England. It occurs throughout northern, central and southern Europe (including the Mediterranean region) into the Middle East and Iran; it also occurs in the USA and Canada.

1.3 In Great Britain this species is classified as *Rare*.

2. Current factors causing loss or decline

2.1 Not known

3. Current action

3.1 None known.

4. Action plan objectives and targets

4.1 Maintain all extant populations in a viable condition.

4.2 Ensure the establishment and maintenance of five new viable populations across the historic range by 2010.

5. Proposed action with lead agencies

A survey of extant colonies and historic sites should be undertaken for this species. This will establish its current status and provide information to allow targeting of the other measures recommended. Priorities will include appropriate management of all extant sites, based on a better understanding of the beetles' ecological requirements, and protection for each colony from damaging activities. Experimental work should also be undertaken to assess the feasibility of reintroducing viable populations to other sites.

5.1 Policy and legislation

5.1.1 Where appropriate, include the requirements of the species when preparing or revising prescriptions for agri-environment or woodland grant schemes. (ACTION: EN, FE, MAFF)

5.2 Site safeguard and management

5.2.1 Where possible, ensure that all occupied habitat is appropriately managed by 2008, for example through uptake of relevant agri-environment schemes. (ACTION: EN)

5.2.2 Ensure that the species is included in site management documents for all relevant SSSIs. (ACTION: EN)

5.2.3 Consider notifying as SSSIs any sites found holding key populations of the species, where this is necessary to secure their long-term protection and appropriate management. (ACTION: EN)

5.3 Species management and protection

5.3.1 Consider reintroducing *Malachius aeneus* to a series of sites within the former range, if necessary to establish five new viable populations by 2010. (ACTION: EN)

5.4 Advisory

5.4.1 Advise landowners and managers of the presence of this species and the importance of beneficial management for its conservation. (ACTION: EN, MAFF)

5.4.2 As far as possible, ensure that all relevant agri-environment project officers, and members of regional agri-environment consultation groups, are advised of locations of this species, its importance, and the management needed for its conservation. (ACTION: EN, MAFF)

5.5 Future research and monitoring

5.5.1 Undertake surveys to determine the status of this species. (ACTION: CCW, EN)

5.5.2 Conduct targeted autecological research to elucidate the causes of decline and inform habitat management. (ACTION: EN)

5.5.3 Establish a regular monitoring programme for this species. (ACTION: EN)

5.5.4 Pass information gathered during survey and monitoring of this species to a central database for incorporation in national and international databases. (ACTION: CCW, EN)

5.6 Communications and publicity

5.6.1 Promote opportunities for the appreciation of the species and the conservation issues associated with its habitat. This should be achieved through articles within appropriate journals, as well as by a publicity leaflet. (ACTION: EN)

5.7 Links with other action plans

5.7.1 This action plan should be considered in conjunction with that for lowland calcareous grassland.

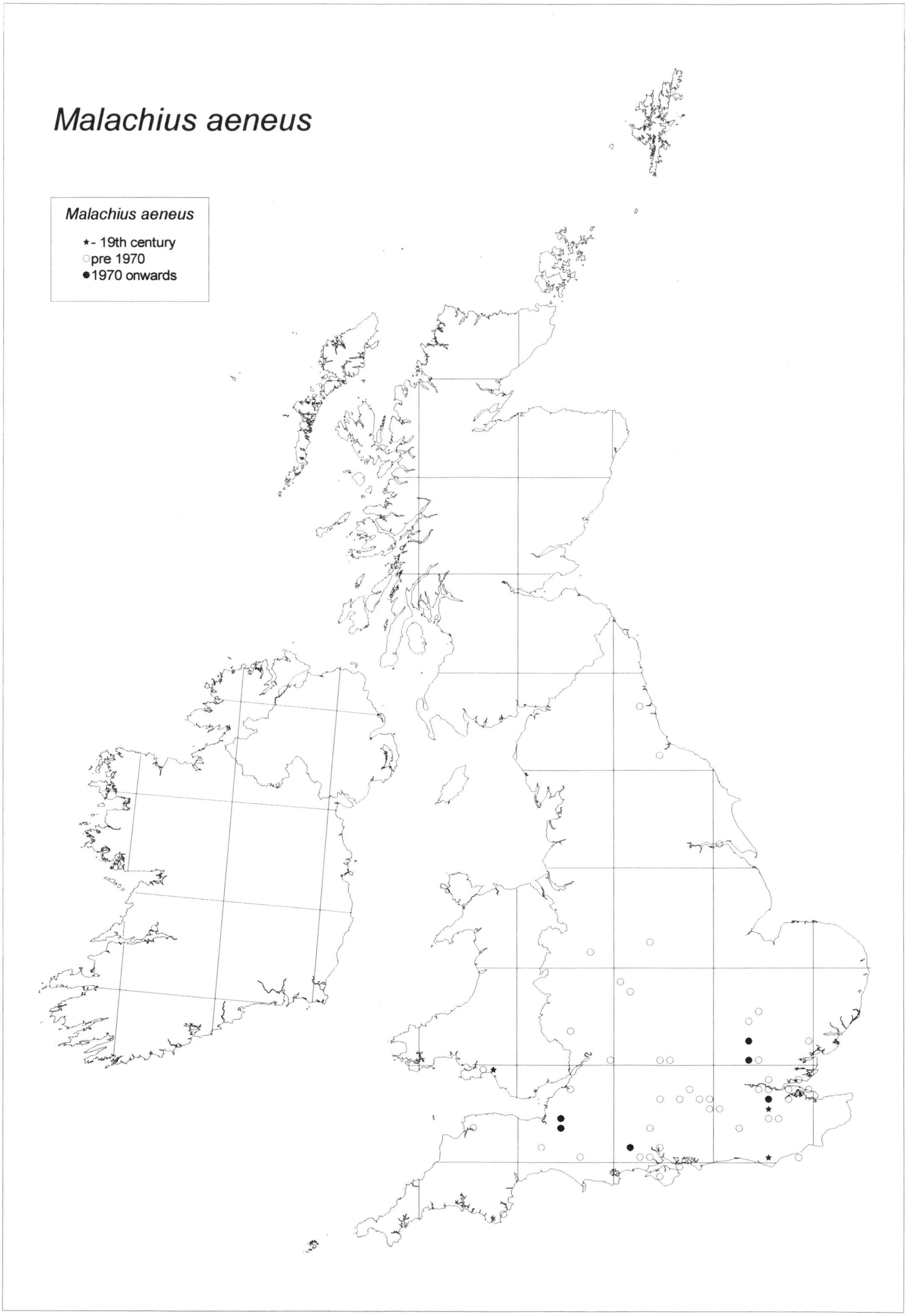

Distribution of Malachius aeneus - a false soldier beetle in Britain, by 10km square.
Source: English Nature - Invertebrate Site Register.

Melanapion minimum (a weevil)
Action plan

1. Current status

1.1 *Melanapion minimum* occurs on willows and sallows in woodland, on the margins of woods, along the sides of ponds, rivers and other watercourses, and in carr. The larvae are inquilines in galls of sawflies of the genus *Pontania*, including *P. collecteana* and *P. proxima*. It has been recorded as an inquiline in galls of Cecidomyidae (gall midges) in Europe, and this may also occur in Britain. The biology of *Melanapion minimum* has been very little studied either here or in Europe.

1.2 There are post 1970 records from the Bure Marshes (east Norfolk), Bedford Purlieus (Northamptonshire), Whiteford Burrows (Glamorganshire) and, less certainly, Warwickshire. However, in historic times the weevil was much more widely distributed, though always local. It was sporadically distributed throughout England, occurred in North and South Wales, and was recorded from Dumfriesshire and Kirkcudbrightshire. It seems to have disappeared from most of these areas during the last 30 years. It is not threatened internationally, and is widely distributed and common throughout central-western and southern Europe. In northern Europe, where it is rather rare and local though usually abundant where it occurs, it has been found in Denmark, south-east Norway, south and central Sweden, Finland and Russian Karelia. It is widely distributed within the Palaearctic region westwards from Mongolia and central Asia.

1.3 In Great Britain this species is now classified as *Rare*.

2. Current factors causing loss or decline

2.1 Not known

3. Current action

3.1 Three of its recent sites are SSSIs and both Bure Marshes and Whiteford Burrows are NNRs contained within candidate SACs.

4. Action plan objectives and targets

4.1 Maintain populations at all known sites.

4.2 Enhance populations at all known sites by 2010.

4.3 Ensure that viable populations are maintained at a minimum of six, well-separated sites, distributed throughout England, and including at least one in each of lowland Scotland and Wales, by 2010.

5. Proposed action with lead agencies

A survey of extant colonies and historic sites should be undertaken for this species. This will establish its current status and provide information to allow targeting of the other measures recommended. Priorities will include appropriate management of all extant sites, based on a better understanding of the beetles' ecological requirements. Experimental work should also be undertaken to assess the feasibility of reintroducing viable populations to other sites.

5.1 Policy and legislation

5.1.1 Where appropriate, include the requirements of the species when preparing or revising prescriptions for agri-environment or woodland grant schemes. (ACTION: CCW, EN, FC, MAFF, SNH, SOAEFD, WOAD)

5.2 Site safeguard and management

5.2.1 Where possible, ensure that all occupied habitat is appropriately managed by 2005, for example through SSSI or agri-environment scheme management agreements. (ACTION: CCW, EN, FC, MAFF, SNH, WOAD)

5.2.2 Ensure that the species is included in site management documents for all relevant SSSIs. (ACTION: CCW, EN, SNH)

5.2.3 Consider notifying as SSSIs sites with key populations of the species, where this is necessary to secure their long-term protection and appropriate management. (ACTION: CCW, EN, SNH)

5.3 Species management and protection

5.3.1 Consider reintroducing to a series of sites within the former range, if necessary to ensure that there are six viable populations by 2010. (ACTION: CCW, EN, SNH)

5.4 Advisory

5.4.1 Advise landowners and managers of the presence of the species and the importance of beneficial management for its conservation. (ACTION: CCW, EN, SNH)

5.5 Future research and monitoring

5.5.1 Undertake surveys to determine the status of the species by 2008. (ACTION: CCW, EN, SNH)

5.5.2 Conduct targeted autecological research to elucidate the causes of decline and inform habitat management. (ACTION: CCW, EN, SNH)

5.5.3 Establish a regular monitoring programme for the species. (ACTION: CCW, EN, SNH)

5.5.4 Pass information gathered during survey and monitoring of this species to a central database for incorporation into national and international databases. (ACTION: CCW, EN, SNH)

5.6 Communications and publicity

5.6.1 Promote opportunities for the appreciation of the species and the conservation issues associated with its habitat. This should be achieved through articles within appropriate journals, as well as by a publicity leaflet. (ACTION: CCW, EN, SNH)

5.7 Links with other action plans

5.7.1 This action plan should be considered in conjunction with those for coastal sand dunes, fens, lowland raised bog, and wet woodlands.

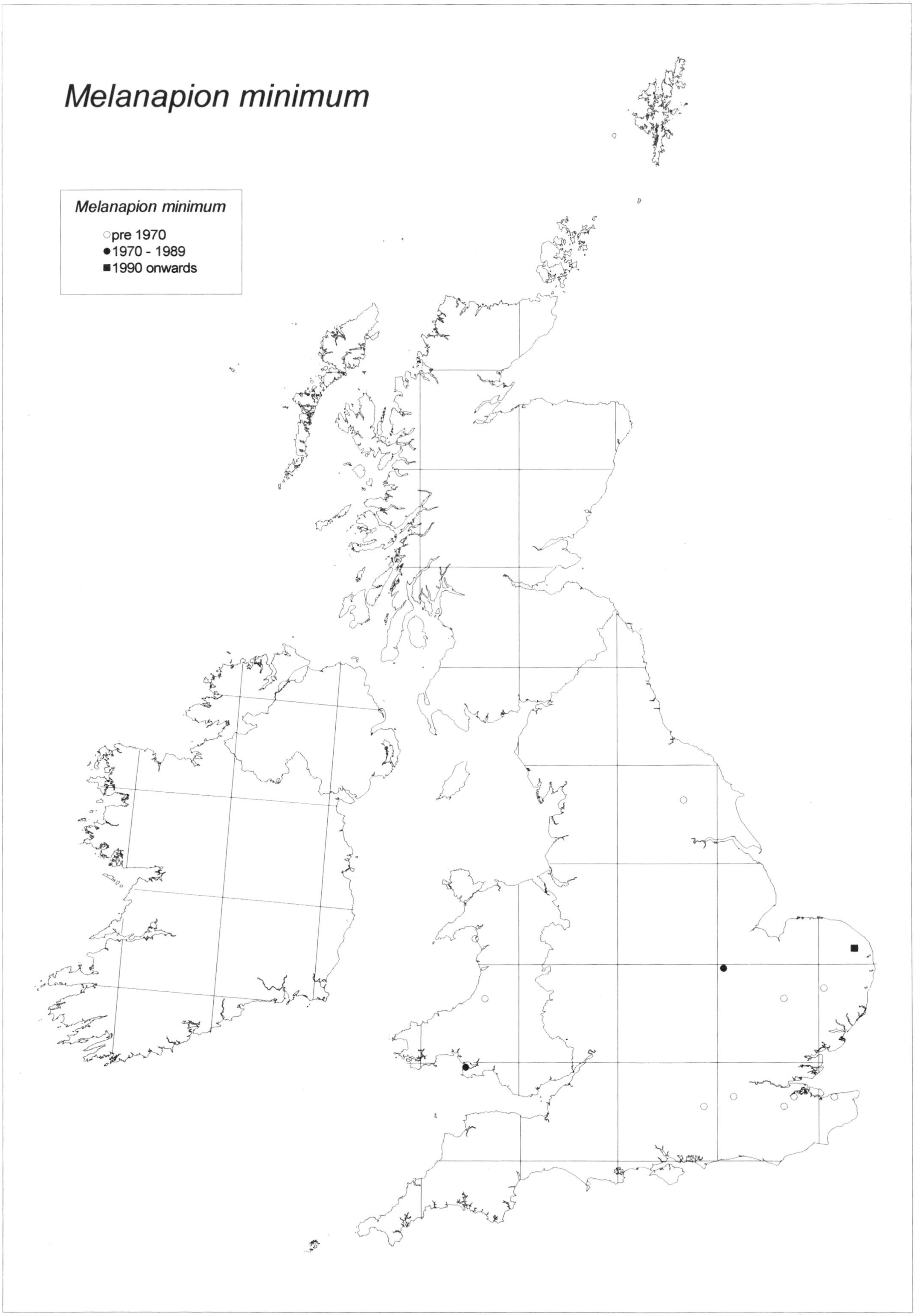

Distribution of Melanapion minimum - a weevil in Britain, by 10km square.
Source: English Nature - Invertebrate Site Register and the Countryside Council for Wales records.

Melanotus punctolineatus (a click beetle) Action Plan

1. Current status

1.1 In Britain *Melanotus punctolineatus* breeds in areas of sparsely vegetated coastal dune. The larvae feed on the roots of grasses, such as marram, and are likely also to be opportunistic predators on other invertebrates. The life cycle takes at least two years, and the species probably passes the winter as an adult within the pupal cell. Adults usually emerge in May and June, and may be found crawling over the surface of the sand or climbing grass stems. Some continental authors call this beetle *Melanotus niger* (Fabricius, 1792), an earlier but probably invalid name.

1.2 Over the 20th century all of the records for this species have been from the south coast of Kent between Littlestone-on-Sea and Sandwich. Records show that the core population is associated with the coastal dunes between Deal and the River Stour (Pegwell Bay). There are isolated 19th century records from Surrey, Essex, Middlesex, Berkshire and Glamorganshire. Most of these sites were lost to urban development long ago, but there are still considerable expanses of dune systems in South Wales. Subtle climatic change may also have contributed to the decline. There have been no records in the British Isles (excluding the Channel Islands) since adults and larvae were collected in a small sand pit on the Sandwich Bay Estate in 1986. *Melanotus punctolineatus* is found widely in central and western Europe (including the Channel Islands), the Mediterranean area and Asia Minor.

1.3 In Great Britain this species is classified as *Endangered*.

2. Current factors causing loss or decline

2.1 Habitat loss.

2.2 Stabilisation of dune grassland.

2.3 'Fly tipping'.

3. Current action

3.1 All modern records are from within the Sandwich Bay/Hacklinge Marshes SSSI.

4. Action plan objectives and targets

4.1 Maintain populations at all known sites.

4.2 Enhance the population size at all known sites by 2010.

4.3 Restore to suitable sites along the south Kent coast to ensure the existence of three viable populations by 2010.

5. Proposed action with lead agencies

The objectives of this plan will be achieved by implementing appropriate habitat management on extant sites, and by reintroducing populations to suitable sites within the former range of the species. A survey of all historic sites on the south Kent coast, to determine current distribution and status, and identify potentially suitable habitat, is a priority. Research will need to be undertaken to elucidate the ecological requirements of this species.

5.1 Policy and legislation

5.1.1 Address the requirements of this species in the LEAP process and in relevant WLMPs and Shoreline Management Plans. (ACTION: EA, IDBs, LAs, MAFF)

5.2 Site safeguard and management

5.2.1 Where possible, ensure that all occupied habitat is appropriately managed, including the rejuvenation of areas of active foredune, by 2008. This may be achieved through site management agreements. (ACTION: EA, EN, LAs)

5.3 Species management and protection

5.3.1 Reintroduce *Melanotus punctolineatus* to a series of sites within the former range, if necessary to establish three viable populations by 2010. (ACTION: EN)

5.4 Advisory

5.4.1 Advise landowners and managers of the presence of the species and the importance of beneficial management for its conservation. (ACTION: EN)

5.5 Future research and monitoring

5.5.1 Undertake surveys, including dune systems on the South Wales coast, to determine the status of this species. (ACTION: CCW, EN)

5.5.2 Conduct targeted autecological research to inform habitat management. (ACTION: EN)

5.5.3 Establish a regular monitoring programme for the species. (ACTION: EN)

5.5.4 Pass information gathered during survey and monitoring of the species to a central database for incorporation in national and international databases. (ACTION: CCW, EN)

5.6 Communication and publicity

5.6.1 Promote opportunities for the appreciation of the species and the conservation issues associated with coastal sand dunes. This should be achieved through articles within appropriate journals, as well as by a publicity leaflet. (ACTION: EN)

5.7 Links with other action plans

5.7.1 Implementation of this action plan could benefit other species of coastal sand dunes, including the spider-hunting wasp *Evagetes pectinipes*.

5.7.2 This plan should be considered in conjunction with that for coastal sand dunes.

Melanotus punctolineatus

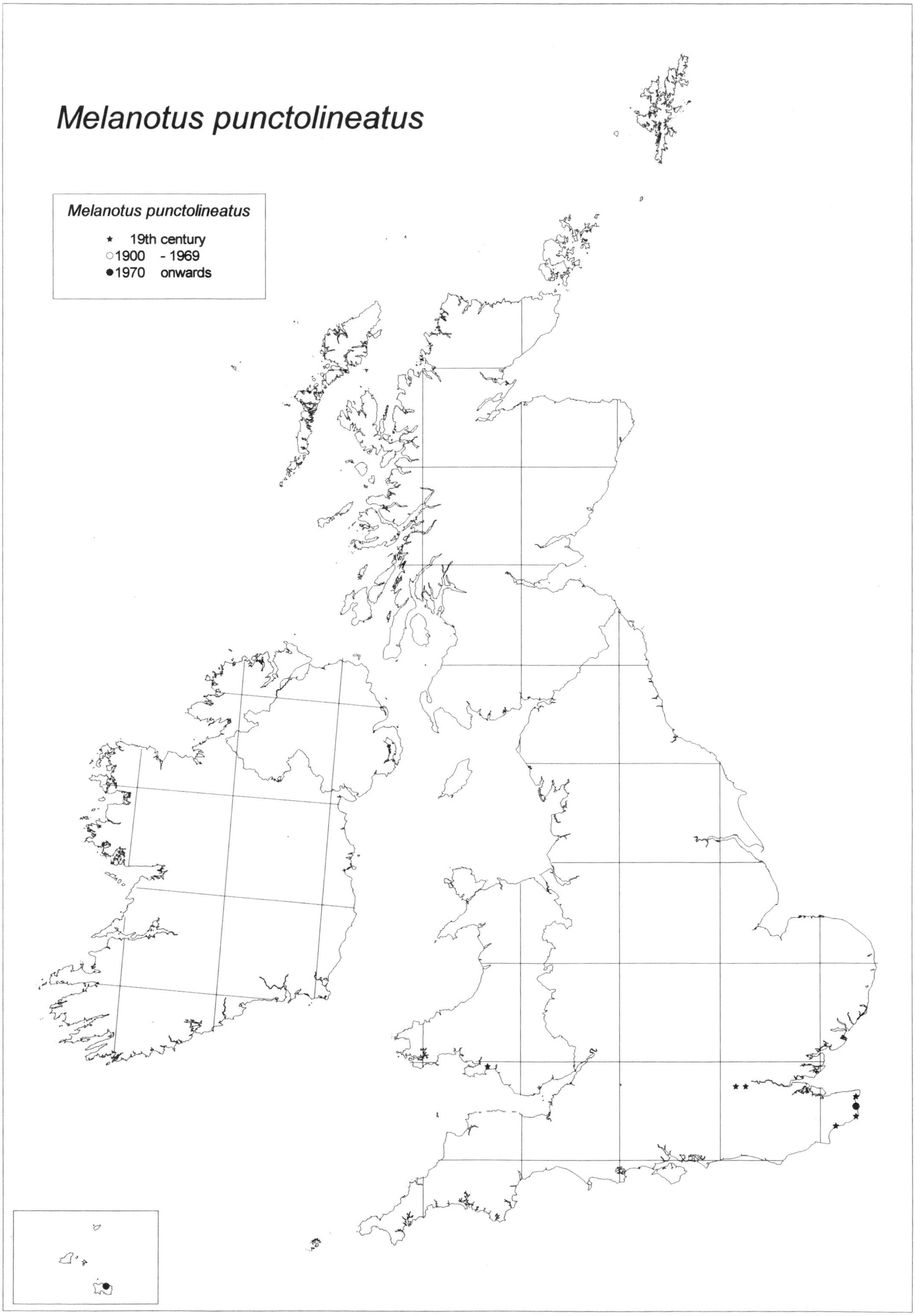

Distribution of Melanotus punctolineatus - a click beetle in Britain, by 10km square.
Source: H.Mendel, 1988. Provisional atlas of the click beetles (Coleoptera: Elateroidea) of the British Isles, Biological Records Centre (ITE) and English Nature - Invertebrate Site Register.

Pachytychius haematocephalus (a weevil) Action Plan

1. Current status

1.1 *Pachytychius haematocephalus* is a weevil whose hostplant is bird's-foot trefoil. Larvae feed in the pods on unripe seeds in summer and the species overwinters as an adult.

1.2 This species was discovered in Britain in 1872 at Gosport, Hampshire, where it has persisted to the present day. The site is a very small area of the lower part of an earth bank raised against the seaward walls of Gilkicker Fort, which is scheduled as an ancient monument. It has also been recorded from Browndown Ranges, just along the coast, in September 1973, but has not been found subsequently, a single specimen was found at Charmouth, Dorset, in October 1947. There are no other Dorset records, despite recent searching. A record from Wiltshire in 1872 is regarded as dubious. It is one of only two species of a southern European genus which reach central Europe. It does not extend into Denmark and Fennoscandia and is much commoner in southern France than in the north, where it is absent from Brittany but does occur in the Channel Islands.

1.3 In Great Britain this species is classified as *Endangered*.

2. Current factors causing loss or decline

2.1 Coastal erosion.

2.2 Encroachment by scrub, especially turkey oak.

2.3 Disturbance to the host plant from trampling by visitors to the fort may be a threat.

2.4 Unsympathetic coastal defence works.

3. Current action

3.1 A survey of Gilkicker Point, commissioned by Hampshire County Council, has been completed.

3.2 Proposals for conserving the weevil at Gilkicker Point have been formulated by Hampshire County Council.

4. Action plan objectives and targets

4.1 Enhance the population at Gilkicker Point by 2010.

4.2 Introduce a population to a suitable south coast site by 2010, if not refound in any of its former localities.

4.3 Initiate a programme of captive breeding to provide material for introductions.

5. Proposed action with lead agencies

The priority action of this plan is to ensure that the existing population is adequately protected and its habitat is appropriately managed. The creation of additional, adjacent habitat will be required to counter the effects of coastal erosion. Surveys of historic localities should be undertaken, followed by introductions of this species to suitable sites along the south coast of England, if this is deemed necessary. To inform habitat management and introductions, a captive breeding programme should be initiated.

5.1 Policy and legislation

5.1.1 Consider extending the existing Gilkicker Lagoon SSSI to include the fort bank. (ACTION: EN)

5.1.2 Incorporate the requirements of this species in relevant Shoreline Management Plans. (ACTION: LAs, MAFF)

5.2 Site safeguard and management

5.2.1 Ensure appropriate management of Gilkicker Point for the species by 2000. (ACTION: EN, EH, Hampshire CC)

5.2.2 Increase the available habitat at the known site and adjacent areas by 2004. (ACTION: EN, English Heritage, Hampshire CC)

5.3 Species management and protection

5.3.1 Consider introducing *Pachytychius haematocephalus* to a suitable south coast site by 2010. (ACTION: EN)

5.3.2 Establish a captive breeding programme to provide material for possible introductions and ecological research. (ACTION: EN)

5.4 Advisory

5.4.1 Advise landowners and managers of the presence of this species and the importance of beneficial management for its conservation. (ACTION: EN)

5.5 Future research and monitoring

5.5.1 Undertake further surveys to determine the status of this species. (ACTION: EN, MoD)

5.5.2 Undertake targeted autecological research to inform habitat management. (ACTION: EN)

5.5.3 Establish a regular monitoring programme for this species. (ACTION: EN)

5.5.4 Pass information gathered during survey and monitoring of this species to a central database for incorporation into national and international databases. (ACTION: EN, MoD)

5.6 Communications and publicity

5.6.1 Promote opportunities for the appreciation of the species and the conservation issues associated with its habitat. This should be achieved through articles within appropriate journals as well as by a publicity leaflet. (ACTION: EN, EH, Hampshire CC)

5.7 Links with other action plans

5.7.1 None proposed.

Pachytychius haematocephalus

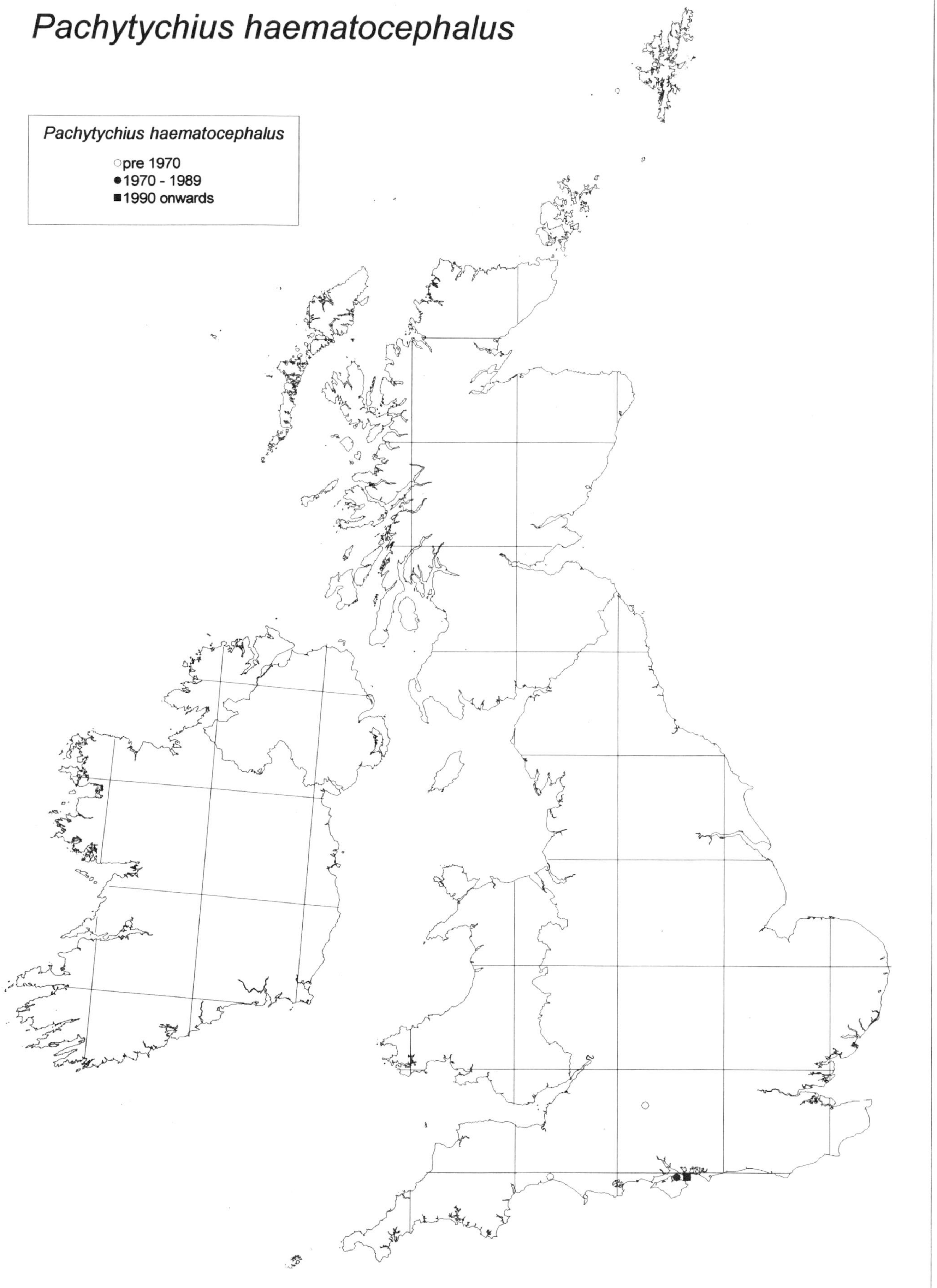

Distribution of Pachytychius haematocephalus - a weevil in Britain, by 10km square.
Source: English Nature - Invertebrate Site Register.

Paracymus aeneus (a water beetle) Action Plan

1. Current status

1.1 *Paracymus aeneus* lives in saline pools above the high-water mark, usually in association with vegetation at the edge of ponds.

1.2 There are recent published records for the Isle of Wight, and the species has recently been rediscovered in south Essex. *Paracymus aeneus* is confined to 2 ten km grid squares in England, having only ever been known from a total of six. It is common along the Mediterranean coasts and at saline localities inland as far as central Germany and the Caspian. In northern Europe it reaches southern Norway, Denmark and the southern tip of Sweden.

1.3 In Great Britain this species is currently classified as *Vulnerable*. It is given full protection under Schedule 5 of the Wildlife and Countryside Act 1981.

2. Current factors causing loss or decline

2.1 Loss of habitat by coastal development, particularly rubbish infill.

2.2 Construction of sea defences.

3. Current action

3.1 This species was rediscovered as a result of survey work, supported by EN, in Essex in 1991. The status of *Paracymus aeneus* in the Isle of Wight was assessed in 1995 through survey work commissioned by EN.

3.2 Both sites are within SSSIs, one of which was extended to include the beetle's locality, which are contained within the Solent and Isle of Wight Lagoons candidate SAC and the Essex Estuaries candidate SAC .

4. Action plan objectives and targets

4.1 Ensure that viable populations are maintained within saltmarsh systems currently occupied in the Isle of Wight and Essex.

5. Proposed action with lead agencies

The objectives of this plan will be achieved by protecting existing populations from damaging activities, and by creating additional habitat through the creation of shallow ponds around the high-water mark. Additional survey work needs to be undertaken to determine the status of this species, and research should be conducted into the ecological requirements of this species. Reintroductions will only be considered if either of the two known populations become extinct.

5.1 Policy and legislation

5.1.1 Address the requirements of this species in the LEAP process and in relevant Shoreline Management Plans. (ACTION: EA, LAs, MAFF)

5.2 Site safeguard and management

5.2.1 Where possible, ensure that all habitat is appropriately managed by 2008, for example through site management agreements. (ACTION: EN)

5.2.2 Ensure that the habitat requirements of *Paracymus aeneus* are taken into account in any relevant development policies, plans and proposals, particularly relating to coastal defence and protection. (ACTION: EA, EN, LAs, MAFF)

5.2.3 Where possible, increase the available habitat at known sites and adjacent areas. (ACTION: EA, EN)

5.2.4 Ensure that this species is included in site management documents for the two relevant SSSIs. (ACTION: EN)

5.3 Species management and protection

5.3.1 In the event of population failure at the Isle of Wight or Essex sites, prepare a contingency plan for reintroductions. (ACTION: EN)

5.4 Advisory

5.4.1 Advise landowners and managers of the presence of this species and the importance of beneficial management for its conservation. (ACTION: EN)

5.5 Future research and monitoring

5.5.1 Undertake further surveys to determine the status of this species. (ACTION: EN)

5.5.2 Conduct targeted autecological research to inform habitat management. (ACTION: EN)

5.5.3 Establish a regular monitoring programme for the species. (ACTION: EN)

5.5.4 Pass information gathered during survey and monitoring of this species to a central database for incorporation in national and international databases. (ACTION: EN)

5.5.5 Encourage research on the ecology and conservation of this species on an international level, and use the experience gained towards its conservation in the UK. (ACTION: EN, JNCC)

5.6 Communications and publicity

5.6.1 Promote opportunities for the appreciation of the species and the conservation issues associated with its habitat. This should be achieved through articles within appropriate journals, as well as by a publicity leaflet. (ACTION: EN)

5.7 Links with other action plans

5.7.1 This action plan should be considered in conjunction with those for coastal saltmarsh, and saline lagoons.

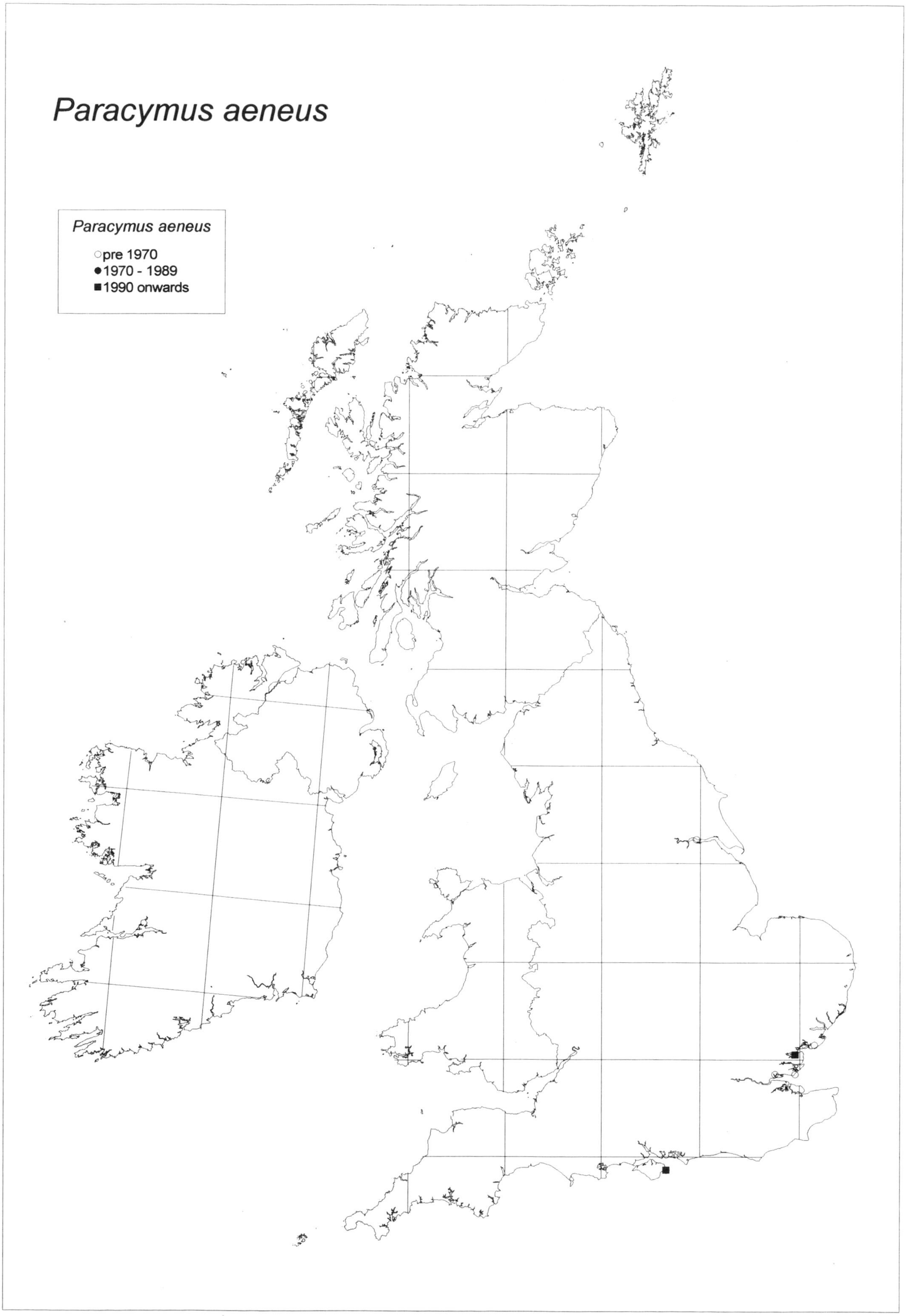

Distribution of Paracymus aeneus - a water beetle in Britain, by 10km square.
Source: Balfour-Browne Club - Water Beetle Recording Scheme.

Procas granulicollis (a weevil) Action Plan

1. Current status

1.1 *Procas granulicollis* is an enigmatic and poorly-understood species. It was described in 1848 and then lost sight of, or assumed to be conspecific with *P. armillatus,* until its identity as a true species was established in 1990. It inhabits woodland clearings or wood edges where there is light shading from well-dispersed trees. It is associated with bracken and climbing corydalis. Adults feed on the latter in early summer, but all attempts to find the larva and elucidate the species' life history have been unsuccessful. Larvae in the group of weevils to which *P. granulicollis* belongs feed internally, but this would be impossible in climbing corydalis, the stem of which is too narrow. It is possible that the larvae feed in stems of bracken, but attempts to find them have, so far, proven abortive.

1.2 *Procas granulicollis* is endemic to Great Britain. Since 1990 it has been discovered at a number of sites, mainly in southern Scotland, northern England and Wales, but including Surrey. It is now known from 16 sites, but is almost certainly under recorded.

1.3 In Great Britain this species is now classified as *Indeterminate.*

2. Current factors causing loss or decline

2.1 Not known

3. Current action

3.1 Most of the sites from which this species has been recorded are SSSIs or NNRs. For example, all four known Scottish populations are on SSSIs, and one of these is a NNR.

3.2 SNH commissioned a survey of known and potential sites in 1996.

4. Action plan objectives and targets

4.1 Maintain populations at all known sites.

4.2 Clarify the taxonomic status of *Procas granulicollis.*

5. Proposed action with lead agencies

The principal actions necessary to deliver the objectives of this plan are to undertake research to determine the larval ecology of the species, and to clarify its taxonomic status. Once the ecological requirements are known, appropriate management should be instigated at key sites, particularly in relation to the significance of bracken habitats in woodland.

5.1 Policy and legislation

5.1.1 Where appropriate, include the requirements of *P. granulicollis* in the preparation or revision of agri-environment or woodland grant schemes. (ACTION: CCW, EN, FC, MAFF, SNH, SOAEFD, WOAD)

5.2 Site safeguard and management

5.2.1 Where possible, ensure the appropriate management of known sites by 2004, for example through SSSI or agri-environment scheme management agreements. (ACTION: CCW, EN, FC, MAFF, SNH, SOAEFD, WOAD)

5.2.2 Ensure that the habitat requirements of *Procas granullicolas* are taken into account in any relevant development policies, plans or proposals. (ACTION: CCW, EN, LAs, SNH)

5.2.3 Ensure that this species is included in site management documents for all relevant SSSIs (ACTION: CCW, EN, SNH)

5.2.4 Consider notifying as SSSIs sites holding key populations of this species, where this is necessary to secure long-term protection and appropriate management. (ACTION: CCW, EN, SNH)

5.3 Species management and protection

5.3.1 None proposed.

5.4 Advisory

5.4.1 Advise landowners and managers of the presence of this species and the importance of beneficial management for its conservation. (ACTION: CCW, EN, SNH)

5.5 Future research and monitoring

5.5.1 Undertake further surveys to determine the status of this species. (ACTION: CCW, EN, SNH)

5.5.2 Establish a regular monitoring programme for this species. (ACTION: CCW, EN, SNH)

5.5.3 Conduct targeted autecological research to inform habitat management. (ACTION: CCW, EN, SNH)

5.5.4 Pass information gathered during survey and monitoring of this species to a central database

for incorporation into national and international databases. (ACTION: CCW, EN, SNH)

5.5.5 Undertake studies to clarify the taxonomic relationships of *P. granulicollis* and *P. armillatus*. (ACTION: CCW, EN, SNH)

5.5.6 Collaborate with European specialists to investigate the endemicity of *P. granulicollis*. (ACTION: CCW, EN, JNCC, NHM, SNH)

5.6 Communications and publicity

5.6.1 Promote opportunities for the appreciation of the species and the conservation issues associated with its habitat. This should be achieved through articles within appropriate journals, as well as by a publicity leaflet. (ACTION: CCW, EN, SNH)

5.7 Links with other action plans

5.7.1 This action plan should be considered in conjunction with that for upland oak wood.

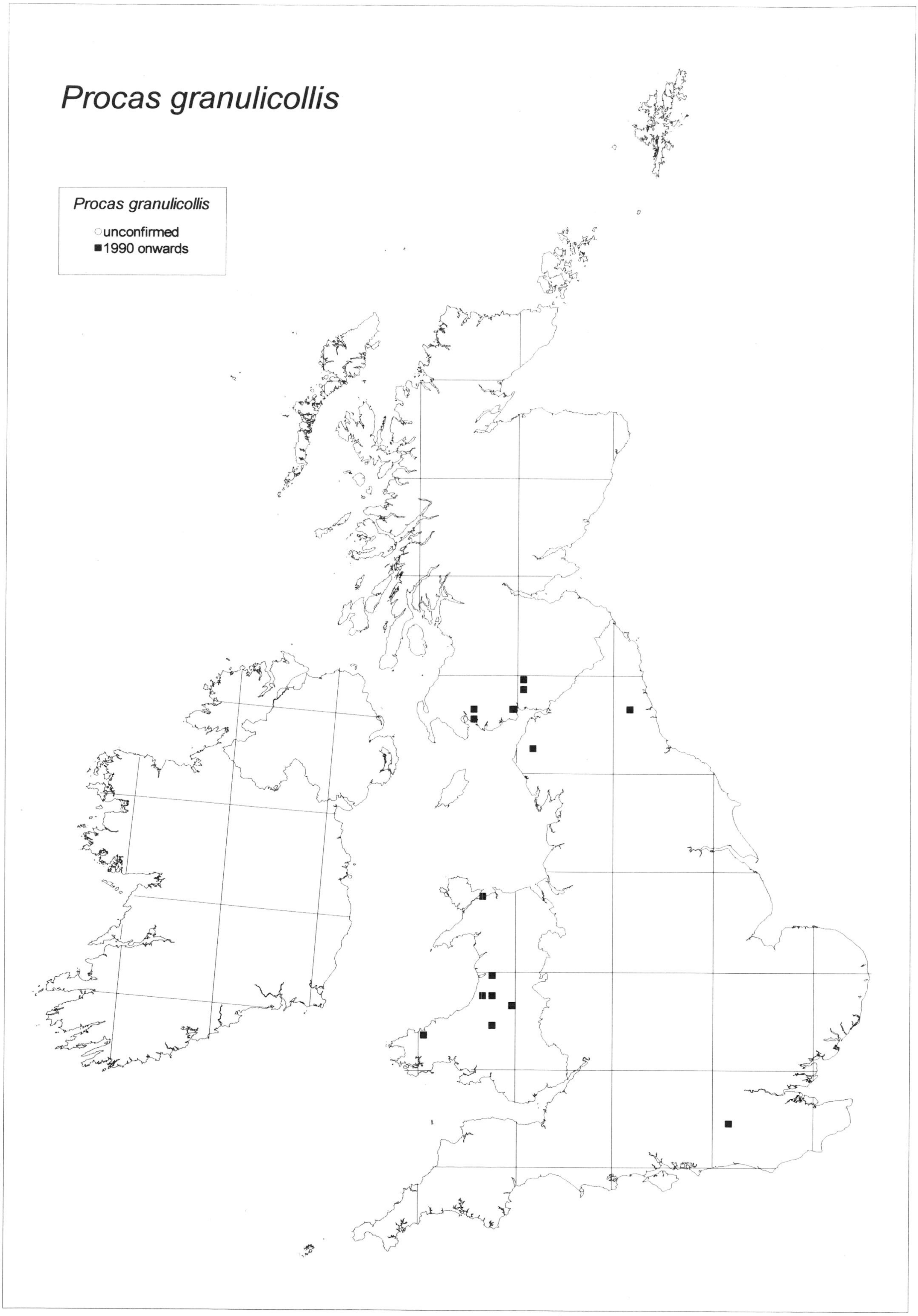

Distribution of Procas granulicollis - a weevil in Britain, by 10km square.
Source: Scottish Natural Heritage, the Countryside Council for Wales and English Nature - Invertebrate Site Register.

Psylliodes sophiae (a flea beetle)
Action Plan

1. Current status

1.1 *Psylliodes sophiae* is a species of disturbed ground and probably also grassland, particularly on sandy soils of the Breckland of East Anglia. It is apparently associated only with the crucifer, flixweed *Descurainia sophiae* (a plant of very sporadic occurrence). The larvae probably mine the pithy flowering stems of flixweed, emerging when fully grown to pupate in the soil. The collection of teneral, new generation, adults during June at Ramsay, Huntingdonshire, suggests that oviposition and larval development occur during April and May.

1.2 Before 1970 it was known from west Suffolk, west Norfolk, Cambridgeshire and Huntingdon; there is also an old record from Bristol, west Gloucestershire which requires confirmation. The most recent records of this species are from Bodney Camp on the edge of Stanford PTA, west Norfolk (1996/97). There are also unconfirmed records from near Lakenheath Warren, west Suffolk (1993/94) and Pashford Poors Fen, a Suffolk Wildlife Trust Reserve (1997). Although recent records are very sparse, the species can occur in reasonable numbers where found. It is widespread throughout north, central and south Europe.

1.3 In Great Britain this species is classified as *Rare*.

2. Current factors causing loss or decline

2.1 Modern treatment of arable weeds using herbicides and seed-cleaning.

2.2 Stabilisation of Breck dunes.

3. Current action

3.1 This species occurs on Pashford Poors Fen, a Suffolk Wildlife Trust Reserve. The Bodney Camp record is from part of the MoD estate.

4. Action plan objectives and targets

4.1 Ensure that all extant populations are maintained in a viable condition.

4.2 Restore populations to three suitable sites within the historic range by 2010.

5. Proposed action with lead agencies

A survey of extant colonies and historic sites should be undertaken for this species. This will establish its current status and provide information to allow targeting of the other measures recommended. Priorities will include appropriate management of all extant sites, based on a better understanding of the beetles' ecological requirements, and protection for each colony from damaging agricultural activities. Experimental work should also be undertaken to assess the feasibility of reintroducing viable populations to other sites.

5.1 Policy and legislation

5.1.1 Where appropriate, include the requirements of the species when preparing or revising prescriptions for agri-environment schemes. (ACTION: EN, MAFF)

5.2 Site safeguard and management

5.2.1 Where possible, ensure that all occupied habitat is appropriately managed, including the creation of disturbed ground, by 2008. This may be achieved through site management agreements or uptake of relevant agri-environment schemes. (ACTION: EN, MoD)

5.2.2 Ensure that *Psylliodes sophiae* is included in site objective and site management statements for any SSSIs on which the species is found. (ACTION: EN)

5.2.3 Consider notifying as SSSIs sites holding key populations of the species, where this is necessary to secure their long-term protection and appropriate management. (ACTION: EN)

5.3 Species management and protection

5.3.1 Reintroduce populations to a series of sites within the former range, if necessary to establish three new viable populations. (ACTION: EN)

5.4 Advisory

5.4.1 Advise landowners and managers of the presence of this species and the importance of beneficial management for its conservation. (ACTION: EN, MAFF)

5.4.2 Ensure that all relevant agri-environment project officers, and members of regional agri-environment consultation groups, are advised of locations for this species, its importance, and the management needed for its conservation. (ACTION: EN, MAFF)

5.5 Future research and monitoring

5.5.1 Undertake surveys to determine the status of this species. (ACTION: EN)

5.5.2 Conduct targeted autecological research to inform habitat management. (ACTION: EN)

5.5.3 Establish a regular monitoring programme for the species. (ACTION: EN)

5.5.4 Pass information gathered during survey and monitoring of this species to a central database for incorporation in national and international databases. (ACTION: EN)

5.6 Communications and publicity

5.6.1 Promote opportunities for the appreciation of the species and the conservation issues associated with its habitat. This should be achieved through articles within appropriate journals, as well as by a publicity leaflet. (ACTION: EN)

5.7 Links with other action plans

5.7.1 Implementation of this action plan could benefit other species of Breck grassland, including the ground beetle *Harpalus froelichi*.

5.7.2 This plan should be considered in conjunction with those for cereal field margins, and lowland dry acidic grassland.

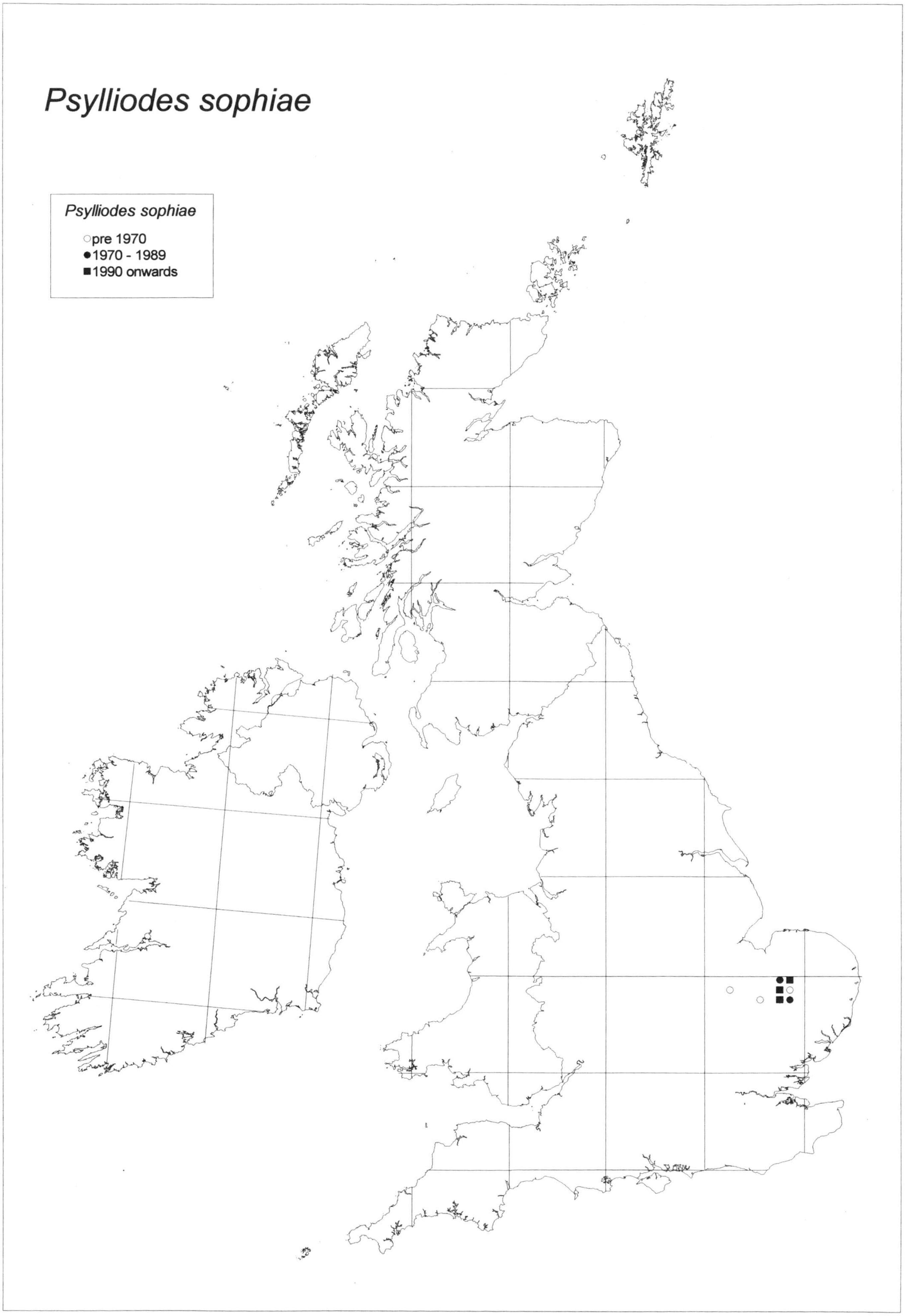

Distribution of Psylliodes sophiae - a flea beetle in Britain, by 10km square.
Source: M.Cox - Natural History Museum and English Nature - Invertebrate Site Register.

Pterostichus aterrimus (a ground beetle) Action Plan

1. Current status

1.1 *Pterostichus aterrimus* is found on muddy or peaty soils at the edges of permanent, standing water bodies, and in very wet ungrazed fen/bog habitats. Areas of bare, wet, but sun-exposed ground among the littoral vegetation may also be needed. *P. aterrimus* has an annual life cycle. It is a spring breeder with summer larvae, and is predatory in both larval and adult stages. It is winged and flight has been recorded.

1.2 *Pterostichus aterrimus* occurred in the Norfolk Broads until early this century, but was last recorded from Norfolk (Stalham) in 1910. From 1969 to 1973 it occurred in *Sphagnum* in the Bishop's Dyke/Denny Wood/Matley Bog area of the New Forest. This site has since partially or completely dried out, and *P. aterrimus* has not been found in Britain since 1973. It has, however, been found at Brackagh Moss in County Armagh, Northern Ireland (1982), and was still present at that site (and was found at six other sites in Armagh and Down) in 1997. It has been recorded at one site in the Irish Republic, and has a wide continental distribution from Spain to Russia.

1.3 In Great Britain this species is classified as *Endangered*.

2. Current factors causing loss or decline

2.1 Drainage of peatland habitat.

2.2 Groundwater abstraction.

3. Current action

3.1 The New Forest is a protected site (Ramsar, SPA, candidate SAC and SSSI), and in Northern Ireland all sites are either designated or proposed ASSIs. Brackagh Moss is an NNR and Derryleckagh a candidate SAC.

4. Action plan objectives and targets

4.1 Maintain populations at all known sites.

4.2 Restore populations to two suitable sites within the historic range in England by 2010.

5. Proposed actions with lead agencies

The processes required to deliver the above objectives involve appropriate management of the species' known habitats, followed by reintroduction of the species to potential sites within its historic British range. Surveys to determine its status, population monitoring, and autecological studies will also need to be undertaken.

5.1 Policy and Legislation

5.1.1 Address the requirements of this species in the LEAP process and in relevant WLMPs. (ACTION: EA, IDBs, LAs, MAFF)

5.1.2 Where appropriate, take account of the species' requirements in response to applications for water abstraction licences. (ACTION: EA, EHS)

5.2 Site safeguard and management

5.2.1 Where possible, ensure that all occupied habitat is appropriately managed by 2008, for example through site management agreements. (ACTION: EHS, EN)

5.2.2 Ensure that the habitat requirements of *Pterostichus aterrimus* are taken into account in any relevant development policies, plans and proposals. (ACTION: EN, LAs)

5.2.3 Ensure that the species is included in site management documents for all relevant SSSIs/ASSIs. (ACTION: EHS, EN)

5.2.4 Consider notifying as SSSI/ASSIs any newly discovered sites holding viable populations of the species, where this is necessary to secure long-term protection and appropriate management. (ACTION: EHS, EN)

5.3 Species management and protection

5.3.1 Reintroduce *Pterostichus aterrimus* to a series of sites within the former range to establish two new viable populations. (ACTION: EN)

5.4 Advisory

5.4.1 Advise landowners and managers of the presence of the species and the importance of beneficial management for its conservation. (ACTION: EHS, EN)

5.5 Future research and monitoring

5.5.1 Undertake surveys to determine the status of the species. (ACTION: EHS, EN)

5.5.2 Conduct targeted autecological research to inform habitat management. (ACTION: EHS, EN)

5.5.3 Establish a regular monitoring programme for this species. (ACTION: EHS, EN)

5.5.4 Pass information gathered during survey and monitoring of this species to a central database for incorporation into national and international databases. (ACTION: EHS, EN)

5.5.5 Encourage research on the ecology and conservation of this species on an international level, and use the experience gained towards its conservation in the UK. (ACTION: EHS, EN, JNCC)

5.6 Communications and publicity

5.6.1 Promote opportunities for the appreciation of this species and the conservation issues associated with its habitat. This should be achieved through articles within appropriate readership journals, as well as by a publicity leaflet. (ACTION: EHS, EN)

5.7 Links with other action plans

5.7.1 Implementation of this action plan could benefit other species of lowland mires, including the large marsh grasshopper *Stethophyma grossum*.

5.7.2 This plan should be considered in conjunction with that for fens.

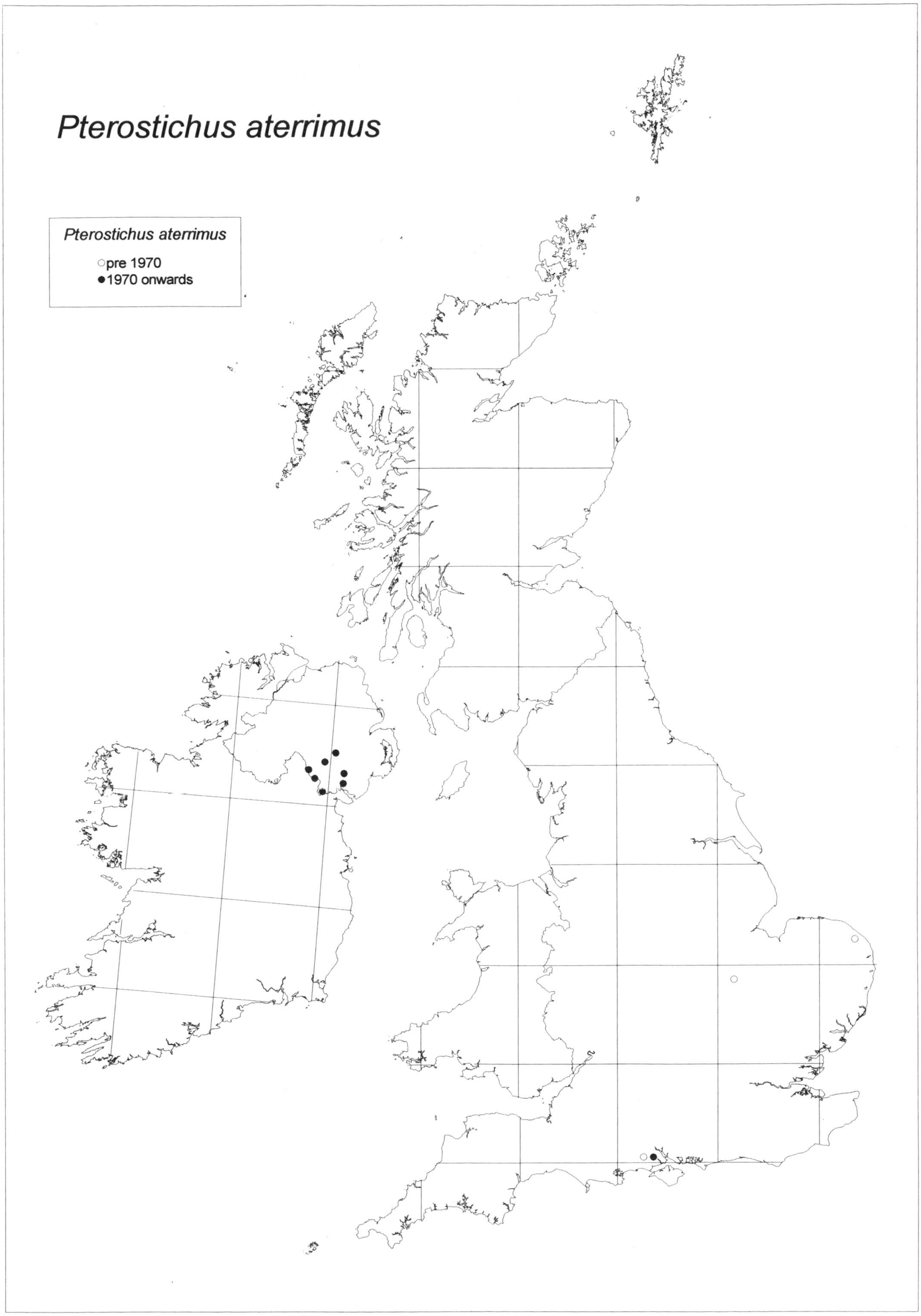

Distribution of Pterostichus aterrimus - a ground beetle in Britain and Northern Ireland, by 10km square.
Source: Luff, M.L. 1998. Provisional atlas of the ground beetles (Coleoptera, Carabidae) of Britain, Biological Records centre (ITE), CEDaR - Ulster Museum and English Nature - Invertebrate Site Register.

Pterostichus kugelanni (a ground beetle) Action Plan

1. Current status

1.1 *Pterostichus kugelanni* is found on heathland with sandy or gravelly soil, but with wet areas present. It is a spring-summer breeding species which may require two years to complete its development in Britain, thus overwintering (probably in tussocks and litter) both as adults and as larvae. Both larvae and adults are presumed to be predatory, but their exact diet is not known. The adults are winged, but whether they are able to disperse by flight in Britain is not known.

1.2 The species has occurred widely from Nottinghamshire to South Wales and the south coast of England. Since 1970 it has been found only at three sites in the New Forest and at a single site on Dartmoor. It has a southern and western European range, from Spain to Hungary.

1.3 In Great Britain this species is classified as *Endangered*.

2. Current factors causing loss or decline

2.1 Inappropriate management of heathland.

2.2 Loss of habitat.

3. Current action

3.1 The New Forest is a protected site (Ramsar, SPA, candidate SAC and SSSI).

4. Action plan objectives and targets

4.1 Maintain populations at all known sites.

4.2 Ensure the establishment and maintenance of five viable populations across the former range by 2010.

5. Proposed action with lead agencies

The processes required to deliver the above objectives involve appropriate management of known habitats for the species, followed by surveys to determine its status, population monitoring, and autecological studies.

5.1 Policy and legislation

5.1.2 Where appropriate, include the requirements of the species when preparing or revising prescriptions for agri-environment schemes. (ACTION: EN, MAFF)

5.2 Site safeguard and management

5.2.1 Where possible, ensure that all occupied habitat is appropriately managed by 2008, including the provision of south-facing patches of bare ground. This may be achieved through SSSI or agri-environment scheme management agreements. (ACTION: Dartmoor National Park, EN, FE)

5.2.2 Ensure that the species in included in site management documents for all relevant SSSIs. (ACTION: EN)

5.3 Species management and protection

5.3.1 Consider reintroducing *Pterostichus kugelanni* to a series of sites within its former range, if necessary to maintain a minimum of five viable populations of the species by 2010. (ACTION: EN)

5.4 Advisory

5.4.1 Advise landowners and managers of the presence of the species and the importance of beneficial management for its conservation. (ACTION: EN)

5.5 Future research and monitoring

5.5.1 Undertake surveys to determine the status of the species. (ACTION: EN, FC)

5.5.2 Conduct targeted autecological research to inform habitat management. (ACTION: EN)

5.5.3 Establish a regular monitoring programme for this species. (ACTION: EN, FC)

5.5.4 Pass information gathered during survey and monitoring of this species to a central database for incorporation into national and international databases. (ACTION: EN)

5.6 Communications and publicity

5.6.1 Promote opportunities for the appreciation of this species and the conservation issues associated with lowland heathland. This should be achieved through articles within appropriate journals as well, as by a publicity leaflet. (ACTION: EN, FC)

5.7 Links with other action plans

5.7.1 Implementation of this action plan could benefit other species of lowland heathland, including the ground beetles *Cicindela sylvatica* and *Amara famelica*.

5.7.2 This plan should be considered in conjunction with that for lowland heathland.

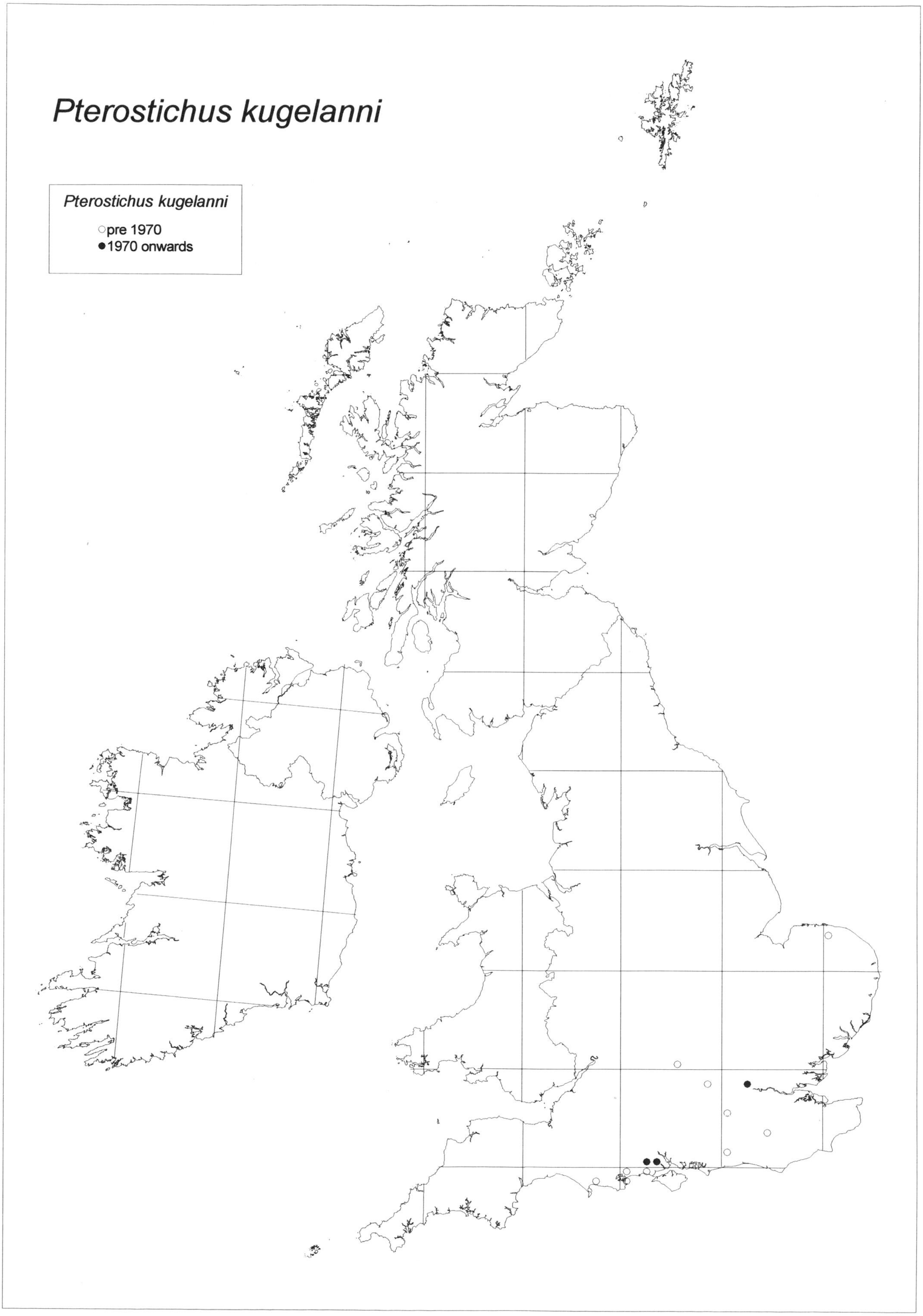

Distribution of Pterostichus kugelanni - a ground beetle in Britain, by 10km square.
Source: Luff, M.L. 1998. Provisional atlas of the ground beetles (Coleoptera, Carabidae) of Britain, Biological Records Centre (ITE) and English Nature - Invertebrate Site Register.

Rhynchaenus testaceus (a jumping weevil) Action Plan

1. Current status

1.1 *Rhynchaenus testaceus* is associated with alder where its larvae mine the leaves; it is not known to feed on any other host in Britain. The specific distinctness between *R. testaceus* and *R. calceatus* is controversial, but the current view is that both are good species. Historically at least, *R. calceatus* is the rarer species and it has a different host (downy birch), but it is possible that some of the older records of *R. testaceus* refer to *R. calceatus*.

1.2 Though always regarded as a scarce species, it has been recorded from many areas of England, southern Scotland, Wales and Northern Ireland (where it has been reported from Counties Down, Antrim and Derry). However, since 1940 the only UK records are from east Cornwall (1978), west Norfolk (1987/88) and Huntingdonshire (1991). It has a Holarctic distribution and is widely distributed in southern Canada and northern USA, including Alaska. It is generally common and widely distributed throughout Europe, occurring in the Nordic countries and extending into Asia and the Mediterranean region.

1.3 In Great Britain this species is now classified as *Vulnerable*.

2. Current factors causing loss or decline

2.1 Not known

3. Current action

3.1 This species has recently been recorded from Holme Fen NNR, MoD Stanford PTA, and a FC nature reserve in Norfolk.

4. Action plan objectives and targets

4.1 Maintain populations at all known sites.

4.2 Enhance populations at all known sites by 2010.

4.3 Ensure that viable populations are maintained at a minimum of six, well-separated sites, within its historical range by 2010.

5. Proposed action with lead agencies

A survey of extant colonies and historic sites should be undertaken for this species. This will establish its current status and provide information to allow targeting of the other measures recommended. Other priorities should include appropriate management of all extant sites, based on a better understanding of the beetles' ecological requirements. Experimental work should also be undertaken to assess the feasibility of reintroducing viable populations to other sites.

5.1 Policy and legislation

5.1.1 Where appropriate, incorporate the requirements of the species in the in preparation or revision of agri-environment or woodland grant schemes. (ACTION: EN, FC, MAFF)

5.1.2 Address the requirements of this species in the LEAP process and in relevant WLMPs. (ACTION: EA, IDBs, LAs, MAFF)

5.2 Site safeguard and management

5.2.1 Where possible, ensure all occupied habitat is appropriately managed by 2008, for example through SSSI or agri-environment/woodland grant scheme management agreements. (ACTION: EA, EN, FE, MAFF, MoD)

5.2.2 Ensure that the species is included in site management documents for all relevant SSSIs. (ACTION: EN)

5.2.3 Consider notifying as SSSIs sites with key populations of the species, where this is necessary to secure their long-term protection and appropriate management. (ACTION: EN)

5.3 Species management and protection

5.3.1 Consider reintroducing *Rhynchaenus testaceus* to a series of sites within the former range, if necessary to ensure the maintenance of six viable populations. (ACTION: CCW, EHS, EN, SNH)

5.4 Advisory

5.4.1 Advise landowners and managers of the presence of this species and the importance of beneficial management for its conservation. (ACTION: EN)

5.5 Future research and monitoring

5.5.1 Undertake surveys to determine the status of this species. (ACTION: CCW, EHS, EN, SNH)

5.5.2 Conduct targeted autecological research to elucidate the causes of decline and inform habitat management. Consideration should be given to the potential effects of alder root disease. (ACTION: EN)

5.5.3 Establish a regular monitoring programme for the species. (ACTION: EN)

5.5.4 Pass information gathered during survey and monitoring of this species to a central database for incorporation in national and international databases. (ACTION: CCW, EHS, EN, SNH)

5.6 Communications and publicity

5.6.1 Promote opportunities for the appreciation of the species and the conservation issues associated with its habitat. This should be achieved through articles within appropriate journals, as well as by a publicity leaflet. (ACTION: EN)

5.7 Links with other action plans

5.7.1 This action plan should be considered in conjunction with that for wet woodlands.

Rhynchaenus testaceus

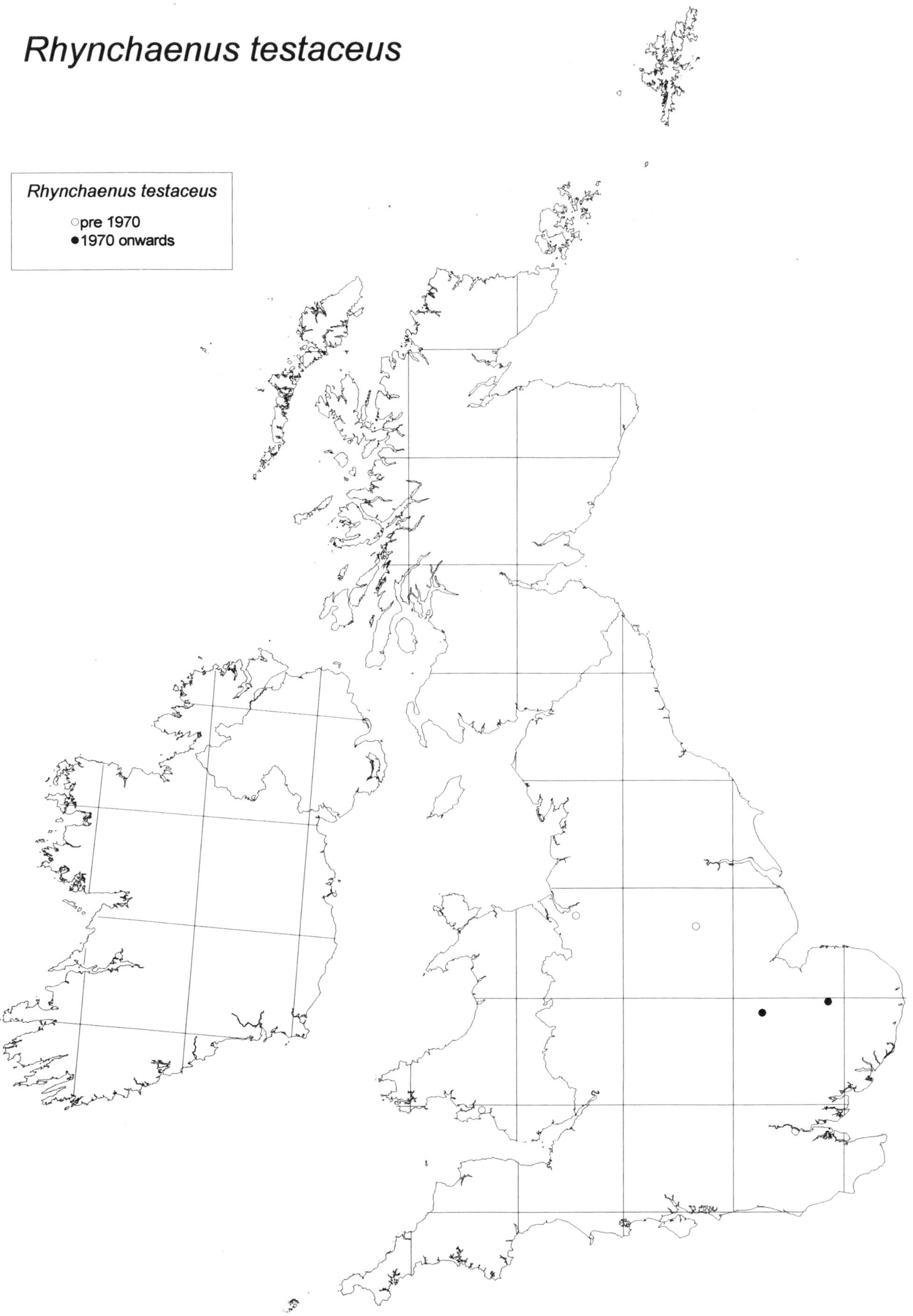

Distribution of Rhynchaenus testaceus - a jumping weevil in Britain, by 10km square.
Source: English Nature - Invertebrate Site Register and the Countryside Council for Wales records.

Badister collaris (= anomalus) (a ground beetle)
Species Statement

1. Current status

1.1 *Badister collaris* occurs on damp, muddy, tree-shaded water margins and in litter and vegetation by standing water, where there is a humus-rich substrate. It has an annual life cycle. It breeds in the spring, with summer larvae, and pupates before overwintering as an adult, probably in tussocks and other locally slightly elevated shelter. Both larvae and adults are predatory, possibly exclusively on small molluscs. *Badister collaris* can fly and has been caught at light traps.

1.2 In Britain the species was first recognised in 1951 from Dorset, but nearly all subsequent occurrences have been from Sussex (Brede and East Guldeford Levels, Powdermill Reservoir, Walland Marsh SSSI), together with one from Kent (Chart Court). Outside Britain it is found locally in north-west Europe, the Balkans and the Middle East. Separation of *Badister collaris* from the related species *B. peltatus* and *B. dilatatus* is difficult, and it can only be done with certainty by microscopical examination of the extracted male genitalia.

1.3 In Great Britain this species is now classified as *Endangered*.

2. Current factors causing loss or decline

2.1 Not known

3. Current action

3.1 Walland Marsh is an SSSI, Brede and East Guldeford Levels are a proposed SSSI.

4. Objective for the species

4.1 Maintain known populations of *Badister collaris*.

5. Proposed action

5.1 Monitoring only. The requirements of the species should be considered in the delivery of the action plans for eutrophic standing waters, and mesotrophic lakes.

Rainbow leaf beetle (*Chrysolina cerealis*)
Species Statement

1. Current status

1.1 The rainbow leaf beetle is a species of montane grassland. The larvae and adults feed on wild thyme, preferring flowers to leaves. During the day, larvae have been found on plants growing in deep, narrow crevices between large boulders, and under stones lying on the grassland surface. Adults are found between April and September, and oviposition occurs during June. In captivity, eggs were mainly laid towards the tip of, and in parallel with, grass blades. On Snowdon, larvae have been found in September and October, also suggesting that this is the main overwintering life stage. However, the presence of fecund adults in April, suggests overwintering as young adults as well as larvae.

1.2 The species is known in the UK only from Caernarvonshire. There are post-1980 records from 6 one km squares, four on Snowdon and two on Cwm Idwal. The site on Snowdon where most adults have been collected is at 630 m above sea level, with a westerly aspect. Here it is considered well established, with one recorder estimating a population of perhaps 1000 individuals in about 1978. Generally, populations remain sparse, in spite of extensive searches. However, this is a difficult species to locate in the field and there is no reliable evidence of decline. This species is widespread throughout northern, central and southern Europe, including the Mediterranean region.

1.3 In Great Britain this species is classified as *Endangered*. The rainbow leaf beetle is specially protected under Section 5 of the Wildlife and Countryside Act 1981.

2. Current factors causing loss or decline

2.1 Not known.

3. Current action

3.1 Both Cwm Idwal and Yr Wyddfa (Snowdon) are NNRs.

3.2 CCW has trialled several monitoring strategies on the Snowdon population in recent years.

3.3 ITE has been observing this species as part of its investigations into the effects of climate change on the distribution of montane invertebrates.

4. Objective for the species

4.1 Maintain known populations of the rainbow leaf beetle.

5. Proposed action

5.1 Monitoring only.

Dyschirius angustatus (a ground beetle) Species Statement

1. Current status

1.1 *Dyschirius angustatus* is a small subterranean ground beetle that lives in burrows of rove beetles of the genus *Bledius* in bare sand at the margins of brackish or fresh water, often on the coast. Its populations can be extremely localised within otherwise apparently suitable habitat. It has an annual life cycle and, as far as is known, is spring breeding. It can probably disperse by flight. *Dyschirius angustatus* is difficult to identify and can be confused with other species of the genus, such as *D. extensus*.

1.2 This beetle has a wide but discontinuous British distribution, with three centres of population in the eastern Scottish Highlands (in river sand/shingle at Nethy Bridge, Fochabers, Bridge of Avon, Colyumbridge and Inverlaidnan), the Solway estuary (Wampool Estuary SSSI), and the Sussex coast (Rye Harbour, Camber, Pevensey Levels). In Europe it is primarily a central European species, but with isolated outlying populations in Scotland and northern Scandinavia.

1.3 In Great Britain this species is classified as *Rare*.

2. Current factors causing loss or decline

2.1 Not known.

3. Current action

3.1 Wampool Estuary is an SSSI within the Upper Solway SPA, candidate SAC and Ramsar site. Pevensey Levels are an NNR and proposed Ramsar site; Rye Harbour and Camber are SSSIs.

4. Objective for the species

4.1 Maintain the range of *Dyschirius angustatus*.

5. Proposed action

5.1 Monitoring only. The requirements of this species should be considered in the delivery of the action plans for coastal saltmarsh, and coastal sand dunes.

Hydroporus cantabricus (a diving beetle) Species Statement

1. Current status

1.1 *Hydroporus cantabricus* occurs in shallow pools on peat on exposed heathland in southern England. It is found in ruts created by vehicles and in small pools associated with artillery practice. Abroad *H. cantabricus* occurs in wooded bogs and base-rich fens. *H. cantabricus* has been found as teneral adults in pitfall traps in June, indicating that it breeds in spring in temporary pools. Its life cycle is otherwise unknown.

1.2 This species is known in Britain from only three 10 km squares on the Isle of Purbeck and in neighbouring heathland south of the River Frome, Dorset. The last record was from Studland Heath NNR in 1993. There are also recent published records for Jersey. *H. cantabricus* is a Palearctic 'Atlantic' species, known from western France, Belgium, northern Spain and Portugal. Eastern European records almost certainly refer to *H. hebaueri*.

1.3 In Great Britain this species is currently classified as *Rare*.

2. Current factors causing loss or decline

2.1 Loss of heathland habitats through agricultural improvement, afforestation and urban encroachment.

2.2 Climate change resulting in loss of temporary pools on lowland heaths.

3. Current action

3.1 This species occurs on the Studland Heath NNR and has been recorded from some other lowland heath SSSIs.

4. Objective for the species

4.1 Maintain existing populations of *Hydroporus cantabricus*.

5. Proposed action

5.1 Monitoring only. The requirements of the species should be taken into account in the delivery of the action plan for lowland heathland.

Diptera

Blera fallax (a hoverfly) Action Plan

1. Current status

1.1 *Blera fallax* is a fly of native pine woods, where the larvae feed in wet rot-holes associated with the secondary decay of pine wood. Existing populations breed in wet pockets of decay in large pine stumps (minimum surface diameter about 40 cm). Less than 10% of large stumps in these areas have suitable wet pockets of decay. As decay proceeds wet areas dry out, thus fresh inputs are needed to ensure new breeding sites are available. In the remaining breeding sites there are very few trees or stumps of sufficient size where new wet pockets of decay might occur. The lack of breeding sites inhibits the recovery of *B. fallax*.

1.2 Until recently *Blera fallax* was recorded from only seven sites within the UK. These are in Aberdeenshire, Moray and Inverness-shire. It was regularly seen until the 1940s, but it has been recorded less than six times in the past 25 years. Most historical records are from Strathspey, centred on the area between Kingussie in the south and Grantown in the north. Recent surveys have shown that the distribution has apparently declined, with the only remaining populations on Speyside. In Europe, *B. fallax* is generally restricted to mountainous areas, where it is declining and probably under threat.

1.3 In Great Britain *Blera fallax* is classified as *Endangered*.

2. Current factors causing loss or decline

2.1 Inappropriate woodland management.

2.2 Paucity of breeding sites.

2.3 There is a potential threat from over collecting.

3. Current action

3.1 The Malloch Society, with support from SNH, is undertaking surveys for this species.

3.2 Some of the sites with recent records are within SSSIs and on the RSPB reserve at Abernethy Forest.

4. Action plan objectives and targets

4.1 Maintain the population size at all known sites.

4.2 Enhance the population size at all known sites by 2010.

4.3 Extend the range of *Blera fallax* into native pine woods.

5. Proposed action with lead agencies

The main action for this species must be to ensure appropriate management of the sites known to have populations of this hoverfly. With the current shortage of suitable breeding sites it is important to investigate the possibility of increasing the size of the populations by creating artificial breeding sites in pine stumps. Further research is needed to help understand habitat use by this fly, particularly in relation to native pine woods and the management of re-afforestation proposals within areas of existing pine stumps.

5.1 Policy and legislation

5.1.1 Consider adding *Blera fallax* to Schedule 5 of the Wildlife and Countryside Act 1981 by 2010. (ACTION: DETR, JNCC)

5.1.2 Take account of the requirements of *B. fallax* when considering felling and forestry schemes in native pinewood areas. (ACTION: FC, SNH)

5.2 Site safeguard and management

5.2.1 Where possible, ensure that all occupied habitat is appropriately managed by 2008, for example through site management agreements. (ACTION: FC, LAs, SNH)

5.2.2 Where possible, increase the available habitat at known sites and in adjacent areas, and attempt to link up existing fragments of habitat. (ACTION: FC, SNH)

5.2.3 Ensure that this species is included in site management documents for all of the SSSIs where it occurs. (ACTION: SNH)

5.3 Species management and protection

5.3.1 None proposed.

5.4 Advisory

5.4.1 Advise landowners and managers of the presence of this fly and the importance of beneficial management for its conservation. This should include notifying land managers of the location of important tree-stump breeding sites. (ACTION: SNH)

5.4.2 Develop and disseminate guidelines to protect *Blera fallax* for use with landowners; FC, LA, RSPB and SNH area staff; Highland Birchwoods and the Cairngorms Partnership. (ACTION: LAs, FC, SNH)

5.5 **Future research and monitoring**

5.5.1 Monitor the distribution and abundance of *Blera fallax* within its core areas. (ACTION SNH)

5.5.2 Monitor and assess the quality and quantity of suitable stumps within the core areas. (ACTION: SNH)

5.5.3 Undertake surveys for *B. fallax* breeding sites in native pine woods in Strathspey, Deeside, Rannoch, and in Easter and Wester Ross by 2005. (ACTION: SNH)

5.5.4 Pass information gathered during survey and monitoring of this species to a central database for incorporation in national and international databases. (ACTION: SNH)

5.6 **Communications and publicity**

5.6.1 Promote opportunities for the appreciation of this fly and the conservation of dead wood in Scottish woodlands. This should be achieved through articles within appropriate journals, as well as by publicity leaflets. (ACTION SNH)

5.7 **Links to other action plans**

5.7.1 Implementation of this action plan could benefit other species of the habitat, including the cuckoo wasp *Chrysura hirsuta,* the bee *Osmia uncinata* and the spider *Clubiona subsultans.*

5.7.2 This plan should be considered in conjunction with that for native pine woodland.

(Map not provided, for site confidentiality.)

Bombylius discolor (dotted bee-fly) Action Plan

1. Current status

1.1 This bee-fly is a parasitoid of some of the larger solitary bees (probably in the genus *Andrena*), which are active in the spring, although the exact hosts have yet to be determined. Large colonies of the host bees have specific nesting sites, usually involving bare ground into which they burrow. The bee-fly requires flowers for nectar, although the plant species concerned are not known. It is almost certain that the bee-fly can only thrive where large congregations of nesting bees of certain species are established. A metapopulation structure, involving several such colonies, may be required in order to allow for fluctuations in abundance of the host bees at any particular colony.

1.2 The dotted bee-fly underwent a major decline and retraction in range at the time that many species of solitary bees crashed during the 1960s-1970s. This coincided with intensification of agriculture and other land use, though the climatic conditions in the early 1960s may have contributed towards the trend. Though recorded from most southern counties, including inland populations in Cambridgeshire, Warwickshire and Worcestershire, for the most part only certain coastal sites in southern England and South Wales have maintained viable populations of this species. In 1996-97 the dotted bee-fly appeared in good numbers in a few inland districts (mainly south Gloucestershire and a site in Warwickshire), apparently in response to the resurgence in numbers of various species of solitary bees following a sequence of hot summers. The species has a wide range in Europe.

1.3 In Great Britain this species is classified as *Nationally Scarce*.

2. Current factors causing loss or decline

2.1 The decline of host bee populations, caused by the loss of nesting sites and reduction of suitable flowers, as a result of intensification of agriculture.

3 Current action

3.1 Some of the known populations are on SSSIs and NNRs.

4. Action plan objectives and targets

4.1 Maintain populations at all known sites.

4.2 Enhance population size at the more viable sites.

4.3 Ensure that there are 20 strong populations, representative of the historic geographic range by 2010.

5. Proposed action with lead agencies

The objective of this plan will be achieved by enhancing the viability of colonies of the host bees at population levels which will remain robust during periods of decline. This is as much a matter of wider countryside quality as conservation site management. Therefore, this action plan will need to embrace wide strategic objectives on both conservation sites and in the wider countryside.

5.1 Policy and legislation

5.1.1 Where appropriate, include the requirements of the dotted bee-fly when preparing or revising prescriptions for agri-environment schemes. (ACTION: CCW, EN, MAFF, WOAD)

5.2 Site safeguard and management

5.2.1 Where possible, ensure that all occupied habitat is appropriately managed by 2005, for example through SSSI or agri-environment scheme management agreements. (ACTION: CCW, EN, MAFF, WOAD)

5.2.2 Ensure that the habitat requirements of the dotted bee-fly are taken into account in any relevant development policies, plans and proposals. (ACTION: CCW, EN, LAs)

5.2.3 Ensure that the dotted bee-fly is listed in site management documents for all relevant SSSIs. (ACTION: CCW, EN)

5.2.4 Consider notifying sites supporting viable populations of the dotted bee-fly as SSSIs, where this is necessary to secure their long-term protection and appropriate management. (ACTION: CCW, EN)

5.3 Species management and protection

5.3.1 Consider reintroducing populations to sites where this species has become extinct, if this is necessary to maintain 20 viable populations across the geographic range. (ACTION: CCW, EN)

5.4 Advisory

5.4.1 Advise landowners and managers of the presence of the species and the importance of beneficial management for its conservation. (ACTION: CCW, EN, MAFF, WOAD)

5.4.2 As far as possible, ensure that all relevant agri-environment project officers, and members of regional agri-environment consultation groups, are advised of locations of this species, its importance, and the management needed for its conservation. (ACTION: CCW, EN, MAFF, WOAD)

5.5 Future research and monitoring

5.5.1 Undertake surveys to determine the status of this species. (ACTION: CCW, EN)

5.5.2 Conduct targeted autecological research to inform habitat management by 2005. (ACTION: CCW, EN)

5.5.3 Establish a regular monitoring programme for the dotted bee-fly and its hosts at key sites. (ACTION: CCW, EN)

5.5.4 Pass information gathered during survey and monitoring of this species to a central database so that it can be incorporated in national databases. (ACTION: CCW, EN)

5.6 Communications and publicity

5.6.1 Promote opportunities for the appreciation of the dotted bee-fly and the conservation issues associated with its habitat. (ACTION: CCW, EN)

5.7 Links with other action plans

5.7.1 This action plan should be considered in conjunction with that for maritime cliffs and slopes.

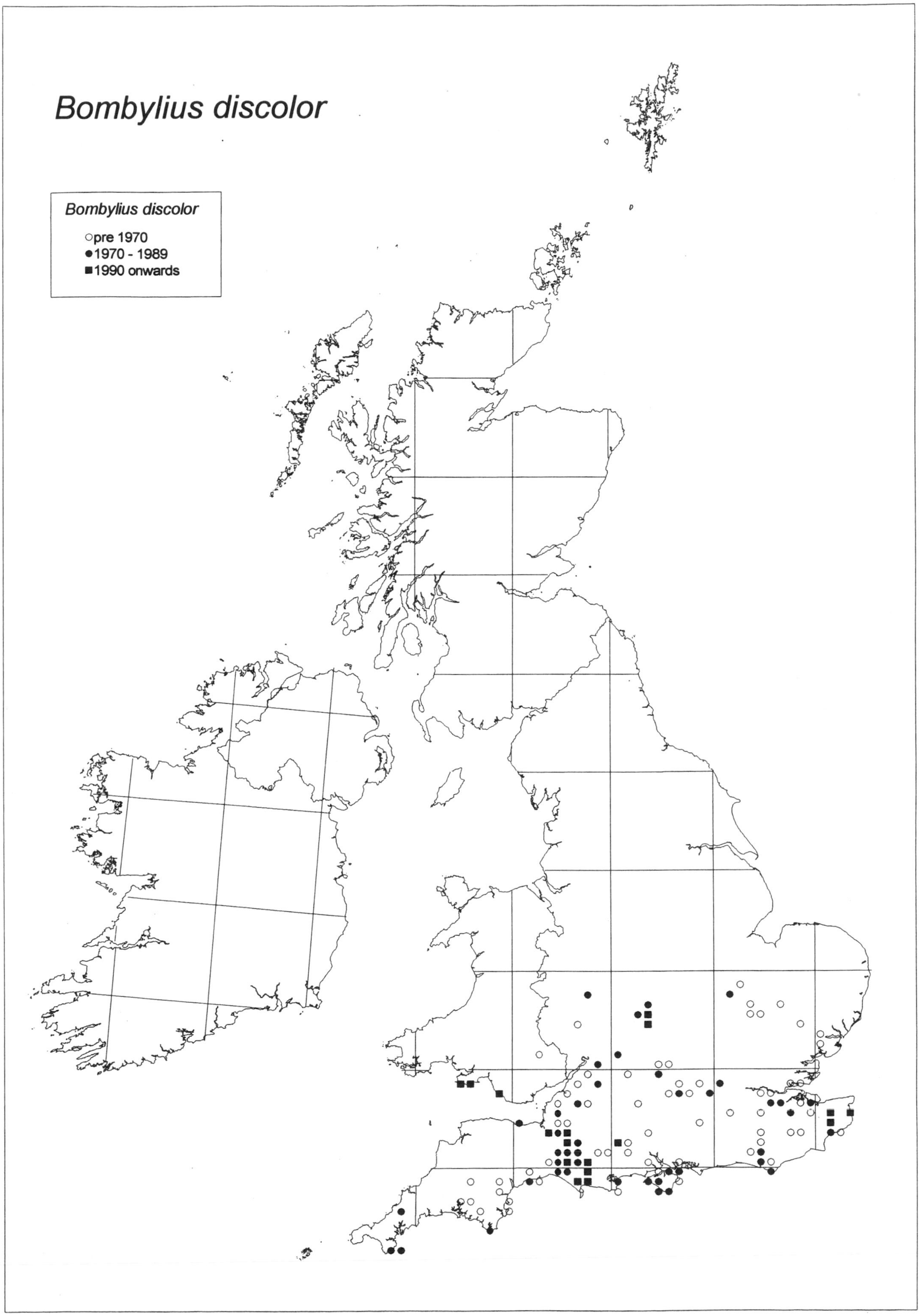

Distribution of Bombylius discolor - dotted bee-fly in Britain, by 10km square.
Source: J. Ismay, Hope Entomological Collections - University Museum of Natural History Oxford, C.M. Drake - Larger Brachycera Recording Scheme and English Nature - Invertebrate Site Register.

Bombylius minor (heath bee-fly) Action Plan

1. Current status

1.1 The heath bee-fly is a species of open heathland where it is a parasitoid of solitary bees of the genus *Colletes*, especially *C. daviesianus*. It uses burrows where the bees nest in vertical sand-banks and possibly also on flat ground. The bee-fly has a strong association with nectar sources on flower-rich path edges (verge heath) and other such situations, but the degree of dependency is uncertain since it also visits bell heather flowers.

1.2 In the UK this species is mainly confined to southern heathland, where it has suffered a contraction in range; it is currently known from only a few sites in Dorset. Here it is highly localised and in most cases at very low population levels. The species' stronghold is the Godlingstone and Studland NNR complex, with other populations on Arne NNR and Wool Heath. The bee-fly is still present on the Isle of Man. It was recorded from the New Forest in 1893 and from the extreme western fringe of the Forest in 1946 and 1959. It is assumed to have become extinct in the Bournemouth - Poole area, and to the north where it was recorded at Holt Heath in 1941. There are single, old records from Devon and Wales. This bee-fly is widely distributed in temperate and southern Europe but its status is uncertain. The taxonomy of the genus is in need of revision.

1.3 In Great Britain this species is classified as *Vulnerable*.

2. Current factors causing loss or decline

2.1 Loss and fragmentation of heathland habitat, including verge heath, owing to development and scrub encroachment.

2.2 Inappropriate heathland management.

2.3 Loss or shading of vertical sand banks, with consequent decline in numbers of the host bees.

3. Current action

3.1 All known populations are on NNRs and SSSIs included within the Dorset Heaths candidate SAC.

3.2 EN commissioned a survey of the East Dorset Heaths in 1995.

4. Action plan objectives and targets

4.1 Maintain populations at all known sites.

4.2 Extend current range, by appropriate management of five sites adjacent to existing sites, by 2010.

5. Proposed action with lead agencies

The priorities for the heath bee-fly are to gain a better understanding of its autecology and habitat requirements, and to increase the amount of nesting sites for host bees by appropriate management. It will be necessary to restore the habitat mosaic on which this species depends, including vertical sand banks and verge heath.

5.1 Policy and legislation

5.1.1 Where appropriate, include the requirements of the species when preparing or revising prescriptions for agri-environment schemes. (ACTION: EN, MAFF)

5.2 Site safeguard and management

5.2.1 Where possible, ensure that occupied sites are appropriately managed, including the maintenance and creation of vertical sandy banks, by 2005. Appropriate management could be achieved through SSSI or agri-environment scheme management agreements. (ACTION: EN, MAFF).

5.2.2 Where possible, increase the available habitat at known sites and in adjacent areas, and attempt to link up existing fragments of habitat. (ACTION: EN, MAFF)

5.2.3 Ensure that the habitat requirements of the heath bee-fly are taken into account in any relevant development policies, plans and proposals. (ACTION: EN, LAs)

5.2.4 Ensure that the heath bee-fly is listed in site management documents for all relevant SSSIs. (ACTION: EN)

5.3 Species management and protection

5.3.1 None proposed.

5.4 Advisory

5.4.1 Advise landowners and managers of the presence of the species and the importance of beneficial management for its conservation. (ACTION: EN, MAFF)

5.4.2 As far as possible, ensure that all relevant agri-environment project officers, and members of regional agri-environment consultation groups, are advised of locations of this species, its importance, and the management needed for its conservation. (ACTION: EN, MAFF)

5.5 **Future research and monitoring**

5.5.1 Undertake further surveys to determine the status of this species. (ACTION: EN)

5.5.2 Conduct targeted autecological research to inform habitat management. (ACTION: EN)

5.5.3 Establish a regular monitoring programme for the heath bee-fly and its hosts. (ACTION: EN)

5.5.4 Pass information gathered during survey and monitoring of this species to a central database so that it can be incorporated in national databases. (ACTION: EN)

5.6 **Communications and publicity**

5.6.1 Promote opportunities for the appreciation of this species and the conservation issues associated with its habitat. (ACTION: EN)

5.7 **Links with other action plans**

5.7.1 Implementation of this action plan could benefit other species of lowland heathland, including the bee-fly *Thyridanthrax fenestratus*, the heath tiger beetle *Cicindella sylvatica* and the sand lizard *Lacerta agilis*.

5.7.2 This action plan should be considered in conjunction with that for lowland heathland.

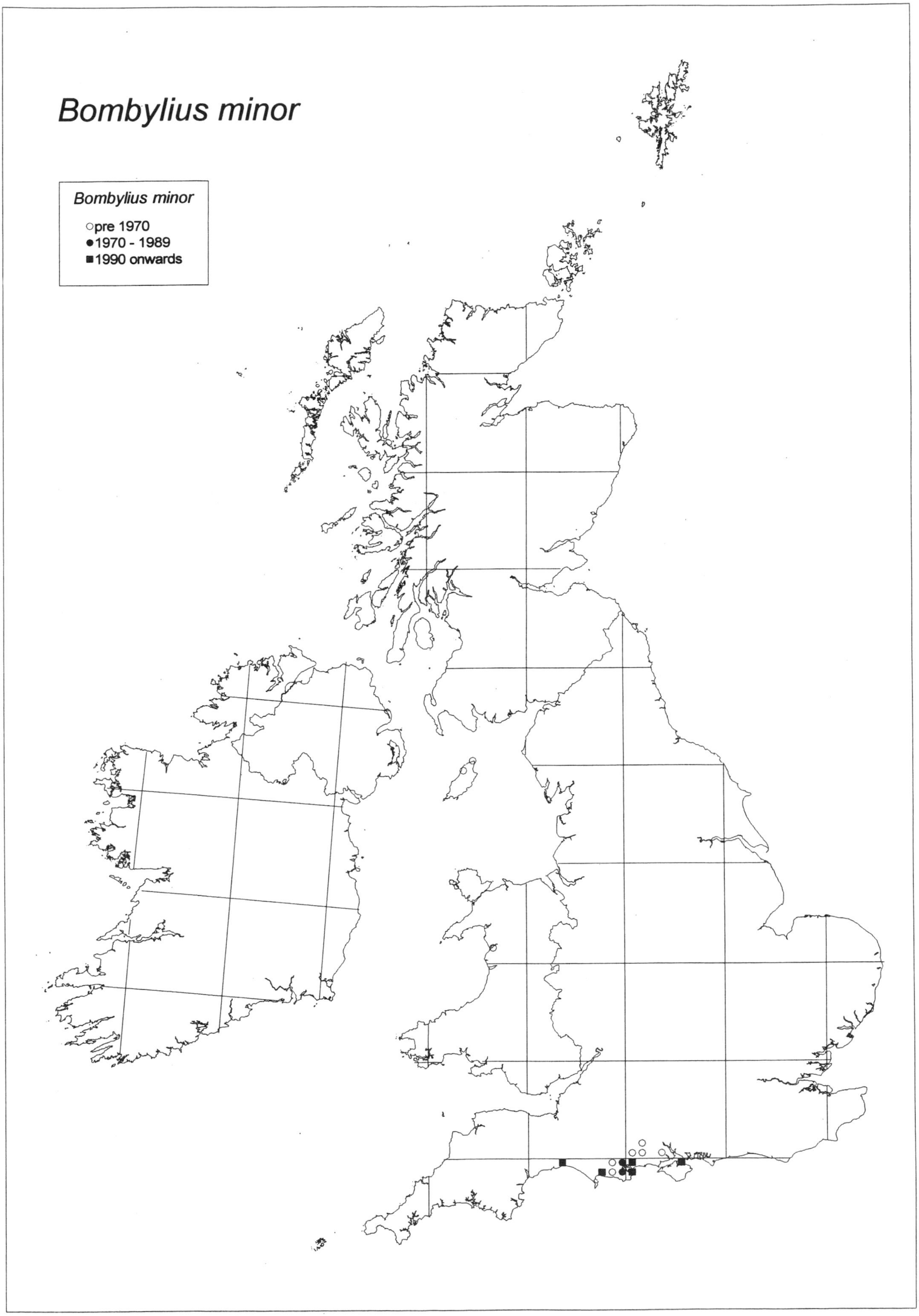

Distribution of Bombylius minor - heath bee-fly in Britain, by 10km square.
Source: A.Stubbs, 1996. The Status of the Bee Flies Bombylius minor and Villa circumdata, with particular reference to the East Dorset Heaths - English Nature report. C.M. Drake - Larger Brachycera Recording Scheme.

Cliorismia (= Psilocephala) rustica (a stiletto fly) Action Plan

1. Current status

1.1 *Cliorismia rustica* is a species of lowland rivers where the adults are associated with sandy river banks, especially where sand shoals have built up at flood level. Shading alders or other trees and bushes are generally present, but bare sand in open sunny conditions is usually part of the habitat mosaic, although the ecological requirements of the species are poorly understood. Larvae of stiletto flies are terrestrial soil predators so those of *Cliorismia rustica* are assumed to live in loose sand, either in sunny situations or in the shade.

1.2 This species is mainly recorded from the Welsh Marches of England and Wales, including the River Monnow and the River Usk, plus isolated localities in West Sussex and north-east Yorkshire. Despite greatly increased recording effort in recent years, few new localities have been found, and the presence of the fly at some of its older localities has not been confirmed. The species has a wide distribution in Europe, but its status in most countries is largely unspecified.

1.3 In Great Britain this species (under the name *Psilocephala rustica*) is classified as *Rare*.

2. Current factors causing loss or decline

2.1 The removal of sandy sediment from rivers and river banks for aggregate and the deepening and canalisation of water courses.

2.2 Reductions in river flow as a result of water abstraction.

3. Current action

3.1 Several populations occur within the River Usk candidate SAC. One SSSI in West Sussex includes a short stretch of river supporting this species.

4. Action plan objectives and targets

4.1 Maintain populations at all known sites.

5. Proposed action with lead agencies

The objectives of this plan will be achieved by securing sympathetic management of sandy river margins, and by maintaining natural hydrological and geomorphological processes on occupied rivers. Surveys will be necessary to clarify the status of this species, followed by autecological research to investigate its habitat requirements.

5.1 Policy and legislation

5.1.1 Address the requirements of this species in the LEAP process and in relevant WLMPs. (ACTION: EA, IDBs, LAs, MAFF)

5.1.2 Take account of the requirements of this species in response to applications for water abstraction or sand extraction from rivers. (ACTION: EA)

5.2 Site safeguard and management

5.2.1 Where possible, ensure that all occupied sites are appropriately managed by 2005, for example through site management agreements. (ACTION: CCW, EA, EN)

5.2.2 Ensure that the species is included in site management documents for all relevant SSSIs. (ACTION: CCW, EN)

5.2.3 Consider notifying as SSSIs sites holding key populations of the species, where this is necessary to secure their long-term protection and appropriate management. (ACTION: CCW, EN)

5.3 Species management and protection

5.3.1 None proposed.

5.4 Advisory

5.4.1 Advise landowners and managers of the presence of this species and the importance of beneficial management for its conservation. (ACTION: CCW, EA, EN)

5.5 Future research and monitoring

5.5.1 Undertake surveys to determine the status of this species. (ACTION: CCW, EN)

5.5.2 Conduct targeted autecological research to inform habitat management. (ACTION: CCW, EN)

5.5.3 Establish a regular monitoring programme for this species. (ACTION: CCW, EN)

5.5.4 Pass information gathered during survey and monitoring of this species to a central database so that it can be incorporated in national databases. (ACTION: CCW, EN)

5.6 Communications and publicity

5.6.1 Promote opportunities for the appreciation of this species and the conservation issues associated with this habitat. This should be achieved through articles within appropriate journals, as well as by a publicity leaflet. (ACTION: CCW, EN)

5.7 Links with other action plans

5.7.1 Implementation of this action plan could benefit other species of sandy river banks, including the cranefly *Rhabdomastix laeta* (= *hilaris*).

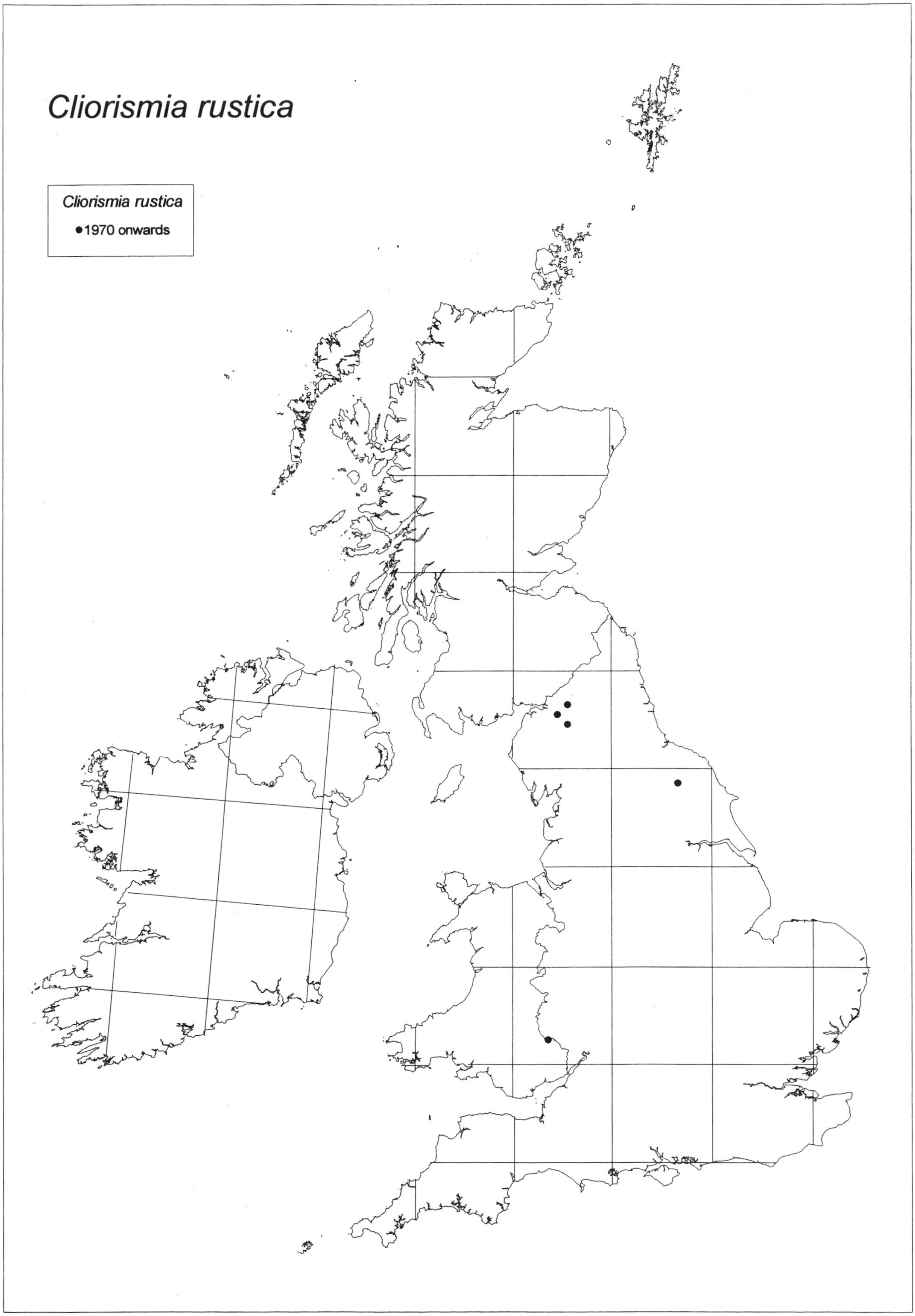

Distribution of Cliorismia rustica - a stiletto fly in Britain, by 10km square.
Source: English Nature - Invertebrate Site Register and C.M. Drake - Diptera Recording Scheme.

Doros profuges (= *conopseus*) (a hoverfly) Action Plan

1. Current status

1.1 The life history of *Doros profuges* is uncertain, but probably complex and highly specialised. The biology of the larvae is unknown, but it is believed to have a commensal or predatory relationship within nests of the ant *Lasius fuliginosus* in woodland or around isolated trees. Most records of adults are from scrub or wood edge on calcareous grasslands. Adults may visit flowers for nectar and they are often found near brambles. *Doros profuges* is a large, spectacular, wasp-mimic and one of the most enigmatic British hoverflies.

1.2 *Doros profuges* is seldom seen and historically has been regarded as a great rarity, with a wide but very patchy distribution. In recent years it has been found mainly on the western chalk rim of the Weald, on the North Downs of Surrey, the South Downs of West Sussex and the Hampshire fringe, where there appear to be several well established colonies. There is a recent record from Wiltshire and it is also present around Morecambe Bay. In Scotland it has been recorded on Arran and at a coastal site on Mull. It has seemingly become extinct recently from a site in Essex where it was found over a period of 100 years, and it has not been seen recently at several other historic sites in Dorset, Somerset, Kent, Worcestershire and Cambridgeshire. There is an old record for Caernarvonshire and this elusive species may still occur in Wales. The species has a wide range in temperate and southern Europe but is generally scarce; in the more northern parts it is rare and its status is apparently just as uncertain and precarious as in Britain.

1.3 In Great Britain this species is classified as *Vulnerable*.

2. Current factors causing loss or decline

2.1 Not known.

3. Current action

3.1 Recent records are mainly from SSSIs.

4. Action plan objectives and targets

4.1 Maintain populations at all known sites.

4.2 Enhance the population size at all known sites by 2010.

5. Proposed action with lead agencies

The priorites of this action plan are to determine the local distribution at currently occupied sites, and to research the habitat requirements and ecology of the larvae. Once this is known, it will be necessary to instigate appropriate conservation management in order to enhance populations.

5.1 Policy and legislation

5.1.1 Where appropriate, include the requirements of the species when preparing or revising prescriptions for agri-environment schemes. (ACTION: EN, MAFF, SNH, SOAEFD)

5.2 Site safeguard and management

5.2.1 Where possible, ensure that occupied sites are appropriately managed by 2005, for example through SSSI or agri-environment scheme management agreements. (ACTION: EN, MAFF, SNH, SOAEFD)

5.2.2 Ensure that the species is included in site management documents for all relevant SSSIs. (ACTION: EN, SNH)

5.2.3 Consider notifying as SSSIs sites holding key populations of the species, where this is necessary to secure their long-term protection and appropriate management. (ACTION: EN, SNH)

5.3 Species management and protection

5.3.1 None proposed.

5.4 Advisory

5.4.1 Advise landowners and managers of the presence of the species and the importance of beneficial management for its conservation. (ACTION: EN, MAFF, SNH, SOAEFD)

5.4.2 As far as possible, ensure that all relevant agri-environment project officers, and members of regional agri-environment consultation groups, are advised of locations of this species, its importance, and the management needed for its conservation. (ACTION: EN, MAFF, SNH, SOAEFD)

5.5 Future research and monitoring

5.5.1 Undertake surveys to determine the status of this species. (ACTION: CCW, EN, SNH)

5.5.2 Conduct targeted autecological research to elucidate the causes of decline and inform habitat management. (ACTION: EN, SNH)

5.5.3 Establish regular monitoring of this species at key sites. (ACTION: EN, SNH)

5.5.4 Pass information gathered during survey and monitoring of this species to a central database so that it can be incorporated in national databases. (ACTION: EN, SNH)

5.6 Communications and publicity

5.6.1 Promote opportunities for the appreciation of this species and the conservation issues associated with this habitat. This should be achieved through articles within appropriate journals, as well as by a publicity leaflet. (ACTION: EN, SNH)

5.7 Links with other action plans

5.7.1 This action plan should be considered in conjunction with those for lowland calcareous grassland, and limestone pavement.

Doros profuges

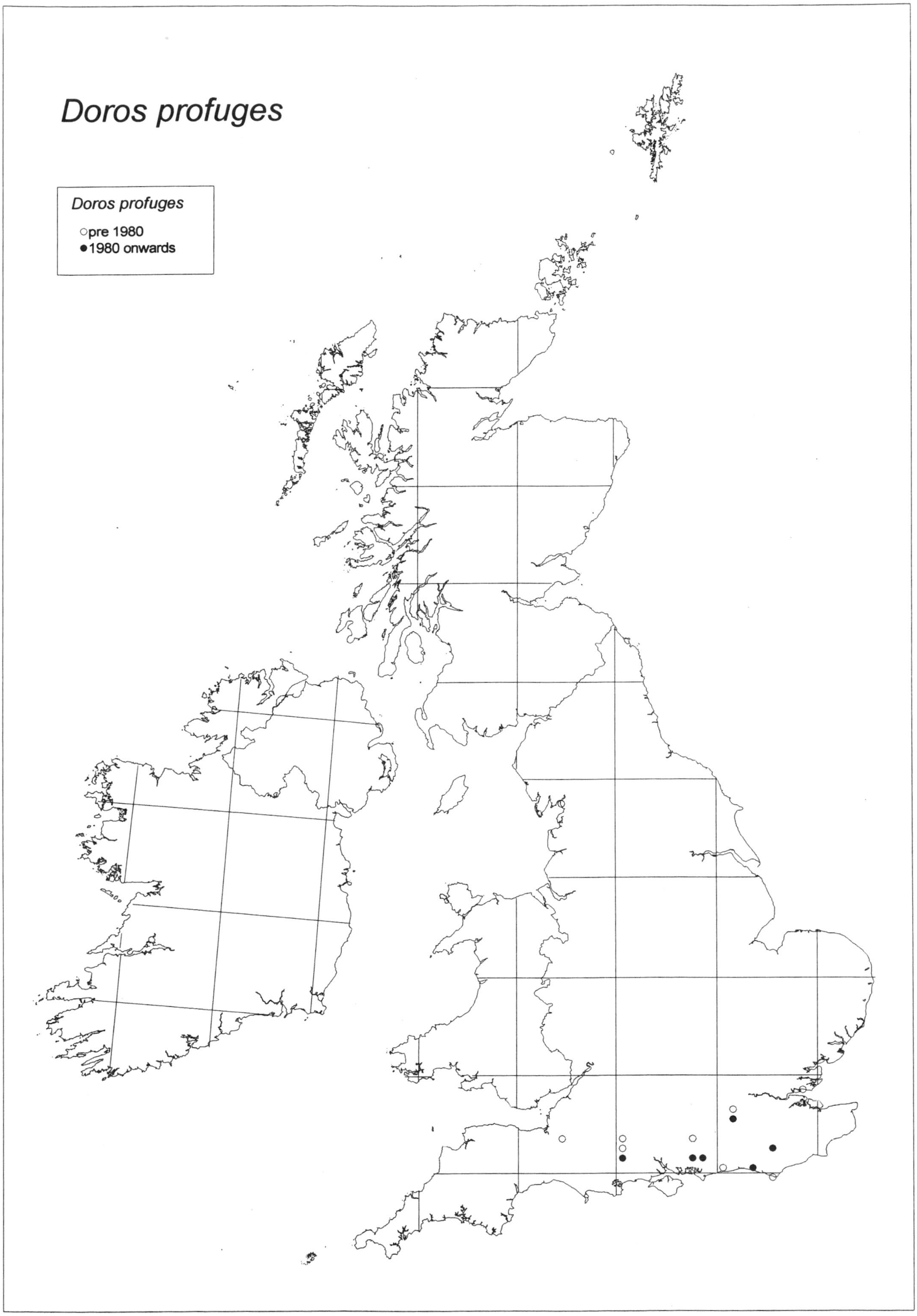

Distribution of Doros profuges - a hoverfly in Britain, by 10km square.
Source: S. Ball & R. Morris, 1992. Working maps of hoverflies, and English Nature - Invertebrate Site Register.

Dorycera graminum (a picture-winged fly) Action Plan

1. Current status

1.1 *Dorycera graminum* is associated with grassland but there is no consistent interpretation of habitat requirements. At least some sites where the species has been reported contain areas of wet grassland or marsh. However, adults have also been found on dry grassland of low botanical diversity. Larval ecology is unknown, which is the position with most British Ulidiidae, but rotting vegetation has been suggested as the most likely larval habitat. Adults have been frequently been found in association with umbellifers.

1.2 This species has undergone a marked decline in numbers and range in recent decades. Old records show that it was formerly widespread in southern England, extending north to Worcestershire, Huntingdonshire and Suffolk, and with a disjunct occurrence in the coastal belt between Elgin and Inverness. From the numbers of specimens in collections, it seems to have been relatively plentiful in some districts. However, in recent years it has been recorded only from Kent, Essex, Oxford, Surrey and Worcestershire. In Europe this is a widespread species in the temperate and southern belts.

1.3 In Great Britain this species is currently classified as *Rare*.

2. Current factors causing loss or decline

2.1 Not known

3. Current action

3.1 Many sites where this species has been reported are SSSIs. Croome Park (Worcestershire) and Morden Hall (Surrey) are owned and managed by the National Trust.

4. Action plan objectives and targets

4.1 Maintain populations at all known sites.

4.2 Enhance the population size at all known sites by 2010.

5. Proposed action with lead agencies

To achieve the objectives of this plan it will be necessary to clarify the ecological requirements of this species by survey and autecological research. Following this, sympathetic management will need to be initiated in order to maintain and enhance populations.

5.1 Policy and legislation

5.1.1 Where appropriate, include the requirements of this species when preparing or revising prescriptions for agri-environment schemes. (ACTION: EN, MAFF, SNH, SOAEFD)

5.2 Site safeguard and management

5.2.1 Where possible, ensure that all occupied sites are appropriately managed by 2005, for example through SSSI or agri-environment scheme management agreements. (ACTION: EN, MAFF, SNH, SOAEFD)

5.2.2 Ensure that the habitat requirements of this species are taken into account in any relevant development policies, plans and proposals. (ACTION: EN, LAs, SNH)

5.2.3 Ensure that the species is included in site management documents for all relevant SSSIs. (ACTION: EN, SNH)

5.2.4 Consider notifying as SSSIs sites holding key populations of the species, where this is necessary to secure their long-term protection and appropriate management. (ACTION: EN, SNH)

5.3 Species management and protection

5.3.1 None proposed.

5.4 Advisory

5.4.1 Advise landowners and managers of the presence of this species and the importance of beneficial management for its conservation. (ACTION: EN, MAFF, SNH, SOAEFD)

5.4.2 As far as possible, ensure that all relevant agri-environment project officers, and members of regional agri-environment consultation groups, are advised of locations of this species, its importance, and the management needed for its conservation. (ACTION: EN, MAFF, SNH, SOAEFD)

5.5 Future research and monitoring

5.5.1 Undertake surveys to determine the status of this species. (ACTION: EN, SNH)

5.5.2 Conduct targeted autecological research to elucidate the causes of decline and inform habitat management. (ACTION: EN, SNH)

5.5.3 Establish a regular monitoring programme for this species. (ACTION: EN, SNH)

5.5.4 Pass information gathered during survey and monitoring of this species to a central database so that it can be incorporated into national and international databases. (ACTION: EN, SNH)

5.6 Communications and publicity

5.6.1 Promote opportunities for the appreciation of this species and the conservation issues associated with its habitat. This should be achieved through articles within appropriate journals, as well as by a publicity leaflet. (ACTION: EN, SNH)

5.7 Links with other action plans

5.7.1 None proposed.

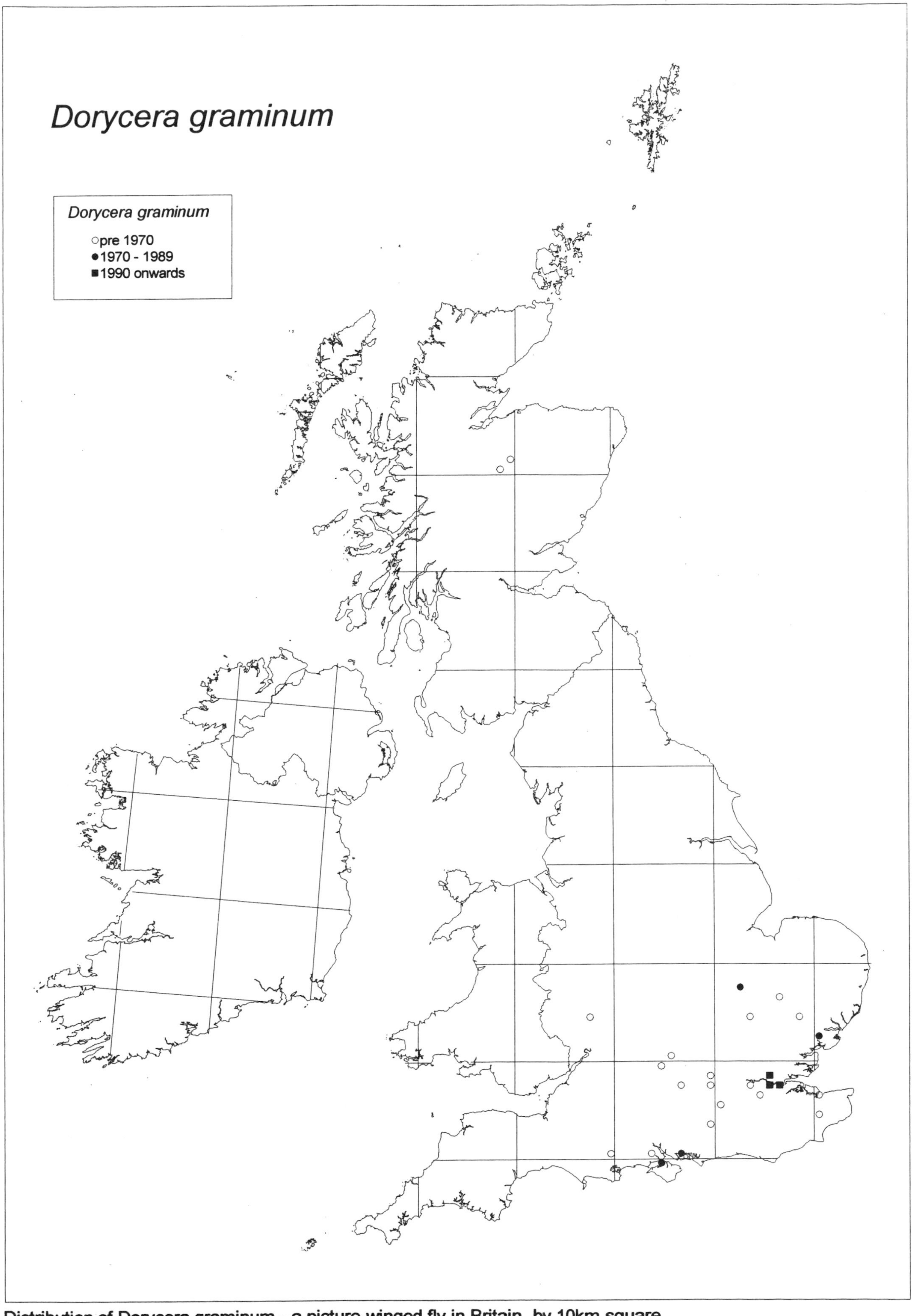

Distribution of Dorycera graminum - a picture-winged fly in Britain, by 10km square.
Source: J. Ismay, Hope Entomological Collections - University Museum of Natural History Oxford, and English Nature - Invertebrate Site Register.

Eristalis cryptarum (a hoverfly) Action Plan

1. Current status

1.1 This hoverfly is associated with valley mire on heathland and moorland, and possibly with other wetland, where its aquatic rat-tailed larvae are assumed to live in saturated peat in flushes, pools or stream edges The adults have been seen at flowers, including bramble, in drier areas, suggesting that a habitat mosaic within and beyond the valley mire is important.

1.2 Historically, *Eristalis cryptarum* was found in all counties of south-west England eastwards to the New Forest. However, it has suffered a major contraction in range, having lost strong populations in the New Forest and east Dorset in the post-war period. The last remaining British location is a small cluster of sites on Dartmoor. The species has a wide range in northern and temperate Europe and is recorded from central Siberia. In Denmark it has declined to *Endangered* status, possibly close to extinction.

1.3 In Great Britain this species is classified as *Vulnerable*.

2. Current factors causing loss or decline

2.1 Not known.

3. Current action

3.1 The Dartmoor population is within the SSSI.

4. Action plan objectives and targets

4.1 Maintain populations at all known sites.

4.2 Enhance the population size at all known sites by 2010.

4.3 Ensure that there are viable populations at five sites within the historic range, including Cornwall, the New Forest and east Dorset by 2010.

5. Proposed action with lead agencies

The priority actions of this plan are to undertake survey of potentially suitable valley mires on Dartmoor and the historic sites for this species, and to conduct research to identify the habitat requirements of the larvae and adults. Appropriate management may then be necessary to maintain and enhance populations. Reintroductions to former sites within the historic range should be considered if necessary to ensure the existence of five viable populations within the historic range.

5.1 Policy and legislation

5.1.1 Address the requirements of this species in the LEAP process and in relevant WLMPs. (ACTION: EA, IDBs, LAs, MAFF)

5.1.2 Where appropriate, include the requirements of the species when preparing or revising prescriptions for agri-environment schemes. (ACTION: EN, MAFF)

5.2 Site safeguard and management

5.2.1 Where possible, ensure that occupied sites are appropriately managed by 2005. (ACTION: Dartmoor National Park, EN, FC, MAFF)

5.2.2 Ensure that the species is included in site management documents for all relevant SSSIs. (ACTION: EN)

5.2.3 Consider notifying as SSSIs sites holding key populations of the species, where this is necessary to secure long-term protection and appropriate management. (ACTION: EN)

5.3 Species management and protection

5.3.1 Consider reintroducing to a series of sites within the former range if necessary to ensure that there are five viable populations. (ACTION: EN)

5.4 Advisory

5.4.1 Advise landowners and managers of the presence of this species and the importance of beneficial management for its conservation. (ACTION: EN, Dartmoor National Park, MAFF)

5.4.2 As far as possible, ensure that all relevant agri-environment project officers, and members of regional agri-environment consultation groups, are advised of locations of this species, its importance, and the management needed for its conservation. (ACTION: EN, MAFF)

5.5 Future research and monitoring

5.5.1 Undertake surveys to determine the status of this species. (ACTION: Dartmoor National Park, EN)

5.5.2 Conduct targeted autecological research to elucidate the causes of decline and inform habitat management. (ACTION: EN)

5.5.3 Establish a regular monitoring programme for this species. (ACTION: Dartmoor National Park, EN)

5.5.4 Pass information gathered during survey and monitoring of this species to a central database so that it can be incorporated in national databases. (ACTION: EN)

5.6 Communications and publicity

5.6.1 Promote opportunities for the appreciation of this species and the conservation issues associated with this habitat. This should be achieved through articles within appropriate journals, as well as by a publicity leaflet. (ACTION: EN)

5.7 Links with other action plans

5.7.1 This action plan should be considered in conjunction with that for lowland heathland.

Eristalis cryptarum

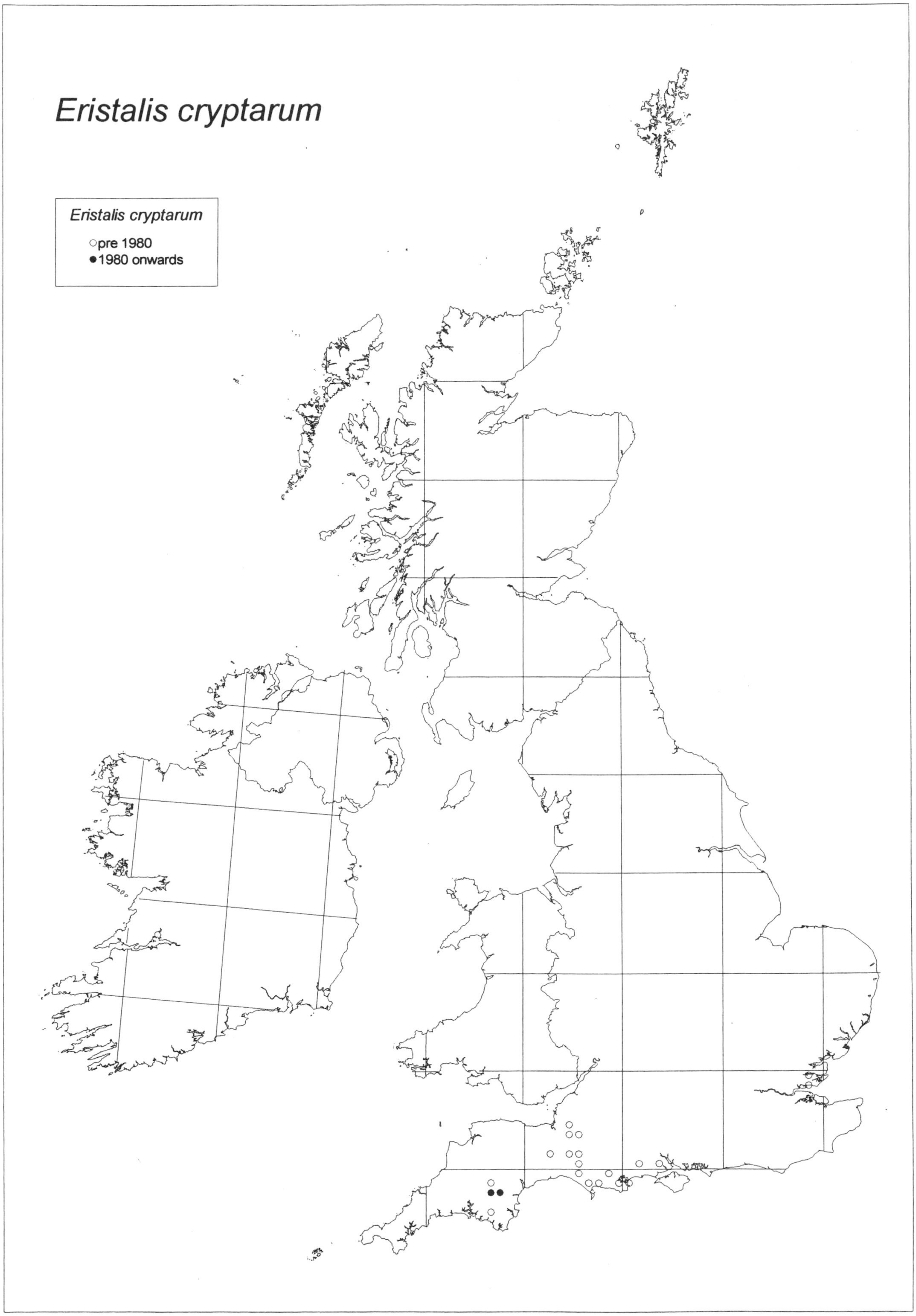

Distribution of Eristalis cryptarum - a hoverfly in Britain, by 10km square.
Source: S. Ball & R. Morris, 1992. Working maps of hoverflies, and English Nature - Invertebrate Site Register.

Hammerschmidtia ferruginea (a hoverfly) Action Plan

1. Current status

1.1 The larvae of *Hammerschmidtia ferruginea* are found in wet decaying cambium that builds up under the bark of recently fallen or dead standing trees, and large branches of aspen with a diameter of at least 30 cm. Wet decaying cambium builds up for about four years in any one branch or tree before the bark cracks and it dries out. Population sizes have never been monitored, but the number of larvae present in individual pieces of fallen wood is generally under 50, and they may be vulnerable to over collecting. Only aspen stands which extend over 4.5 ha are large enough to maintain the continuity of fresh inputs of suitably sized fallen timber needed for *H. ferruginea*. Most aspen stands in Scotland are small, less than 1.5 ha. In the Highlands, only 14 aspen stands extend over 4.5 ha and *H. ferruginea* is virtually absent from the numerous smaller stands, particularly those beyond 1 km of the core stands.

1.2 *H. ferruginea* is rare and thought to be endangered in Europe. It is an indicator of ancient woodlands of international importance in Europe. In 1990-93, *H. ferruginea* was known from eight sites in the British Isles. Intensive survey throughout Scotland during 1990-3, including all previous locations, extended its known distribution to 12 sites in 8 ten km squares in the north-east of Scotland. The main stronghold is Strathspey between Newtonmore in the south and Grantown in the north. Other sites are in the valley of the Findhorn, Easter Ross, Wester Ross, south-east Sutherland and Deeside.

1.3 In Great Britain this species is classified as *Endangered*.

2. Current factors causing loss or decline

2.1 Removal of dead standing and fallen timber.

2.2 Loss of aspen woodlands to road and building development.

2.3 Small size and isolation of aspen stands.

2.4 Insufficient regeneration.

3. Current action

3.1 The Malloch Society surveyed all suitable aspen stands between 1990 and 1993.

3.2 Populations are present on one NNR and others are on land managed by RSPB, FE and LAs.

4. Action plan objectives and targets

4.1 Maintain populations at all known sites

4.2 Enhance the population size at all known sites by 2010.

4.3 Restore populations to three suitable sites by 2010.

5. Proposed action with lead agencies

The objectives of this plan will be achieved by ensuring sympathetic management is in place in sites supporting populations of *Hammerschmidtia ferruginea;* and by increasing the range of the species, extending core aspen stands, regeneration around the fringes, and by linking up isolated stands within 1 km of these areas.

5.1 Policy and legislation

5.1.1 Consider adding *Hammerschmidtia ferruginea* to Schedule 5 of the Wildlife and Countryside Act 1981. (ACTION: DETR, JNCC)

5.1.2 Take account of the requirements of *H. ferruginea* when considering felling and forestry schemes in core aspen areas. (ACTION: FC)

5.1.3 Encourage the use of woodland grant schemes to plant aspen in and around core areas. (ACTION: FC, SNH)

5.2 Site safeguard and management

5.2.1 Where possible, ensure that all occupied and potential habitat is appropriately managed by 2008. (ACTION: FE, LAs, SNH)

5.2.2 Where possible, increase the available habitat at known sites and adjacent areas, and attempt to link up existing fragments of habitat. (ACTION: FE, SNH)

5.2.3 Ensure that the species is included on site management plans, particularly on land managed by RSPB, FE and LAs and the NNR on which *H. ferruginea* occurs. (ACTION: FE, LAs, SNH)

5.2.4 Ensure that the habitat requirements of *H. ferruginea* are taken into account in any relevant development policies, plans and proposals. (ACTION: LAs, SNH)

5.2.5 Consider notifying as SSSI sites supporting viable populations of *H. ferruginea,* where this is necessary to secure long-term protection and appropriate management. (ACTION: SNH)

5.3 Species management and protection

5.3.1 Ensure that any proposals to introduce beavers will not conflict with the requirements of *Hammerschmidtia ferruginea*. (ACTION: SNH)

5.4 Advisory

5.4.1 Advise landowners and managers of aspen stands over 1.5 ha of the presence of the species and the importance of beneficial management for its conservation. (ACTION: SNH)

5.4.2 Develop and disseminate guidelines to protect *Hammerschmidtia ferruginea* for use with: landowners; FC, LA, RSPB and SNH area staff; Highland Birchwoods and the Cairngorms Partnership. (ACTION: FC, LAs, SNH)

5.5 Future research and monitoring

5.5.1 Monitor the distribution and abundance of *Hammerschmidtia ferruginea* within the core areas once every four years. (ACTION: SNH)

5.5.2 Monitor the quantity of suitably aged fallen and dead standing timber within the core areas. (ACTION: SNH)

5.5.3 Pass information gathered during survey and monitoring of this species to a central database so that it can be incorporated in national databases. (ACTION: SNH)

5.6 Communications and publicity

5.6.1 Promote opportunities for the appreciation of *H. ferruginea* and the conservation issues associated with aspen woodlands in Scotland. (ACTION: FA, LAs, SNH)

5.7 Links with other action plans

5.7.1 Implementation of this action plan could benefit other species of aspen woodlands, including the dark-bordered beauty moth *Epione parallelaria*.

5.7.2 This plan should be considered in conjunction with that for wet woodlands.

(Map not provided, for site confidentiality.)

Lipsothrix ecucullata (a cranefly)
Action Plan

1. Current status

1.1 Adult *Lipsothrix ecucullata* are found on or close to wet seepages in damp, deciduous woodlands, but they avoid acid conditions. This species has never been reared, but others in the genus occur in similar situations and breed in very soft, well-decayed sapwood and heartwood of fallen timber lying partially immersed in water, where the larvae feed on fungal mycelia.

1.2 In Europe *L. ecucullata* is rare, with a northern bias in its distribution. The status of this species in the UK is uncertain. There are records from nine well-dispersed sites within Scotland, six of which (in Stirlingshire, Perthshire and Moray) have post-1972 records.

1.3 In Great Britain this species is classified as *Vulnerable*.

2. Current factors causing loss or decline

2.1 Not known

3. Current action

3.1 One of the recent records is from an SSSI.

4. Action plan objectives and targets

4.1 Maintain populations at all known sites.

4.2 Enhance the population size at all known sites by 2010.

5. Proposed action with lead agencies

To achieve the objectives for *Lipsothrix ecucullata*, the first step must be to carry out a baseline survey to determine the distribution, status and breeding sites of the species within Scotland. Once this information is available, the next step will be to protect and maintain the integrity of woodland and woodland seepages at the existing sites, and at others that may be found. Autecological research will be necessary in order to elucidate the threats faced by this species.

5.1 Policy and legislation

5.1.1 Take account of the requirements of *L. ecucullata* when considering felling and forestry schemes and woodland grant schemes in damp woodlands. (ACTION: FC, SNH)

5.1.2 Incorporate the requirements of this species in relevant catchment management plans. (ACTION: SEPA)

5.2 Site safeguard and management

5.2.1 Where possible, ensure that all occupied habitat is appropriately managed by 2005. (ACTION: FE, LAs, SNH)

5.2.2 Where possible, increase the available habitat at known sites and adjacent areas. (ACTION: FE, SNH)

5.2.3 Ensure that the species is included in site management documents for all relevant SSSIs. (ACTION: SNH)

5.3 Species management and protection

5.3.1 None proposed.

5.4 Advisory

5.4.1 Advise landowners and managers of the presence of this species and the importance of beneficial management for its conservation. (ACTION: FC, SNH)

5.4.2 Develop and disseminate guidelines to protect *L. ecucullata* for use with: landowners; FC, FWAG, LA and SNH area staff. (ACTION: FC, LAs, SNH)

5.5 Future research and monitoring

5.5.1 Undertake surveys to determine the range and status of this species. (ACTION: SNH)

5.5.2 Conduct targeted autecological research to elucidate the causes of decline and inform habitat management. (ACTION: SNH)

5.5.3 Establish a regular monitoring programme for this species. (ACTION: SNH)

5.5.4 Pass information gathered during survey and monitoring of this species to a central database for incorporation in national and international databases. (ACTION: SNH)

5.6 Communications and publicity

5.6.1 Promote opportunities for the appreciation of *Lipsothrix ecucullata* and the conservation issues associated wet woodlands. This should be achieved through articles within appropriate journals, as well as by publicity leaflets. (ACTION SNH)

5.7 Links with other action plans

5.7.1 This action plan should be considered in conjunction with that for wet woodlands.

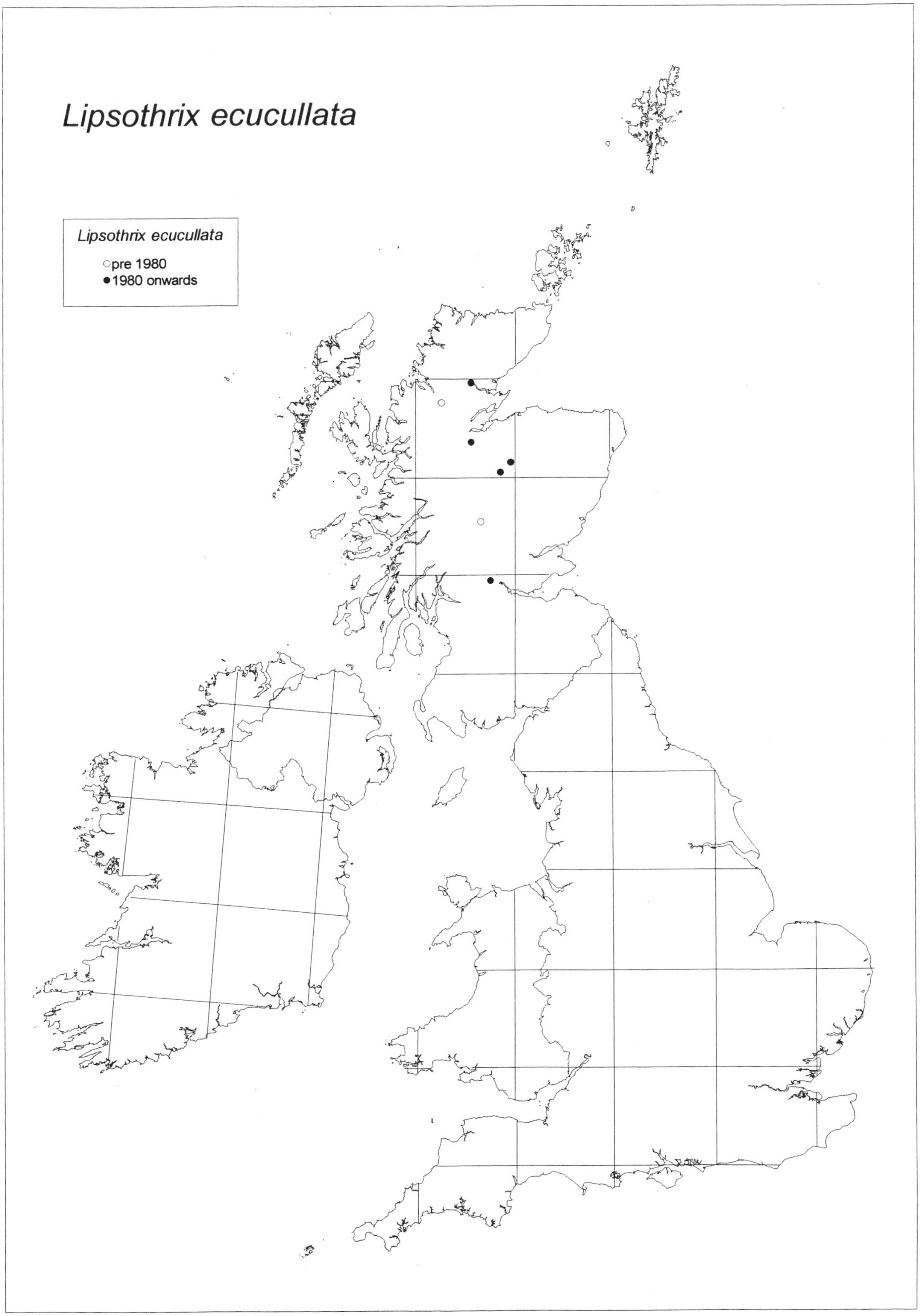

Distribution of Lipsothrix ecucullata - a cranefly in Britain, by 10km square.
Source: English Nature - Invertebrate Site Register

Lipsothrix nervosa (a cranefly) Action Plan

1. Current status

1.1 *Lipsothrix nervosa* is a species of wet, rotting twigs and branches in seepages in deciduous woodland; it is believed to require continuous shade and a constant supply of rotting timber.

1.2 Though having a wide distribution which includes southern England, the south Midlands and South Wales, this species is very localised and for the most part occurs as small populations. Since the 1975/76 drought, and especially during the drought-prone 1990s, the species has declined markedly in abundance and many of its known sites have dried out. The decline has particularly affected the eastern and central part of its range. There is an unconfirmed Scottish record. This species is endemic to the UK.

1.3 In Great Britain this species is classified as *Local*.

2. Current factors causing loss or decline

2.1 The loss or degradation of woodland seepages through woodland clearance, conifer afforestation, drainage or water abstraction.

3. Current action

3.1 Small populations are known to occur on some SSSIs.

4. Action plan objectives and targets

4.1 Maintain populations at all known sites.

5. Proposed action with lead agencies

Meeting the objectives of this plan will be depend on clarifying the status and ecological requirements of this species. Appropriate management of woodland seepages will need to be instigated, particularly efforts to maintain suitable hydrological conditions.

5.1 Policy and legislation

5.1.1 Take account of the requirements of *L. nervosa* when considering felling and forestry schemes and woodland grant schemes in deciduous woodlands. (ACTION: CCW, EN, FC)

5.1.2 Address the requirements of this species in the LEAP process and in relevant WLMPs. (ACTION: EA, IDBs, LAs, MAFF)

5.2 Site safeguard and management

5.2.1 Ensure that sites supporting key populations are appropriately managed by 2008, with particular reference to maintaining beneficial hydrological conditions. Appropriate management could be achieved through site management agreements. (ACTION: CCW, EN)

5.2.2 Ensure that the species is included in site management documents for all relevant SSSIs. (ACTION: CCW, EN)

5.3 Species management and protection

5.3.1 None proposed.

5.4 Advisory

5.4.1 Advise landowners and managers of the presence of this species and the importance of beneficial management for its conservation. (ACTION: CCW, EN)

5.5 Future research and monitoring

5.5.1 Undertake surveys to determine the status of this species. (ACTION: CCW, EN)

5.5.2 Conduct targeted autecological research to inform habitat management. (ACTION: CCW, EN)

5.5.3 Establish a regular monitoring programme for this species at key sites. (ACTION: CCW, EN)

5.5.4 Pass information gathered during survey and monitoring of this species to a central database so that it can be incorporated in national databases. (ACTION: CCW, EN)

5.6 Communications and publicity

5.6.1 Promote opportunities for the appreciation of this species and the conservation issues associated with this habitat. This should be achieved through articles within appropriate journals, as well as by a publicity leaflet. (ACTION: CCW, EN)

5.7 Links with other action plans

5.7.1 None proposed.

(Map data unavailable at time of going to press.)

Lipsothrix nigristigma (a cranefly) Action Plan

1. Current status

1.1 *Lipsothrix nigristigma* is associated with woodland streams, where the larvae live in wet, rotting, fallen trees and branches lying in the stream, especially those in log jams. The exact ecological needs have yet to be elucidated.

1.2 The only recent British records were made in 1995 at two sites near Telford, Shropshire, where log jams were unusually well developed. Before these discoveries the species was known in Britain only from the type specimen taken in Lancashire in 1924. Abroad, the species is known from Romania, Lithuania, the Crimea and Georgia. However, there is the possibility that *Lipsothrix nigristigma* is conspecific with *L. nobilis*, which is reported from Austria, Czechoslovakia, Germany, France and 'Yugoslavia', where the distribution is probably mainly confined to in the Alpine belt.

1.3 In Great Britain this species is classified as *Endangered*.

2. Current factors causing loss or decline

2.1 The removal of log jams and other fallen timber from streams.

3. Current action

3.1 None known.

4. Action plan objectives and targets

4.1 Maintain populations at all known sites.

4.2 Ensure that there are 10 viable populations in existence by 2010.

5. Proposed action with lead agencies

To achieve the objectives of this plan it will be necessary to clarify the distribution of this species in the UK and to investigate its autecology. When a clearer understanding of its status and requirements is available, appropriate management will need to be undertaken. Translocation may be necessary to establish additional populations.

5.1 Policy and legislation

5.1.1 Take account of the requirements of *L. nigristima* when considering relevant felling and forestry schemes and woodland grant schemes in deciduous woodlands. (ACTION: CCW, EN, FC)

5.1.2 Address the requirements of this species in the LEAP process. (ACTION: EA)

5.2 Site safeguard and management

5.2.1 Where possible, ensure that sites supporting key populations are appropriately managed by 2005. (ACTION: EA, EN)

5.2.2 Ensure that the species is included in site management documents for all relevant SSSIs. (ACTION: EN)

5.2.3 Consider notifying as SSSIs sites holding key populations of the species, where this is necessary to secure long-term protection and appropriate management. (ACTION CCW, EN)

5.3 Species management and protection

5.3.1 Consider establishing new populations by translocation if this is necessary to maintain 10 viable populations. (ACTION: CCW, EN)

5.4 Advisory

5.4.1 Advise landowners and managers of the presence of this species and the importance of beneficial management for its conservation. (ACTION: CCW, EA, EN)

5.5 Future research and monitoring

5.5.1 Undertake surveys to determine the status of this species. (ACTION: CCW, EN)

5.5.2 Conduct targeted autecological research to inform habitat management. (ACTION: EN)

5.5.3 Establish a regular monitoring programme for this species. (ACTION: EN)

5.5.4 Pass information gathered during survey and monitoring of this species to a central database so that it can be incorporated in national databases. (ACTION: EN)

5.6 Communications and publicity

5.6.1 Promote opportunities for the appreciation of this species and the conservation issues associated with dead wood in streams. This should be achieved througha articles within appropriate journals, as well as by a publicity leaflet. (ACTION: EA, EN)

5.7 Links with other action plans

5.7.1 Implementation of this action plan could benefit other species of wooded streams, including the cranefly *Lipsothrix errans*.

(Map data unavailable at time of going to press.)

Thyridanthrax fenestratus (mottled bee-fly) Action Plan

1. Current status

1.1 The mottled bee-fly is a species of open, heather-dominated heathland, where it is often found along sandy paths and in other sparsely vegetated sandy areas. It is considered to be either a parasitoid of the sand wasp *Ammophila pubescens* or of the caterpillars which the wasp collects to feed its larvae in burrows in bare sand, although the association requires confirmation. The bee-fly has a requirement for hot microclimates and for flowers which the adults visit to feed on nectar.

1.2 This species is now confined to southern heathland in Dorset, the New Forest and the Weald in Hampshire, Surrey, West Sussex and, possibly, Berkshire. There is a very old record for north Norfolk but none for the Breck or other heaths in East Anglia. The species has seemingly gone from some former sites, such as in mid Surrey, and has become scarce on many other sites. Although some good populations remain, the distribution has become much more restricted in recent decades as open heaths have become smaller and fragmented, and management problems have increased. The mottled bee-fly has a wide north-central European distribution but its status is unknown.

1.3 In Great Britain this species is classified as *Rare*.

2. Current factors causing loss or decline

2.1 Inappropriate heathland management.

2.2 Encroachment by scrub and trees.

2.3 Uncontrolled heathland fires.

2.4 Damage to paths and open areas by increasing recreational use, especially horse riding, or by intense military use.

3. Current action

3.1 EN commissioned a preliminary report on the ecology of this species in 1994.

3.2 All known populations of the mottled bee-fly are on NNRs or SSSIs, and some are included within relevant candidate SACs.

4. Action plan objectives and targets

4.1 Ensure all known sites support viable populations by 2010.

5. Proposed action with lead agencies

The priority actions for this species are to undertake surveys to determine the distribution and status of this species, and to resolve the ecological relationships of host sand wasp and the bee-fly and their ecological requirements. Sympathetic management of occupied habitat on sandy heathlands will be necessary to maintain and enhance populations, as will the linking up of heathland fragments to facilitate colonisation of restored habitat.

5.1 Policy and legislation

5.1.1 Where appropriate, include the requirements of the species when preparing or revising prescriptions for agri-environment schemes. (ACTION: EN, MAFF)

5.2 Site safeguard and management

5.2.1 Where possible, ensure that all occupied sites are appropriately managed, including the provision and maintenance of bare, compacted sand, and the avoidance of excessive disturbance by 2005. Appropriate management could be achieved through SSSI or agri-environment scheme management agreements. (ACTION: EN, MAFF)

5.2.2 Where possible, increase the available sandy heathland habitat at known sites and adjacent areas, and attempt to link up existing fragments of heathland. (ACTION: EN, MAFF)

5.2.3 Incorporate specific targets and management for the mottled bee-fly in MoD site management plans for relevant sites. (ACTION: MoD)

5.2.4 Ensure that the habitat requirements of the mottled bee-fly are taken into account in any relevant development policies, plans and proposals. (ACTION: EN, LAs)

5.2.5 Ensure that the species is included in site management documents for all relevant SSSIs. (ACTION: EN)

5.3 Species management and protection

5.3.1 None proposed.

5.4 Advisory

5.4.1 Advise landowners and managers of the presence of the species and the importance of beneficial management for its conservation. (ACTION: EN, MAFF)

5.4.2 As far as possible, ensure that all relevant agri-environment project officers, and members of regional agri-environment consultation groups, are advised of locations of this species, its importance, and the management needed for its conservation. (ACTION: EN, MAFF)

5.5 **Future research and monitoring**

5.5.1 Undertake surveys to determine the status of this species. (ACTION: EN)

5.5.2 Conduct further targeted autecological research, particularly on the ecological relationships of the bee-fly and its host sand wasp, to inform habitat management. (ACTION: EN)

5.5.3 Establish a regular monitoring programme for this species at key sites. (ACTION: EN)

5.5.4 Determine the impact of horse riding and military activity, and investigate measures to overcome any detrimental effects. (ACTION: EN, MoD)

5.5.5 Pass information gathered during survey and monitoring of this species to a central database so that it can be incorporated in national databases. (ACTION: EN, JNCC)

5.6 **Communications and publicity**

5.6.1 Promote opportunities for the appreciation of this species and the conservation issues associated with this habitat. This should be achieved through articles in appropriate journals, as well as by a publicity leaflet. (ACTION: EN)

5.6.2 Use this species to highlight the impact of recreational pressure on heathland. (ACTION: EN)

5.7 **Links with other action plans**

5.7.1 Implementation of this action plan could benefit other species of dry heathland, including: the sand lizard *Lacerta agilis*, the bee-fly *Bombylius minor*, the hoverfly *Chrysotoxum octomaculatum* and the heath tiger beetle *Cicindella sylvatica*.

5.7.2 This plan should be considered in conjunction with that for lowland heathland.

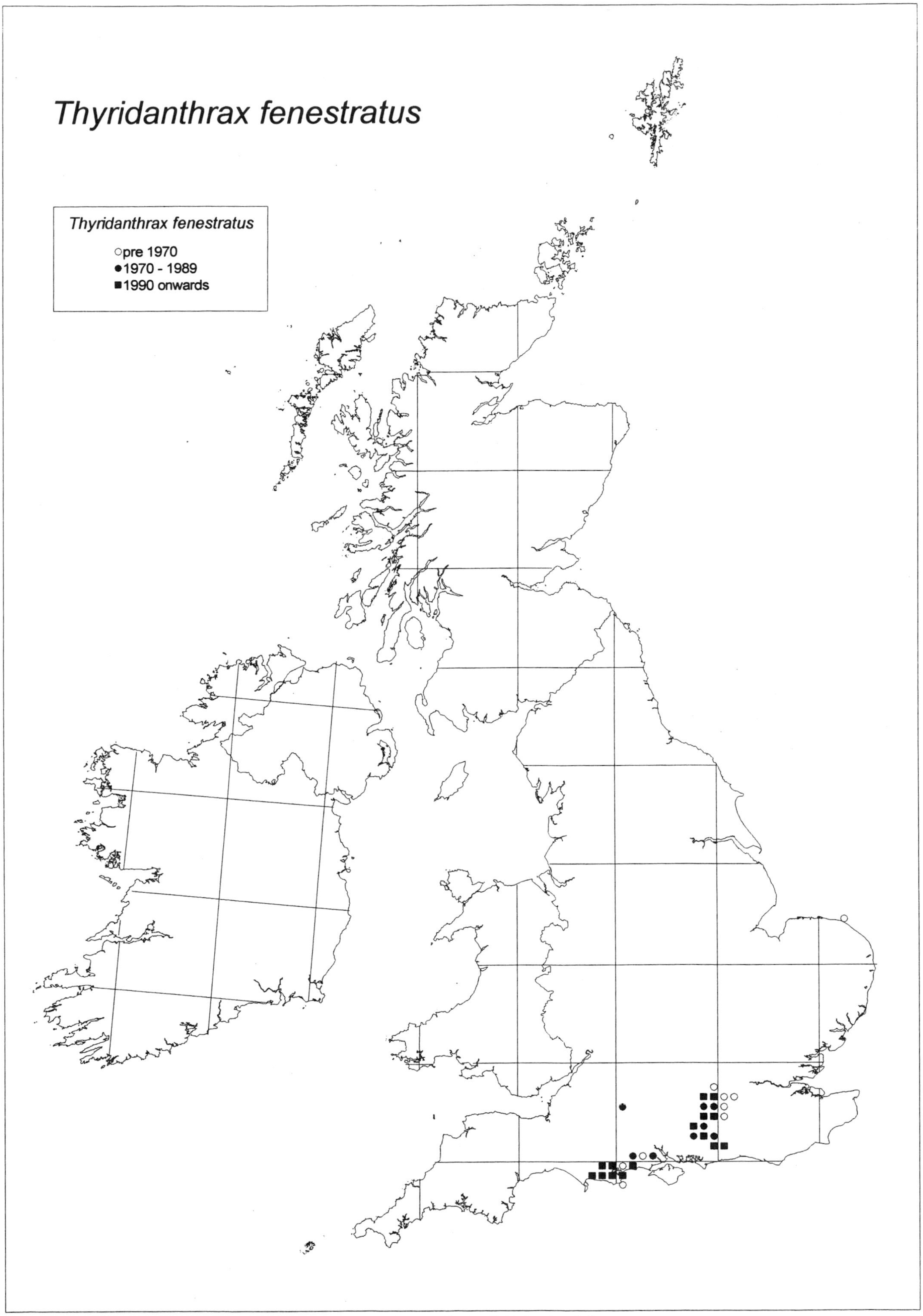

Distribution of Thyridanthrax fenestratus - mottled bee-fly in Britain, by 10km square.
Source: Provisional atlas of the larger brachycera (diptera) of Britain and Ireland, Biological Records Centre (ITE), C.M. Drake - Larger Brachycera Recordong Scheme and English Nature - Invertebrate Site Register.

Lipsothrix errans (a cranefly) Species Statement

1. Current status

1.1 *Lipsothrix errans* is a species of wet rotting fallen trees and branches in shaded, woodland streams, although the exact ecological needs have yet to be elucidated.

1.2 Though having a wide distribution which includes Wales, northern England and Scotland, records have always been sparse. Despite greatly increased recording effort in recent years, few new records are available. *L. errans* has a wide distribution across the temperate belt of Europe but it is generally scarce.

1.3 In Great Britain this species is classified as *Nationally Scarce*.

2. Current factors causing loss or decline

2.1 The removal of log jams and fallen timber and branches from streams.

3. Current action

3.1 The species has been recorded on a few SSSIs.

4. Objective for the species

4.1 Maintain the range of *Lipsothrix errans*.

5. Proposed action

5.1 Monitoring only. This species could benefit from the action plans for other species of wooded streams, including the cranefly *Lipsothrix nigristigma*.

Myolepta potens (a hoverfly)
Species statement

1. Current status

1.1 The ecology of this species is unknown although it is presumed that, as with other species of the genus, it breeds in wet rot holes of mature deciduous trees.

1.2 The only British records, based on six specimens, are from two districts in Somerset between 1945 and 1949. It was first taken in Coombe Dingle, west of Bristol, and was later found on two occasions at Eddington and at nearby Loxley Wood. It seems likely that the species was more widespread than these records suggest, so it may still survive in other areas of south-west England. Loxley Wood has been converted to conifer plantation. The European status of *Myolepta potens* is uncertain but firm records exist for few countries. The species is recognised as a quality indicator for dead wood (saproxylic) habitats in Europe.

1.3 In Great Britain this species is classified as *Endangered*.

2. Current factors causing loss or decline

2.1 Loss of old trees with water-filled rot holes.

2.2 Replacement of deciduous woodland with conifers.

3. Current action

3.1 None known.

4. Objective for the species

4.1 Maintain any discovered populations of *Myolepta potens*.

5. Proposed action

5.1 Search only.

Rhabdomastix laeta (= *hilaris*) (a cranefly)
Species Statement

1. Current status

1.1 The cranefly *Rhabdomastix laeta* is a species of rivers with sandy sediment. The larvae of this genus are aquatic, but those of *R. laeta* are unknown. In its more southern sites, this species occurs on relatively small stretches of lowland rivers with sandy shoals, such as the Rother in West Sussex and the Monnow on the Hereford/Gwent border. In the Scottish Highlands the species can occur within upland districts, where rivers such as the Spey have a flood plain and relatively gentle flow. The ecology of the fauna of this habitat is not well known, and the nature and scale of the problems and any required remedies are, at present, unknown.

1.2 *R. laeta* is widespread across the temperate belt of Europe but it is generally scarce. It has been widely recorded in England, Scotland and Wales, but there are few known localities for this quite distinctive species. Despite greatly increased recording effort in recent years, few new records have been made in much of its range. There is concern that river management over recent decades has reduced its range, especially in England where some lowland rivers have been modified.

1.3 In Great Britain this species is classified as *Rare*.

2. Current factors causing loss or decline

2.1 Removal of sandy sediment from rivers for aggregate.

2.2 Deepening and canalisation of water courses.

2.3 Water abstraction from rivers resulting in changes in sedimentation patterns.

3. Current action

3.1 There are records from the River Usk candidate SAC and several SSSIs.

4. Objective for the species

4.1 Maintain the range of *Rhabdomastix laeta*.

5. Proposed action

5.1 Monitoring only. This species could benefit from the action plans for other species of sandy rivers, including the stiletto flies *Cliorismia rustica* and *Thereva lunulata*.

Tipula serrulifera (a cranefly)
Species Statement

1. Current status

1.1 *Tipula serrulifera* is one of the most enigmatic of the British long-palped craneflies since it has proved so elusive in recent decades. The only precise ecological data is for the Pentland Hills (west of Edinburgh) where it was reported in late August from an un-named location comprising treeless grassy heath beside a burn at 200-250 m in a steep-sided glen. Significantly, the population was confined to a strip about 90 m long. At the site on the North York Moors it was recorded in a trap set in *Calluna* with a moss understory, but that does not mean that it breeds in this habitat. *T. serrulifera* belongs to the subgenus *Savtchenkia* whose many species have larvae that live in or under moss, but the early stages of *T. serrulifera* are unknown.

1.2 In Europe this is a species of mountain areas, mainly the Alps, the Central Massif of France, the Pyrenees, and areas of Corsica and Sardinia. It is also known from the Caucasus and Turkey but not from Scandinavia. There are only three British records: the Wyre Forest (1892), the Pentland Hills (1945) and Yarlsey on the North York Moors (late 1970s). The absence of more recent records is more likely to be due to lack of survey rather than to the extinction of the species.

1.3 In Great Britain this species is currently classified as *Endangered*.

2. Current factors causing loss or decline

2.1 Not known.

3. Current action

3.1 None known

4. Objective for the species

4.1 Maintain any discovered populations of *Tipula serrulifera*.

5. Proposed action

5.1 Search only. The requirements of the species should be taken into account in the delivery of the action plan for upland heathland.

Hymenoptera

Andrena ferox (a mining bee) Action Plan

1. Current status

1.1 *Andrena ferox* is a large mining bee which nests gregariously in open situations exposed to the sun. The nest is unusual in that many females use just one tunnel opening to the outside, although each female provisions its own nest cells within this communal tunnel. Such nest sites are perennial, with subsequent generations using the same nest entrance from year to year. Nest sites are therefore highly vulnerable to disturbance or vegetational succession. The bee flies from late April to early June, and forages for pollen at the flowers of a number of tree species, especially oak, although there are also records of individuals at hawthorn and sycamore flowers.

1.2 *Andrena ferox* is a very rarely found mining bee, with confirmed records from the counties of Kent, East Sussex, Hampshire, Berkshire, Avon and Cornwall. The species was recorded twice during 1966 (Kent, Hampshire) and since then only once in Kent, during 1990. *Andrena ferox* is widely distributed, although rare, in central and southern Europe.

1.3 In Great Britain this species is classified as *Endangered*.

2. Current factors causing loss or decline

2.1 The loss of open grasslands with areas of sunny bare ground at the margins and in the rides of broadleaved woodlands.

3. Current action

3.1 None known.

4. Action plan objectives and targets

4.1 Maintain populations at all known sites

4.2 Enhance the population size at all known sites by 2010.

4.3 Restore populations to suitable sites to maintain 10 viable populations within the historic range by 2010.

5. Proposed action with lead agencies

This species is under threat due to the loss of grasslands with areas of bare ground which are open to the sun and adjacent to oak woods. The priority action necessary to halt and reverse the decline of this species is to establish a programme of pre-recovery autecological research, investigating the nectar, pollen and nesting requirements of the species, together with its dispersal ability. This will need to be followed by a programme of informed habitat management.

5.1 Policy and legislation

5.1.1 Where appropriate, include the requirements of the species when preparing or revising prescriptions for agri-environment and woodland grant schemes. (ACTION: EN, FC, MAFF)

5.2 Site safeguard and management

5.2.1 Where possible, ensure that all occupied and nearby potential habitat is appropriately managed by 2008, for example through uptake of agri-environment or woodland grant schemes. (ACTION: EN, FC, MAFF)

5.2.2 Ensure that the habitat requirements of *Andrena ferox* are taken into account in relevant development policies, plans and proposals. (ACTION: EN, LAs)

5.2.3 Ensure that this species is included in site management documents for all relevant SSSIs. (ACTION: EN)

5.2.4 Consider notifying sites supporting viable populations of *Andrena ferox* as SSSIs, where this is necessary to secure their long-term protection and appropriate management. (ACTION: EN)

5.3 Species management and protection

5.3.1 If necessary to maintain 10 viable populations, undertake habitat restoration and/or re-introductions at suitable former or potential sites. (ACTION: EN)

5.4 Advisory

5.4.1 Advise landowners and managers of the presence of the species and the importance of beneficial management for its conservation. (ACTION: EN)

5.5 Future research and monitoring

5.5.1 Undertake surveys to determine the status of the bee by 2005. (ACTION: EN)

5.5.2 Promote ecological research to establish the habitat requirements of this species, the factors limiting breeding success at existing sites, and its dispersal ability. (ACTION: EN)

5.5.3 Establish a regular monitoring programme for the species. (ACTION: EN)

5.5.4 Pass information gathered during survey and monitoring of this species to a central database for incorporation into national and international databases. (ACTION: EN)

5.6 Communications and publicity

5.6.1 Promote opportunities for the appreciation of this species and the conservation issues associated with its habitat. This should be achieved through articles within appropriate journals, as well as by a publicity leaflet. (ACTION: EN)

5.7 Links with other action plans

5.7.1 Implementation of this action plan could benefit the bees *Andrena gravida* and *Nomada ferruginata*.

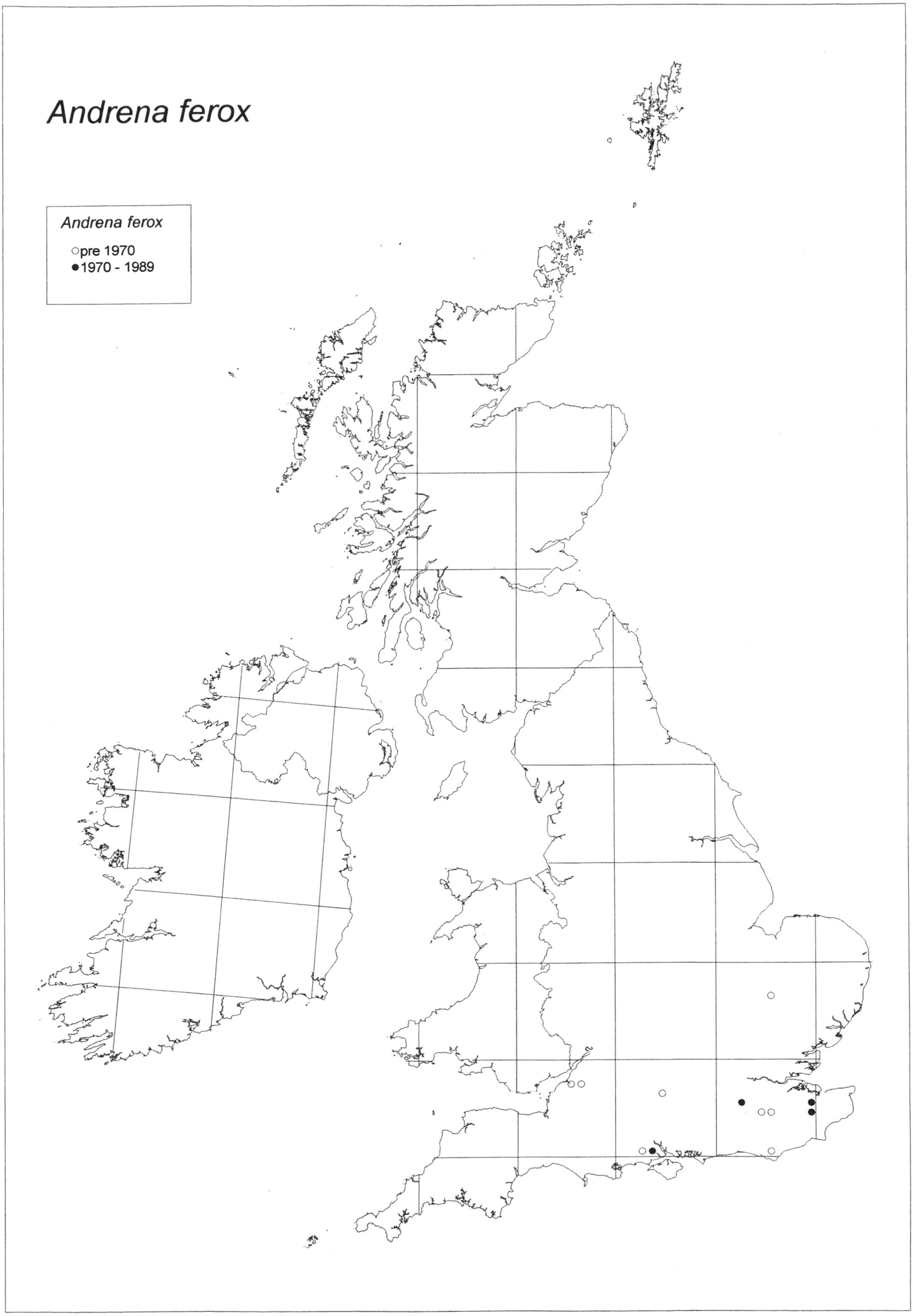

Distribution of Andrena ferox - a mining bee in Britain, by 10km square.
Source: G.R. Else - Recording Scheme and English Nature - Invertebrate Site Register.

Banded mining bee (*Andrena gravida*) Action Plan

1. Current status

1.1 The banded mining bee is a large mining bee which nests in sandy situations exposed to the sun. It flies between late March and May and forages for pollen at the flowers of a number of plant species, including apples, cherries, dandelions and sallows.

1.2 All the confirmed records of this bee come from the counties of Kent, East Sussex and Essex. There were numerous records from within this area in the latter years of the 19th century and the early years of the 20th, particularly from Kent. Following a period of 35 years when no records of this species are known, there have been records from two localities during 1996 (Maidstone, Kent, and Rye Harbour, East Sussex). There are unconfirmed records from Hampshire, Tayside and Borders, although these latter ones are almost certainly the result of mis-identifications. The species is known from Guernsey. The banded mining bee is widespread and locally common in central and southern Europe.

1.3 In Great Britain this species is classified as *Vulnerable*.

2. Current factors causing loss or decline

2.1 Loss of open areas of sandy ground for nesting, and flower-rich sandy grasslands for foraging.

3. Current action

3.1 None known.

4. Action plan objectives and targets

4.1 Maintain populations at all known sites.

4.2 Enhance the population size at all known sites by 2010.

4.3 Restore populations to suitable sites to maintain 10 viable populations within the historic range by 2010.

5. Proposed action with lead agencies

This species is under threat due to the loss of floriferous sandy grasslands with areas of bare ground open to the sun. The priority action necessary to halt or reverse the decline of this species is to establish a programme of pre-recovery autecological research, investigating the nectar, pollen and nesting requirements of the species, together with its dispersal ability. This will need to be followed by a programme of informed habitat management.

5.1 Policy and legislation

5.1.1 Where appropriate, include the requirements of the species when preparing or revising prescriptions for agri-environment schemes. (ACTION: EN, MAFF)

5.2 Site safeguard and management

5.2.1 Where possible, ensure that all occupied and nearby potential habitat is appropriately managed by 2008, for example through agri-environment scheme management agreements. (ACTION: EN, MAFF)

5.2.2 Ensure that the habitat requirements of the banded mining bee are taken into account in relevant development policies, plans and proposals. (ACTION: EN, LAs)

5.2.3 Ensure that this species is included in site management documents for all relevant SSSIs. (ACTION: EN)

5.2.4 Consider notifying sites supporting viable populations of the banded mining bee as SSSIs, where this is necessary to secure their long-term protection and appropriate management. (ACTION: EN)

5.3 Species management and protection

5.3.1 If necessary to maintain 10 viable populations, undertake habitat restoration and/or (re)introductions at suitable former or potential sites. (ACTION: EN)

5.4 Advisory

5.4.1 Advise landowners and managers of the presence of the species and the importance of beneficial management for its conservation. (ACTION: EN)

5.5 Future research and monitoring

5.5.1 Undertake surveys to determine the status of the bee by 2005. (ACTION: EN)

5.5.2 Promote ecological research to establish the habitat requirements of this species, the factors limiting breeding success at existing sites, and its dispersal ability. (ACTION: EN)

5.5.3 Establish a regular monitoring programme for the species. (ACTION: EN)

5.5.4 Pass information gathered during survey and monitoring of this species to a central database for incorporation into national and international databases. (ACTION: EN)

5.6 Communications and publicity

5.6.1 Promote opportunities for the appreciation of this species and the conservation issues associated with its habitat. This should be achieved through articles within appropriate journals, as well as by a publicity leaflet. (ACTION: EN)

5.7 Links with other action plans

5.7.1 Implementation of this action plan could benefit: the sphecid wasps *Cerceris quadricincta* and *Cerceris quinquefasciata;* and the bees *Andrena ferox, Nomada ferruginata, Bombus humilis, B. ruderatus, B. subterraneus* and *B. sylvarum.*

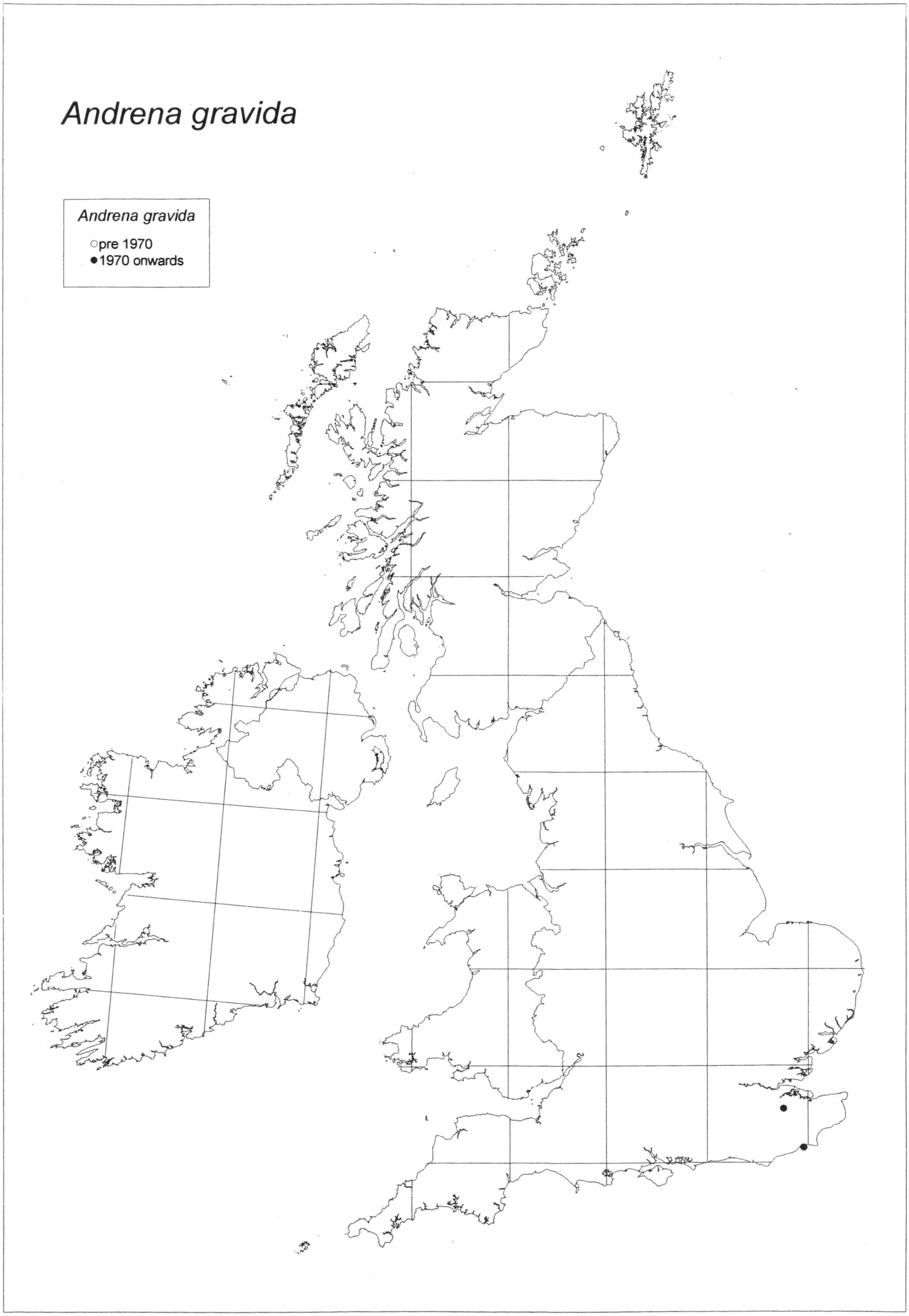

Distribution of Andrena gravida - banded mining bee in Britain, by 10km square.
Source: English Nature - Invertebrate Site Register.

Andrena lathyri (a mining bee)
Action Plan

1. Current status

1.1 *Andrena lathyri* is a large mining bee which flies in mid-spring and is dependent on various vetches (Fabaceae) for forage (*Vicia* spp, especially *V. sativa* and *V. sepium*).

1.2 This bee was first recognised as a British species in 1971, following the discovery of a strong population alongside a disused railway line in Wiltshire. Subsequent study of museum material revealed a further specimen which had been collected during the mid 1950s from a site in central Somerset. Despite the strength of the Wiltshire population in the early 1970s, and numerous subsequent visits to the site during the flight season, only a single specimen has been seen since (a female on 10 May 1990). It is a central European species, with its range extending from southern Fennoscandia to Switzerland, Austria and Turkey.

1.3 In Great Britain this species is classified as *Endangered*.

2. Current factors causing loss or decline

2.1 The loss of open sites on tall sward calcareous or mesotrophic grasslands supporting large populations of vetches.

2.2 Scrub encroachment.

3. Current action

3.1 None known.

4. Action plan objectives and targets

4.1 Maintain populations at all known sites.

4.2 Enhance the population size at all known sites by 2010.

5. Proposed action with lead agencies

The priority action necessary to halt or reverse the decline of this species is to establish a programme of pre-recovery autecological research, investigating the nectar, pollen and nesting requirements of the species, together with its dispersal ability. This will need to be followed by a programme of informed habitat management.

5.1 Policy and legislation

5.1.1 Where appropriate, include the requirements of the species when preparing or revising prescriptions for agri-environment schemes. (ACTION: EN, MAFF)

5.2 Site safeguard and management

5.2.1 Where possible, ensure that all occupied and nearby potential habitat is appropriately managed by 2008, for example through agri-environment scheme management agreements. (ACTION: EN, MAFF)

5.2.2 Ensure that the habitat requirements of the species are taken into account in relevant development policies, plans and proposals. (ACTION: EN, LAs)

5.2.3 Ensure that this species is included in site management documents for all relevant SSSIs. (ACTION: EN)

5.2.4 Consider notifying sites supporting viable populations of *Andrena lathyri* as SSSIs, where this is necessary to secure their long-term protection and appropriate management. (ACTION: EN)

5.3 Species management and protection

5.3.1 None proposed.

5.4 Advisory

5.4.1 Advise landowners and managers of the presence of the species and the importance of beneficial management for its conservation. (ACTION: EN)

5.5 Future research and monitoring

5.5.1 Undertake surveys to determine the status of the bee by the year 2005. (ACTION: EN)

5.5.2 Promote ecological research to establish the habitat requirements of this species, the factors limiting breeding success at existing sites, and its dispersal ability. (ACTION: EN)

5.5.3 Establish a regular monitoring programme for the species. (ACTION: EN)

5.5.4 Pass information gathered during survey and monitoring of this species to a central database for incorporation into national and international databases. (ACTION: EN)

5.6 Communications and publicity

5.6.1 Promote opportunities for the appreciation of this species and the conservation issues associated with its habitat. This should be achieved through articles within appropriate journals, as well as by a publicity leaflet. (ACTION: EN)

5.7 Links with other action plans

5.7.1 Implementation of this action plan could benefit other species of calcareous grasslands, including *Bombus humilis, B. ruderatus, B. subteraneus* and *B. sylvarum*.

5.7.2 This plan should be considered in conjunction with that for lowland calcareous grassland.

Great yellow bumblebee (*Bombus distinguendus*) Action Plan

1. Current status

1.1 Most records of this bee have been associated with extensive areas of meadowland supporting a large number of plant species with long corolla flower types, notably those belonging to the plant families Fabaceae and Lamiaceae. It is one of a number of bumblebee species to have undergone a drastic reduction in range and abundance as a result of the loss of this habitat in the modern agricultural landscape. On the Hebrides during August 1997 it was strongly associated with areas that had been winter-grazed and then allowed to grow throughout the summer. Such areas supported good stands of red clover and common knapweed, both of which were important forage plants. Nests are constructed underground. The number of workers of the great yellow bumblebee per nest is often noted as being particularly low, with workers being of a large size.

1.2 This species is widespread in northern and central Europe and in Asia, although it is declining in many parts of its range. In the UK, there are post-1960 records for scattered localities across England, Scotland and Wales. However, records since 1970 are very strongly biased towards the extreme north of Scotland, with most being from the Outer Hebrides. Searches during 1997 showed there to be good populations associated with machair systems on the islands south of, and including, North Uist. There are also recent (post-1990) records from Orkney, Coll, Tiree and Sutherland. There are pre-1960 records from Northern Ireland.

1.3 In Great Britain this species is classified as *Nationally Scarce*.

2. Current factors causing loss or decline

2.1 Loss of extensive, herb-rich grasslands.

3. Current action

3.1 This species is the subject of an SNH Pre-Recovery Project.

3.2 Some populations are on SSSIs and RSPB reserves.

4. Action plan objectives and targets

4.1 Maintain populations at all known sites.

4.2 Enhance the population size at all known sites by 2010.

5. Proposed action with lead agencies

This bee is under threat from changes in agricultural practices, especially the loss of extensive permanent, flower-rich meadows. The priority action for this species is to generate mechanisms that safeguard remaining habitat as well as restore habitat to its natural range. This will need a programme of autecological research, which will allow the development of advice on site management, and a programme of informed habitat management.

5.1 Policy and legislation

5.1.1 Where appropriate, include the requirements of the species when preparing or revising prescriptions for agri-environment schemes. (ACTION: CCW, DANI, EHS, EN, MAFF, SNH, SOAEFD, WOAD)

5.2 Site safeguard and management

5.2.1 Where possible, ensure that all occupied habitat is appropriately managed by 2008, for example through SSSI or agri-environment scheme management agreements. (ACTION: CCW, DANI, EHS, EN, MAFF, SNH, SOAEFD, WOAD)

5.2.2 Ensure that the habitat requirements of the great yellow bumblebee are taken into account in any relevant development policies, plans and proposals. (ACTION: CCW, EN, EHS, SNH, LAs)

5.2.3 Ensure that this species is included in site management documents for all relevant SSSIs/ASSIs. (ACTION: CCW, EHS, EN, SNH)

5.2.4 Consider notifying as SSSIs/ASSIs sites supporting viable populations of the great yellow bumblebee, where this is necessary to secure long-term protection and appropriate management. (ACTION: CCW, EHS, EN, SNH)

5.3 Species management and protection

5.3.1 None proposed.

5.4 Advisory

5.4.1 Advise landowners and managers of the presence of this species and the importance of beneficial management for its conservation. (ACTION: CCW, Crofters Commission, DANI, EHS, EN, MAFF, SNH, SOAEFD, WOAD)

5.4.2 As far as possible, ensure that all relevant agri-environment project officers, and members of regional agri-environment consultation groups, are advised of locations of this species, its importance, and the management needed for its conservation. (ACTION: CCW, DANI, EHS, EN, MAFF, SNH, SOAEFD, WOAD)

5.5 **Future research and monitoring**

5.5.1 Undertake surveys to determine the range and status of this bee by 2005. (ACTION: CCW, EHS, EN, SNH)

5.5.2 Continue autecological research targeted to identify key habitat features, such as sources of nectar and pollen, nesting sites, and areas used for mating and over-wintering, in order to inform habitat management. (ACTION: CCW, EHS, EN, SNH)

5.5.3 Establish a regular monitoring programme. (ACTION: CCW, EHS, EN, SNH)

5.5.4 Pass information gathered through survey and monitoring of this species to a central database so that it can be incorporated into national databases. (ACTION: CCW, EHS, EN, SNH)

5.6 **Communications and publicity**

5.6.1 Promote opportunities for the appreciation of the bee and the conservation issues associated with its habitat. This should be achieved through articles within appropriate journals as well as by publicity leaflets. (ACTION: CCW, EHS, EN, SNH)

5.7 **Links with other action plans**

5.7.1 Implementation of this action plan could benefit other priority species of herb-rich grassland, including the bee *Colletes floralis* and the corncrake *Crex crex*.

5.7.2 This plan should be considered in conjunction with those for lowland hay meadows, lowland calcareous grassland, and machair.

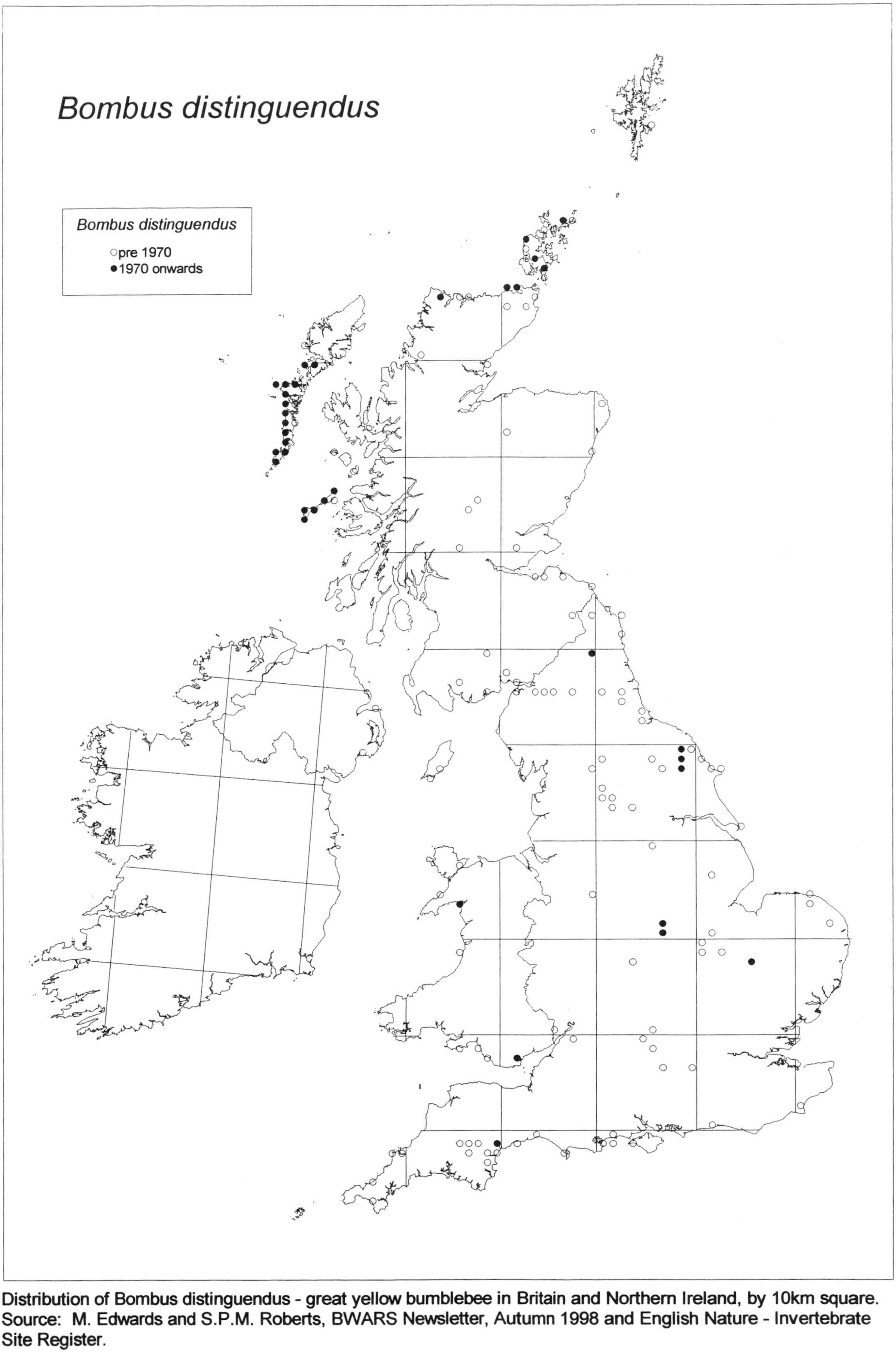

Distribution of Bombus distinguendus - great yellow bumblebee in Britain and Northern Ireland, by 10km square. Source: M. Edwards and S.P.M. Roberts, BWARS Newsletter, Autumn 1998 and English Nature - Invertebrate Site Register.

Bombus humilis (a carder bumblebee) Action Plan

1. Current status

1.1 *Bombus humilis* is a brown carder bumblebee which makes its nest on the surface of the ground at the base of long vegetation, often under accumulated plant litter. It has most often been recorded as associated with areas of grassland supporting a large number of plant species with long corolla flower types, notably those belonging to the plant families Lamiaceae and Fabaceae. It is one of a number of bumblebee species to have undergone a drastic reduction in range and abundance, as a result of the loss of this habitat in the modern agricultural landscape, although it appears to be able to survive in less extensive areas of flower-rich habitat compared with some bumblebee species.

1.2 At the beginning of the 20th century this bumblebee was considered uncommon in southern England. However, it was a widespread species, reaching Yorkshire and Lancashire in the north. By the 1970s it had disappeared from most of its northern and inland localities, although it was still widespread along much of the coast. The species has continued to decline in the eastern half of England, where it is now local and sporadic. It is still readily found along the south-western coast of England, from Dorset westwards, and on the southern coast of Wales. There are also a number of inland localities associated with the larger areas of chalk grasslands, notably Salisbury Plain. There are no records of this species from Scotland or Northern Ireland. *B. humilis* is widespread in Europe.

1.3 In Great Britain this species is classified as *Local*.

2. Current factors causing loss or decline

2.1 Loss of extensive, herb-rich grasslands through agricultural intensification.

2.2 Non-native forms of *Bombus* used for pollination in greenhouses may be a threat, but this requires further investigation.

3. Current action

3.1 Some populations are on SSSIs.

4. Action plan objectives and targets

4.1 Maintain populations at all known sites.

5. Proposed action with lead agencies

This bee is under threat from changes in agricultural practices, especially the loss of extensive permanent, flower-rich meadows. Action is necessary to determine the current status of this species, and to identify population trends. It may subsequently be necessary to undertake autecological research, investigating the nectar, pollen, nesting, mating and overwintering requirements of the species. The dispersal ability of queens, and the size of suitable habitat required to support a viable population of nests, will also need investigation. This may need to be followed by a programme of informed habitat management.

5.1 Policy and legislation

5.1.1 Where appropriate, include the requirements of the species when preparing or revising prescriptions for agri-environment schemes. (ACTION : CCW, EN, MAFF, WOAD)

5.2 Site safeguard and management

5.2.1 Where possible, ensure that all occupied and nearby potential habitat is appropriately managed by 2008, for example through SSSI or agri-environment scheme management agreements. (ACTION: CCW, EN, MAFF, WOAD)

5.2.2 Ensure that the habitat requirements of the species are taken into account in relevant development policies, plans and proposals. (ACTION: CCW, EN, LAs)

5.2.3 Ensure that this species is included in site management documents for all relevant SSSIs. (ACTION: CCW, EN)

5.3 Species management and protection

5.3.1 None proposed.

5.4 Advisory

5.4.1 Advise landowners and managers of the presence of this species and the importance of beneficial management for its conservation. (ACTION: CCW, EN, MAFF, WOAD)

5.4.2 As far as possible, ensure that all relevant agri-environment project officers, and members of regional agri-environment consultation groups, are advised of locations of this species, its importance, and the management needed for its conservation. (ACTION: CCW, EN, MAFF, WOAD)

5.5 Future research and monitoring

5.5.1 Undertake surveys to determine the current status of the bee by the year 2005. (ACTION: CCW, EN)

5.5.2 Promote ecological research to establish the habitat requirements of this species, the factors limiting breeding success at existing sites, and dispersal ability. (ACTION: CCW, EN)

5.5.3 Encourage further research to identify the extent to which the introduction of non-native forms of *Bombus* used for pollination in greenhouses may be a threat to the species. (ACTION: CCW, EN, MAFF, WOAD)

5.5.4 Establish a regular monitoring programme for this species. (ACTION: CCW, EN)

5.5.5 Pass information gathered through survey and monitoring of this species to a central database so that it can be incorporated into national databases. (ACTION: CCW, EN)

5.6 Communications and publicity

5.6.1 Where appropriate use this species to promote appreciation and conservation of threatened species of bee and wasp and their habitats. (ACTION: CCW, EN)

5.7 Links with other action plans

5.7.1 Implementation of this action plan could benefit other species of herb-rich grassland, including the bumblebees *Bombus distinguendus, B. ruderatus, B. subterraneus* and *B. sylvarum*.

5.7.2 This plan should be considered in conjunction with those for lowland hay meadows and lowland calcareous grassland.

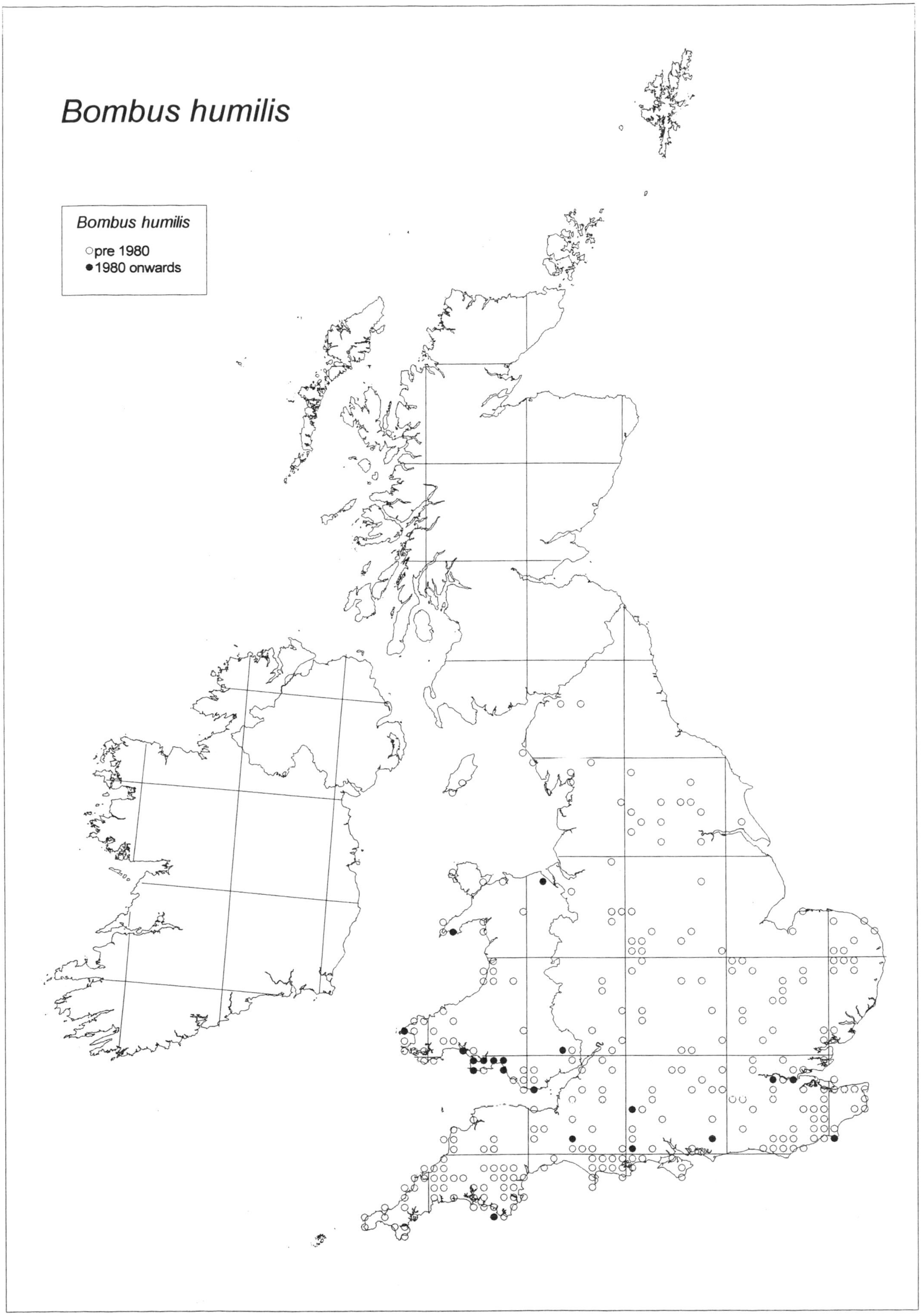

Distribution of Bombus humilis - brown-banded carder bee in Britain, by 10km square.
Source: Atlas of the Bumblebees of the British Isles, Biological Records Centre (ITE), International Bee Research Association, 1980. English Nature - Invertebrate Site Register and Countryside Council for Wales records.

Large garden bumblebee (*Bombus ruderatus*) Action Plan

1. Current status

1.1 The large garden bumblebee has most often been recorded as associated with extensive areas of meadowland supporting a large number plants with long-corolla flower types, notably those belonging to the plant families Lamiaceae and Fabaceae. It is one of a number of bumblebee species to have undergone a drastic reduction in range and abundance as a result of the loss of this habitat in the modern agricultural landscape. It is a very difficult species to separate from its sister species *B. hortorum*, except (in Britain) the all-black form known as variety *harrisellus*. The number of workers of *Bombus ruderatus* per nest is often noted as being particularly high. These may be both yellow-banded or all black from the same nest, which is built underground.

1.2 Although this bumblebee was considered to be very common in southern England at the beginning of the 20th century, by the 1970s it was already considered a scarce but widespread species. The decline has continued since, with fewer than 10 confirmed post-1980 sites for this bee, mostly in East Anglia. There are no confirmed post-1960 records for Wales and no records for Scotland or Northern Ireland. This bee is widespread but declining in Europe.

1.3 In Great Britain this species is classified as *Nationally Scarce*.

2. Current factors causing loss or decline

2.1 Loss of extensive, herb-rich grasslands, especially those containing good stands of plants of the families Lamiaceae and Fabaceae, through agricultural intensification.

2.2 Non-native forms of *Bombus* used for pollination in greenhouses may be a threat, but this requires further investigation.

3. Current action

3.1 Some known populations are on SSSIs.

4. Action plan objectives and targets

4.1 Maintain populations at all known sites.

4.2 Ensure that there are 20 viable populations within the historic range by 2010, by enhancing population sizes at all known sites, or by re-establishing the species at suitable localities.

4.3 If necessary to support 4.2, establish an *ex-situ* programme to provide material for re-introductions.

5. Proposed action with lead agencies

This bee is under threat from changes in agricultural practices, especially the loss of extensive permanent, flower-rich meadows. The priority action necessary to halt or reverse the decline of this species is to establish a programme of autecological research, investigating the nectar, pollen, nesting, mating and overwintering requirements of the species. The dispersal ability of queens, and the size of suitable habitat required to support a viable population of nests, requires investigation. This will need to be followed by a programme of informed habitat management. Reintroductions should be considered if habitat management alone fails to meet the objective of 20 viable populations within the historic range.

5.1 Policy and legislation

5.1.1 Where appropriate, include the requirements of the species when preparing or revising prescriptions for agri-environment schemes. (ACTION : CCW, EN, MAFF, WOAD)

5.2 Site safeguard and management

5.2.1 Where possible, ensure that all occupied and nearby potential habitat is appropriately managed by 2008, for example through SSSI or agri-environment scheme management agreements. (ACTION: CCW, EN, MAFF, WOAD)

5.2.2 Ensure that the habitat requirements of the species are taken into account in relevant development policies, plans and proposals (ACTION: CCW, EN, LAs)

5.2.3 Ensure that this species is included in site management documents for all relevant SSSIs. (ACTION: CCW, EN)

5.2.4 Consider notifying sites supporting viable populations of the large garden bumblebee as SSSIs, where this is necessary to secure long-term protection and appropriate management. (ACTION: CCW, EN)

5.3 Species management and protection

5.3.1 Consider establishing a captive breeding population with a view to undertaking re-introductions. (ACTION: CCW, EN)

5.3.2 If necessary to maintain 20 viable populations, undertake habitat restoration and/or re-introductions at suitable former or potential sites. (ACTION: CCW, EN)

5.4 **Advisory**

5.4.1 Advise landowners and managers of any sites with extant or restored populations of the presence of this species and the importance of beneficial management for its conservation. (ACTION: CCW, EN, MAFF, WOAD)

5.4.2 As far as possible, ensure that all relevant agri-environment project officers, and members of regional agri-environment consultation groups, are advised of locations of this species, its importance, and the management needed for its conservation. (ACTION: CCW, EN, MAFF, WOAD)

5.5 **Future research and monitoring**

5.5.1 Undertake surveys to determine the current status of the bee by the year 2005. (ACTION: CCW, EN)

5.5.2 Promote ecological research to establish the habitat requirements of this species, the factors limiting breeding success at existing sites, dispersal ability and appropriate re-introduction methods. (ACTION: CCW, EN)

5.5.3 Encourage further research to identify the extent to which the introduction of non-native forms of *Bombus* used for pollination in greenhouses may be a threat to the species. (ACTION: CCW, EN, MAFF, WOAD)

5.5.4 Establish a regular monitoring programme for this species. (ACTION: CCW, EN)

5.5.5 Pass information gathered through survey and monitoring of this species to a central database so that it can be incorporated into national databases. (ACTION: CCW, EN)

5.6 **Communications and publicity**

5.6.1 Where appropriate, use this species to promote appreciation and conservation of threatened species of bee and wasp and their habitats. (ACTION: CCW, EN)

5.7 **Links with other action plans**

5.7.1 Implementation of this action plan could benefit other species of herb-rich grassland, including the bumblebees *Bombus distinguendus, B. humilis, B. subterraneus* and *B. sylvarum*.

5.7.2 This plan should be considered in conjunction with those for lowland hay meadows and lowland calcareous grassland.

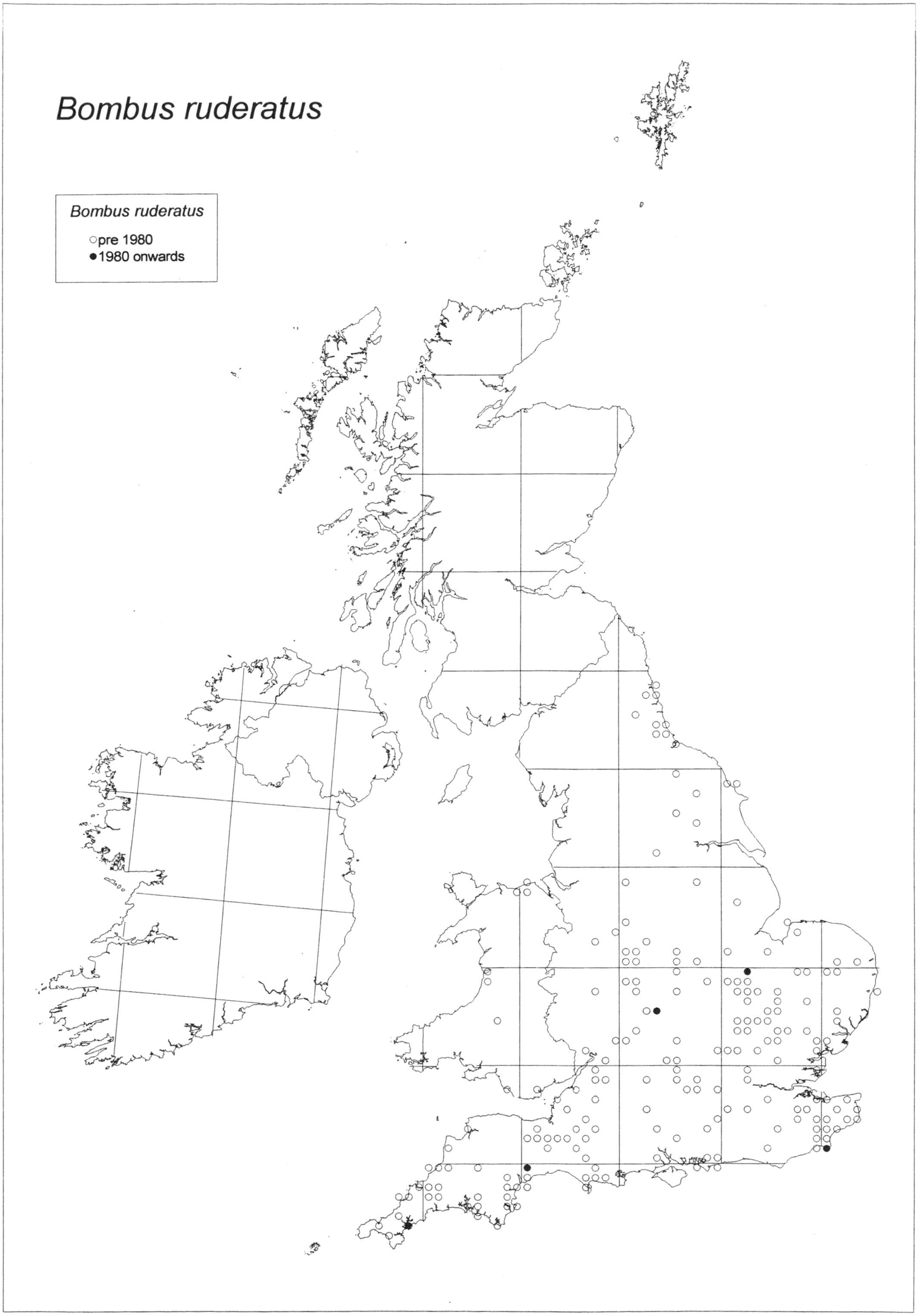

Distribution of Bombus ruderatus - large garden bumblebee in Britain, by 10km square.
Source: Atlas of the Bumblebees of the British Isles, Biological Records Centre (ITE), International Bee Research Association, 1980. English Nature - Invertebrate Site Register and Countryside Council for Wales records.

Short-haired bumblebee (*Bombus subterraneus*) Action Plan

1. Current status

1.1 The short-haired bumblebee, which nests underground, has most often been recorded as associated with extensive areas of grassland (including sand dunes and coastal shingle) supporting a large number of plants with long corolla flower types, notably those belonging to the plant families Lamiaceae and Fabaceae. It has undergone a drastic reduction in range and abundance as a result of the loss of this habitat in the modern agricultural landscape. Although queens and workers of this species are fairly readily distinguished from its sister species *B. distinguendus*, the males of the two species are extremely difficult to separate.

1.2 Although the short-haired bumblebee was considered to be locally common in east Kent and Suffolk at the beginning of the 20th century, the published national distribution map shows records for only 95 ten km squares. Some 22 of these represent post-1960 records, of which nine are in the Dungeness district of Kent. The bee was last recorded in Britain from Dungeness during an extensive survey of the invertebrates of the area in 1988, and was not found in either 1997 or 1998 despite targeted searches. There are no records from Scotland or Northern Ireland, and no confirmed post-1960 records from Wales. This bee is widespread in Europe but declining over much of its former range.

1.3 In Great Britain this species is classified as *Nationally Scarce*.

2. Current factors causing loss or decline

2.1 Loss of extensive, herb-rich grasslands, especially those containing good stands of plants of the families Lamiaceae and Fabaceae, through agricultural intensification.

2.2 Non-native forms of *Bombus* used for pollination in greenhouses may be a threat, but this requires further investigation.

3. Current action

3.1 The last known population was on the Dungeness SSSI.

4. Action plan objectives and targets

4.1 Establish an *ex-situ* breeding programme to provide material for re-introductions and ecological research, using native stock if available.

4.2 Establish and maintain 10 viable populations within the historic range by 2010, by enhancing population sizes at known sites or by re-introducing populations to suitable localities.

5. Proposed action with lead agencies

The short-haired bumblebee is under threat from changes in agricultural practices, especially the loss of extensive permanent, flower-rich meadows. In the first instance, surveys will need to be undertaken to determine whether this bumblebee is still present in Great Britain. The priority action necessary to halt or reverse the decline of this species is then to establish a programme of autecological research, investigating the nectar, pollen, nesting, mating and overwintering requirements of the species. The dispersal ability of queens, and the size of suitable habitat required to support a viable population of nests, will need investigation. This will need to be followed by a programme of informed habitat management. A captive breeding programme should be initiated in order to provide material for reintroductions and research.

5.1 Policy and legislation

5.1.1 Where appropriate, include the requirements of the species when preparing or revising prescriptions for agri-environment schemes. (ACTION: EN, MAFF)

5.2 Site safeguard and management

5.2.1 Where possible, ensure that all occupied and nearby potential habitat is appropriately managed by 2008. (ACTION: EN)

5.2.2 Ensure that the habitat requirements of this species are taken into account in relevant development policies, plans and proposals (ACTION: EN, LAs)

5.2.3 Ensure that this species is included in site management documents for the Dungeness, and any other relevant SSSIs. (ACTION: EN)

5.2.4 If sites with viable populations of this species are found, consider notifying them as SSSIs, where this is necessary to secure their long-term protection and appropriate management. (ACTION: EN)

5.3 Species management and protection

5.3.1 Establish a captive breeding population, preferably using native stock, with a view to undertaking reintroductions. (ACTION: EN)

5.3.2 If necessary to maintain 10 viable populations, undertake habitat restoration and/or re-introductions at suitable former or potential sites. (ACTION: EN)

5.4 **Advisory**

5.4.1 Advise landowners and managers of the presence of this species and the importance of beneficial management for its conservation. (ACTION: EN)

5.5 **Future research and monitoring**

5.5.1 Undertake surveys to determine the current status of the bee by the year 2005. (ACTION: EN)

5.5.2 Promote ecological research to establish the habitat requirements of this species, the factors limiting breeding success at existing sites, dispersal ability, and appropriate reintroduction methods. (ACTION: EN)

5.5.3 Encourage further research to identify the extent to which the introduction of non-native forms of *Bombus* used for pollination in greenhouses may be a threat to the species. (ACTION: EN, MAFF)

5.5.4 Establish a regular monitoring programme for the species. (ACTION: EN)

5.5.5 Pass information gathered through survey and monitoring of this species to a central database so that it can be incorporated into national databases. (ACTION: EN)

5.6 **Communications and publicity**

5.6.1 Use this species to promote appreciation and conservation of threatened species of bee and wasp and their habitats. (ACTION: EN)

5.7 **Links with other action plans**

5.7.1 Implementation of this action plan could benefit other species of herb-rich grassland, including the bumblebees *Bombus distinguendus*, *B. humilis*, *B. ruderatus* and *B. sylvarum*.

5.7.2 This plan should be considered in conjunction with those for lowland hay meadows and lowland calcareous grassland.

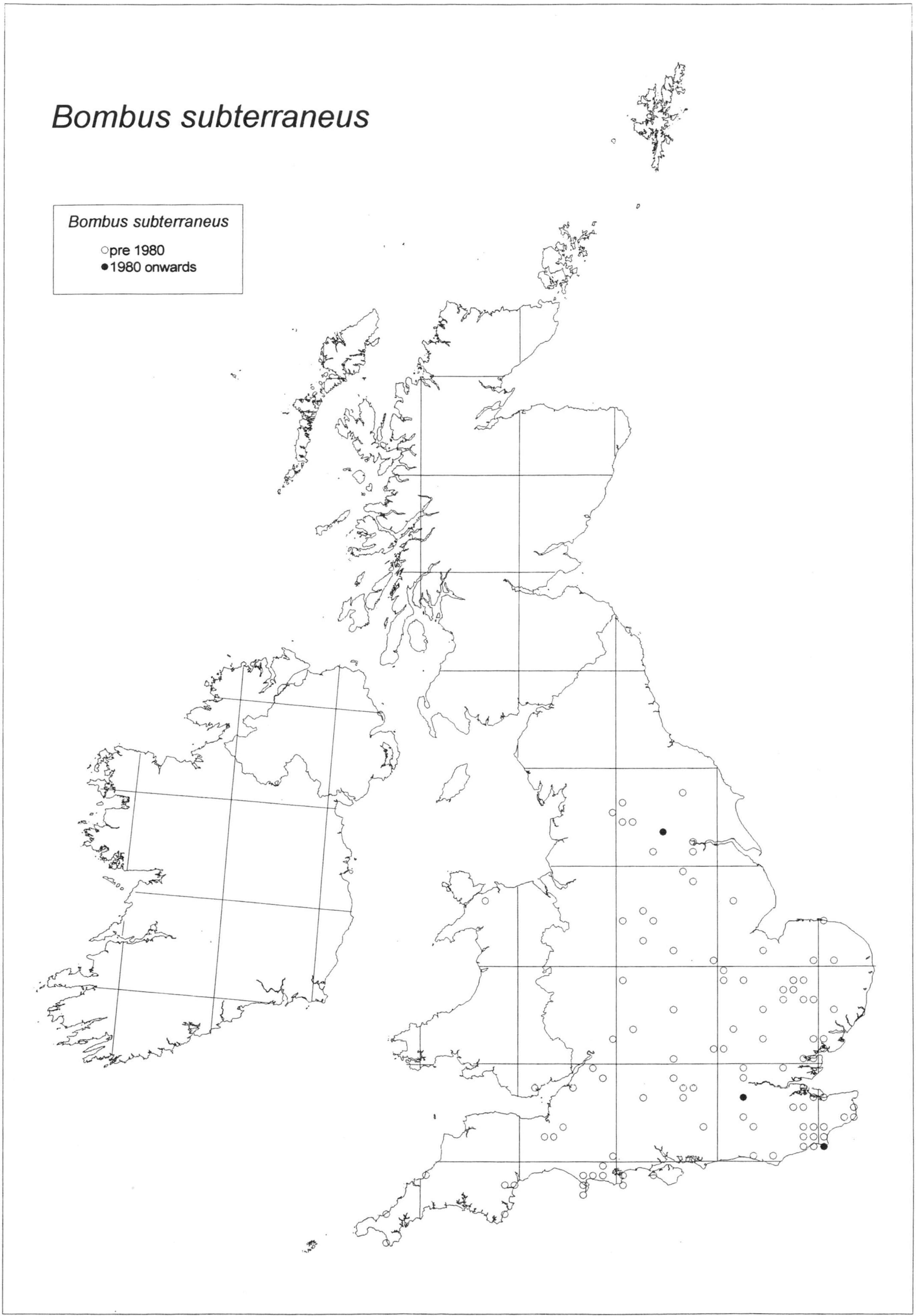

Distribution of Bombus subterraneus - short-haired bumblebee in Britain, by 10km square.
Source: Atlas of the Bumblebees of the British Isles, Biological Records Centre (ITE), International Bee Research Association, 1980 and English Nature - Invertebrate Site Register.

Cerceris quadricincta (a solitary wasp) Action Plan

1. Current status

1.1 *Cerceris quadricincta* is a medium-sized, yellow-and-black wasp which nests gregariously in areas of bare sand in places exposed to the sun. It provisions its nest with weevils. The known sites are sandy grasslands on south-facing slopes.

1.2 The wasp has been known from 10 ten km squares in Kent and Essex. There are four post-1970 records, three from Kent and one from Essex, the latter being from Colchester during 1995. The wasp is rare in southern and central Europe. It also occurs in northern Africa and western Asia.

1.3 In Great Britain this species is classified as *Endangered*.

2. Current factors causing loss or decline

2.1 Loss of open sandy ground for nesting and flower-rich sandy grasslands for foraging.

3. Current action

3.1 None known.

4. Action plan objectives and targets

4.1 Maintain populations at all known sites.

4.2 Enhance the population size at all known sites by 2010.

4.3 Restore populations to suitable sites to maintain 10 viable populations within the historic range by 2010.

5. Proposed action with lead agencies

This species is under threat due to the loss of open sandy grasslands. The priority action necessary to halt or reverse the decline of this species is to establish a programme of pre-recovery autecological research, investigating the prey, nectar and nesting requirements of the species, together with its dispersal ability. This will need to be followed by a programme of informed habitat management.

5.1 Policy and legislation

5.1.1 Where appropriate, include the requirements of the species when preparing or revising prescriptions for agri-environment schemes. (ACTION: EN, MAFF)

5.2 Site safeguard and management

5.2.1 Where possible, ensure that all occupied and nearby potential habitat is appropriately managed by 2008, for example through agri-environment scheme management agreements. (ACTION: EN, MAFF)

5.2.2 Ensure that the habitat requirements of *Cerceris quadricincta* are taken into account in relevant development policies, plans and proposals. (ACTION: EN, LAs)

5.2.3 Ensure that this species is included in site management documents for all relevant SSSIs. (ACTION: EN)

5.2.4 Consider notifying sites supporting viable populations of *Cerceris quadricincta* as SSSIs, where this is necessary to secure their long-term protection and appropriate management. (ACTION: EN)

5.3 Species management and protection

5.3.1 If necessary to maintain 10 viable populations, undertake habitat restoration and/or (re)introductions at suitable former or potential sites. (ACTION: EN)

5.4 Advisory

5.4.1 Advise landowners and managers of the presence of the species and the importance of beneficial management for its conservation. (ACTION: EN)

5.5 Future research and monitoring

5.5.1 Undertake surveys to determine the status of the wasp by 2005. (ACTION: EN)

5.5.2 Promote ecological research to establish the habitat requirements of this species, the factors limiting breeding success at existing sites, dispersal ability, and appropriate reintroduction methods. (ACTION: EN)

5.5.3 Establish a regular monitoring programme for the species. (ACTION: EN)

5.5.4 Pass information gathered during survey and monitoring of this species to a central database for incorporation into national and international databases. (ACTION: EN)

5.6 Communications and publicity

5.6.1 Promote opportunities for the appreciation of this species and the conservation issues associated with its habitat. This should be achieved through articles within appropriate journals, as well as by a publicity leaflet. (ACTION: EN)

5.7 Links with other action plans

5.7.1 Implementation of this action plan could benefit the sphecid wasp *Cerceris quinquefasciata* and the bees *Andrena gravida, Bombus humilis, B. ruderatus, B. subterraneus* and *B. sylvarum*.

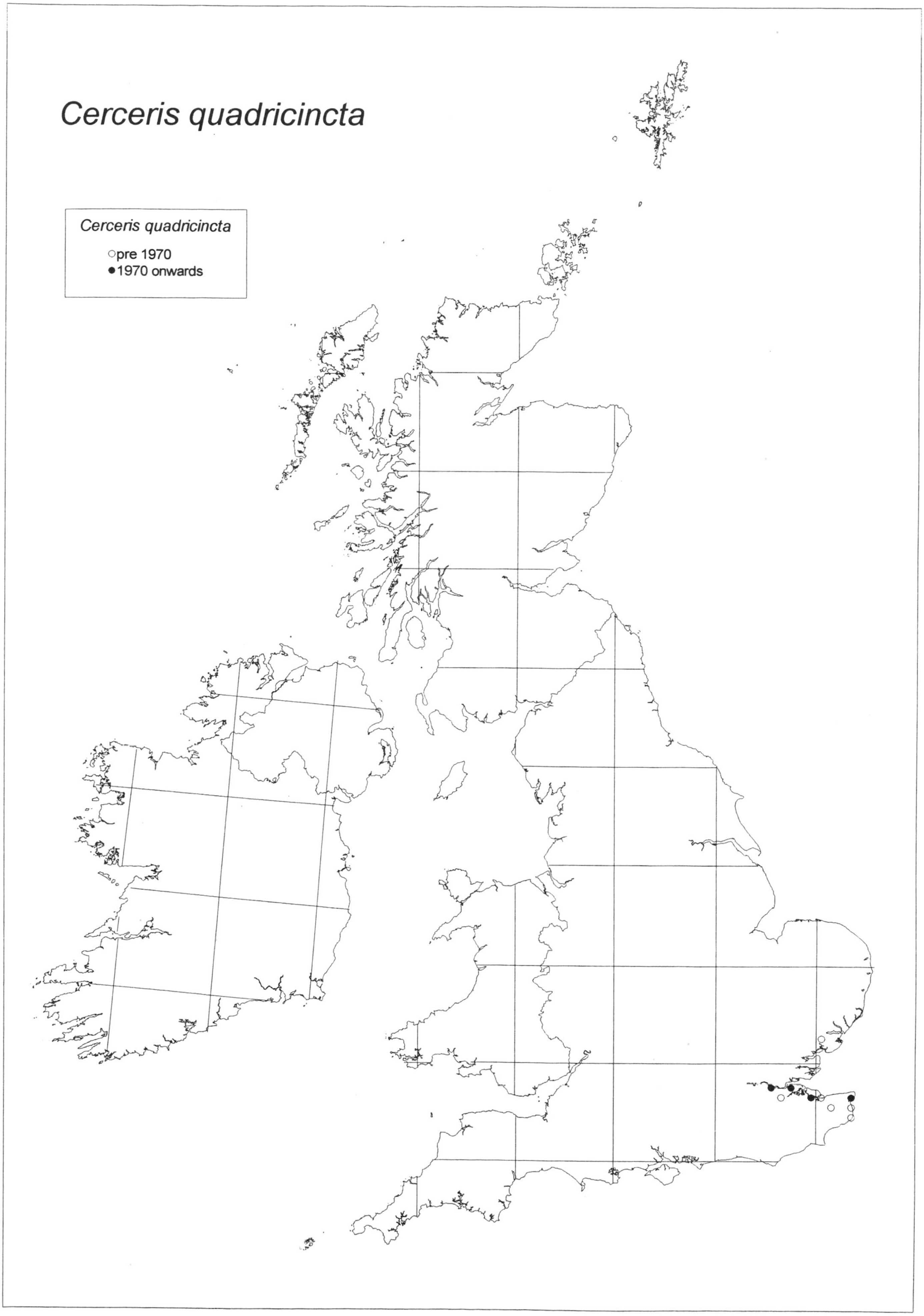

Distribution of Cerceris quadricincta - a solitary wasp in Britain, by 10km square.
Source: Provisional atlas of aculeate hymenoptera of Britain and Ireland, 1997. Biological Records Centre (ITE).

Cerceris quinquefasciata (a solitary wasp) Action Plan

1. Current status

1.1 *Cerceris quinquefasciata* is a medium-sized yellow-and-black wasp which nests gregariously in areas of bare sand in places exposed to the sun. It provisions its nest with weevils. It may be common where it occurs.

1.2 It has been known from 49 ten km squares in southern and eastern England, but has been found in only 14 squares since 1980, largely in south-eastern England (Essex, Kent, Norfolk, Oxfordshire and Suffolk). There are no post-1970 records for the coasts of Dorset, Devon and Cornwall, despite a number of earlier records. The wasp is widespread in southern and central Europe and present, although rare, in southern Fennoscandia. It also occurs in northern Africa and throughout Asia.

1.3 In Great Britain this species is classified as *Rare*.

2. Current factors causing loss or decline

2.1 Loss of open areas of sandy ground for nesting and flower-rich sandy grasslands for foraging.

3. Current action

3.1 Some populations are on SSSIs or nature reserves.

4. Action plan objectives and targets

4.1 Maintain populations at all known sites.

4.2 Enhance the population size at all known sites by 2010.

4.3 Restore populations to suitable sites to maintain 20 viable populations within the historic range by 2010.

5. Proposed action with lead agencies

This species is under threat due to the loss of open sandy grasslands with areas of bare ground open to the sun. The priority action necessary to halt or reverse the decline of this species is to establish a programme of pre-recovery autecological research, investigating the nectar, pollen and nesting requirements of the species, together with its dispersal ability. This will need to be followed by a programme of informed habitat management.

5.1 Policy and legislation

5.1.1 Where appropriate, include the requirements of the species when preparing or revising prescriptions for agri-environment schemes. (ACTION: EN, MAFF)

5.2 Site safeguard and management

5.2.1 Where possible, ensure that all occupied and nearby potential habitat is appropriately managed by 2008, for example through SSSI or agri-environment scheme management agreements. (ACTION: EN, MAFF)

5.2.2 Ensure that the habitat requirements of *Cerceris quinquefasciata* are taken into account in relevant development policies, plans and proposals. (ACTION: EN, LAs)

5.2.3 Ensure that this species is included in site management documents for all relevant SSSIs. (ACTION: EN)

5.2.4 Consider notifying sites supporting viable populations of *Cerceris quinquefasciata* as SSSIs, where this is necessary to secure their long-term protection and appropriate management. (ACTION: EN)

5.3 Species management and protection

5.3.1 If necessary to maintain 20 viable populations, undertake habitat restoration and/or (re)introductions at suitable former or potential sites. (ACTION: EN)

5.4 Advisory

5.4.1 Advise landowners and managers of the presence of the species and the importance of beneficial management for its conservation. (ACTION: EN, MAFF)

5.4.2 As far as possible, ensure that all relevant agri-environment project officers, and members of regional agri-environment consultation groups, are advised of locations of this species, its importance, and the management needed for its conservation. (ACTION: EN, MAFF)

5.5 Future research and monitoring

5.5.1 Undertake surveys to determine the status of the wasp by 2005. (ACTION: EN)

5.5.2 Promote ecological research to establish the habitat requirements of this species, the factors limiting breeding success at existing sites, dispersal ability and appropriate reintroduction methods. (ACTION: EN)

5.5.3 Establish a regular monitoring programme for the species. (ACTION: EN)

5.5.4 Pass information gathered during survey and monitoring of this species to a central database for incorporation into national and international databases. (ACTION: EN)

5.6 Communications and publicity

5.6.1 Promote opportunities for the appreciation of this species and the conservation issues associated with its habitat. This should be achieved through articles within appropriate journals, as well as by a publicity leaflet. (ACTION: EN)

5.7 Links with other action plans

5.7.1 Implementation of this action plan could benefit the sphecid wasp *Cerceris quadricincta,* and the bees *Andrena gravida, Bombus humilis, B. ruderatus, B. subterraneus* and *B. sylvarum.*

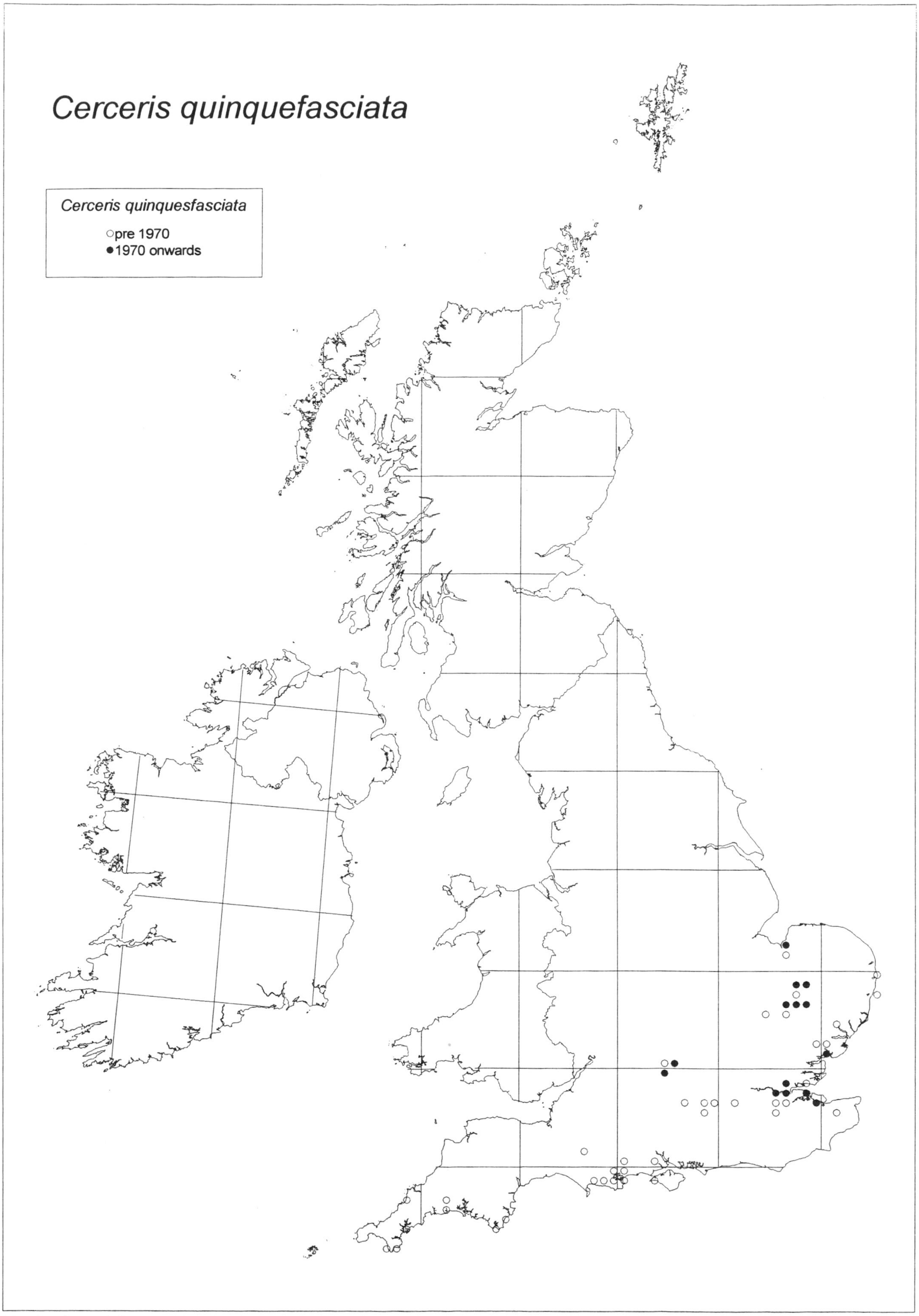

Distribution of Cerceris quinquefasciata - a solitary wasp in Britain and Northern Ireland, by 10km square.
Source: Provisional atlas of aculeate hymenoptera of Britain and Ireland, 1997. Biological Records Centre (ITE).

Chrysis fulgida (a ruby-tailed wasp) Action Plan

1. Current status

1.1 *Chrysis fulgida* has occurred in a variety of habitat types (including fens) but appears to show a preference for heathland sites. It has been recorded in the British literature as a parasitoid on the eumenid wasp *Odynerus spinipes* and the megachiline bee *Osmia leaiana*. It has also been presumed to attack the nests of the sphecid wasp *Trypoxylon figulus*, although this is unlikely. German references list only the eumenid wasps *Symmorphus crassicornis* and *S. murarius* as confirmed hosts; the former is a British species which is known to be present at one of the two extant sites for *Chrysis fulgida*. *Symmorphus crassicornis* nests in vertical banks, including upturned tree root-plates, where one of the modern specimens was found. *Odynerus spinipes* nests in similar situations.

1.2 Records exist for 13 ten km squares in southern England, but *Chrysis fulgida* is seldom common anywhere. There is a small concentration of records from the Surrey/north Hampshire heaths, including the two most recent records which are from north Hampshire. The wasp is widespread in the Eurasian part of the western Palearctic region.

1.3 In Great Britain this species is classified as *Endangered*.

2. Current factors causing loss or decline

2.1 Not known.

3. Current action

3.1 Both recent sites are on SSSIs.

4. Action plan objectives and targets

4.1 Maintain populations at all known sites.

5. Proposed action with lead agencies

The priority action necessary to halt or reverse the decline of this species is to establish a programme of pre-recovery autecological research, investigating the host(s) utilised by the chrysid, and the prey and nesting requirements of the host. This may need to be followed by a programme of informed habitat management.

5.1 Policy and legislation

5.1.1 Where appropriate, include the requirements of the species when preparing or revising prescriptions for agri-environment schemes. (ACTION: EN, MAFF)

5.2 Site safeguard and management

5.2.1 Where possible, ensure that all occupied and nearby potential habitat is appropriately managed by 2008, for example through SSSI or agri-environment scheme management agreements. (ACTION: EN, MAFF)

5.2.2 Ensure that the habitat requirements of *Chrysis fulgida* are taken into account in relevant development policies, plans and proposals. (ACTION: EN, LAs)

5.2.3 Ensure that this species is included in site management documents for all relevant SSSIs. (ACTION: EN)

5.2.4 Consider notifying sites supporting viable populations of *Chrysis fulgida* as SSSIs, where this is necessary to secure their long-term protection and appropriate management. (ACTION: EN)

5.3 Species management and protection

5.3.1 None proposed. (ACTION: EN)

5.4 Advisory

5.4.1 Advise landowners and managers of the presence of the species and the importance of beneficial management for its conservation. (ACTION: EN)

5.5 Future research and monitoring

5.5.1 Undertake surveys to determine the status of the wasp by 2005. (ACTION: EN)

5.5.2 Promote ecological research to establish the habitat requirements of this species, the factors limiting breeding success at existing sites, and dispersal ability. (ACTION: EN)

5.5.3 Establish a regular monitoring programme for the species. (ACTION: EN)

5.5.4 Pass information gathered during survey and monitoring of this species to a central database for incorporation into national and international databases. (ACTION: EN)

5.6 Communications and publicity

5.6.1 Promote opportunities for the appreciation of this species and the conservation issues associated with its habitat. This should be achieved through articles within appropriate journals, as well as by a publicity leaflet. (ACTION: EN)

5.7 Links with other action plans

5.7.1 Implementation of this action plan could benefit the following heathland species: the ground beetles *Amara famelica, Cicindela sylvatica* and *Pterostichus kugellani;* and the wasps *Homonotus sanguinolentus* and *Pseudepipona herrichii.*

5.7.2 This plan should be considered in conjunction with that for lowland heathland.

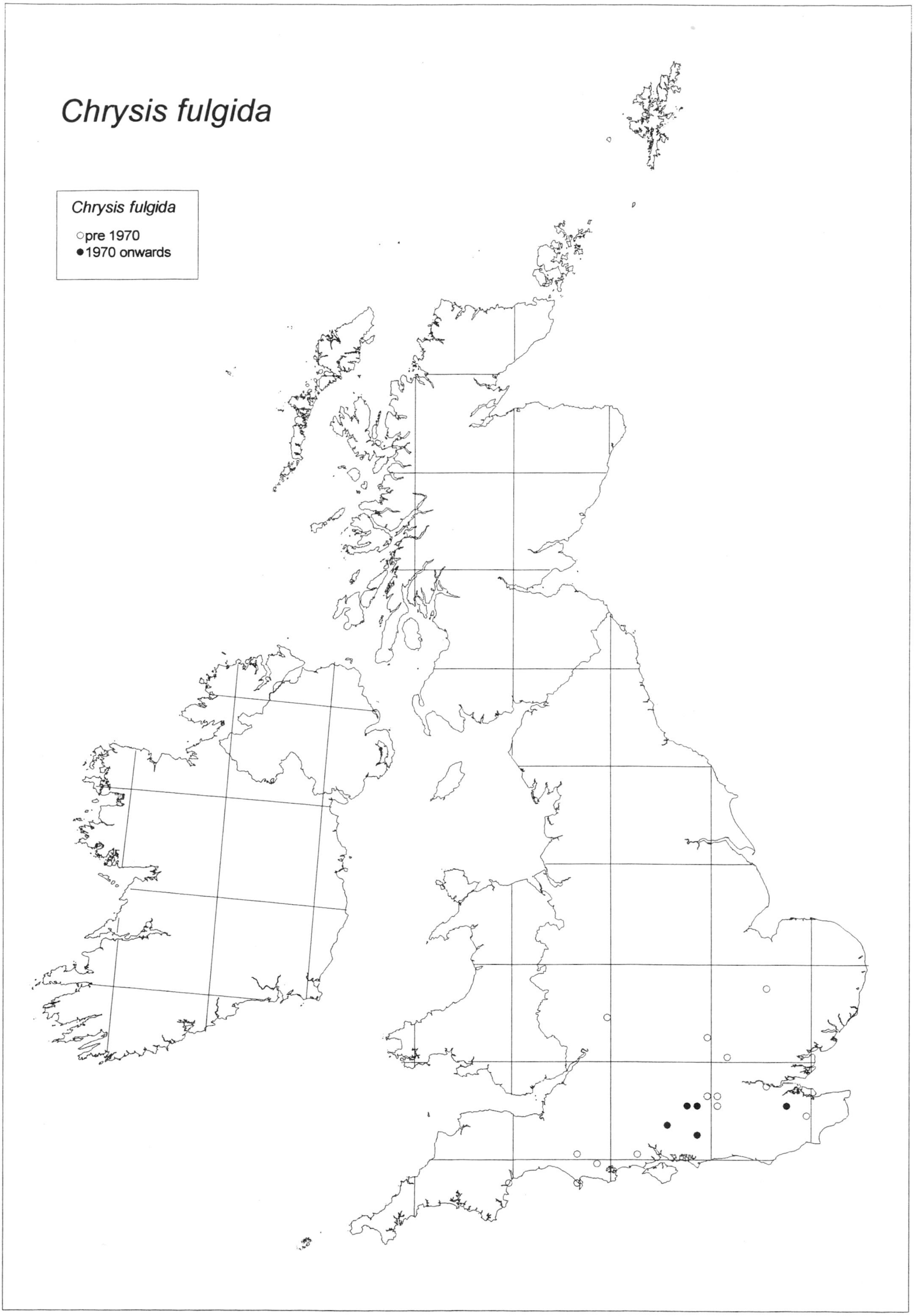

Distribution of Chrysis fulgida - a ruby-tailed wasp in Britain, by 10km square.
Source: English Nature - Invertebrate Site Register and BWARS records.

Colletes floralis (the northern Colletes) Action Plan

1. Current status

1.1 The northern Colletes is one of a small group of boreo-alpine species of bee found in the UK. The female bees forage for nectar from a wide range of flowers and nest in aggregations in light, sandy soil. Nest sites on Barra in the Outer Hebrides are associated with machair grasslands, although on the Scottish mainland it is reported from the marram zone of coastal dunes. In Eire it apparently nests in firmer substrates, including coastal cliffs composed of sandy clay.

1.2 This bee has a Palearctic distribution, being found at low altitudes in northern regions and in montane locations further south. Within the British Isles most records of the northern Colletes are from the western seaboard of Scotland, notably the Outer Hebrides, where it is strongly associated with the machair grasslands. It is also known from Eire, Northern Ireland, and from the Cumbrian coast. Altogether, the bee has been recorded from 15 UK ten km squares.

1.3 In Great Britain this bee is now classified as *Rare*.

2. Current factors causing loss or decline

2.1 Loss of herb-rich dune grasslands due to agricultural intensification.

2.2 As a species with a boreo-alpine distribution, it could be negatively affected by warming of the UK climate.

3. Current action

3.1 Some of the recent records are from SSSIs and other reserves.

4. Action plan objectives and targets

4.1 Maintain populations at all known sites.

5. Proposed action with lead agencies

This bee is under threat from changes in agricultural practices, especially the decline of traditional crofting agriculture leading to agricultural improvement of machair grassland. The priority action necessary to halt or reverse the decline of this species is to establish a programme of autecological research, investigating the nectar, pollen, nesting, mating and overwintering requirements of the species. This will need to be followed by a programme of informed habitat management.

5.1 Policy and legislation

5.1.1 Where appropriate, include the requirements of the northern Colletes when preparing or revising prescriptions for agri-environment schemes, especially ESAs covering machair in Scotland. (ACTION: DANI, EHS, EN, MAFF, SNH, SOAEFD)

5.2 Site safeguard and management

5.2.1 Ensure that the species is included in site management documents for all relevant SSSIs/ASSIs. (ACTION: EN, SNH, EHS)

5.2.2 Consider notifying as SSSIs/ASSIs sites supporting viable populations of the northern Colletes, where this is necessary to their secure long-term protection and appropriate management. (ACTION: EHS, EN, SNH)

5.3 Species management and protection

5.3.1 None proposed.

5.4 Advisory

5.4.1 Advise landowners and managers of the presence of this species and the importance of beneficial management for its conservation. (ACTION: Crofters Commission, DANI, EHS, EN, MAFF, SNH, SOAEFD)

5.4.2 As far as possible, ensure that all relevant agri-environment project officers, and members of regional agri-environment consultation groups, are advised of locations of this species, its importance, and the management needed for its conservation. (ACTION: DANI, EHS, EN, MAFF, SNH, SOAEFD)

5.5 Future research and monitoring

5.5.1 Undertake surveys to determine the range and status of this bee in the UK by 2005. (ACTION: EHS, EN, SNH)

5.5.2 Conduct autecological research targeted to inform habitat management. (ACTION: EHS, EN, SNH)

5.5.3 Undertake regular surveys to monitor the status and extent of known populations. (ACTION: EHS, EN, SNH)

5.5.4 Pass information gathered during survey and monitoring of this species to a central database for incorporation in national and international databases. (ACTION: EHS, EN, SNH)

5.6 Communications and publicity

5.6.1 Promote opportunities for the appreciation of this bee and the conservation issues associated with its habitat. Emphasis should be given to the importance of traditional crofting practices for maintaining the biodiversity of machair grasslands. This should be achieved through articles within appropriate journals, and by publicity leaflets. (ACTION: EHS, EN, SNH)

5.7 Links with other action plans

5.7.1 Implementation of this action plan could benefit other species of the habitat, including the bumblebee *Bombus distinguendus* and the corncrake *Crex crex*.

5.7.2 This plan should be considered in conjunction with that for machair.

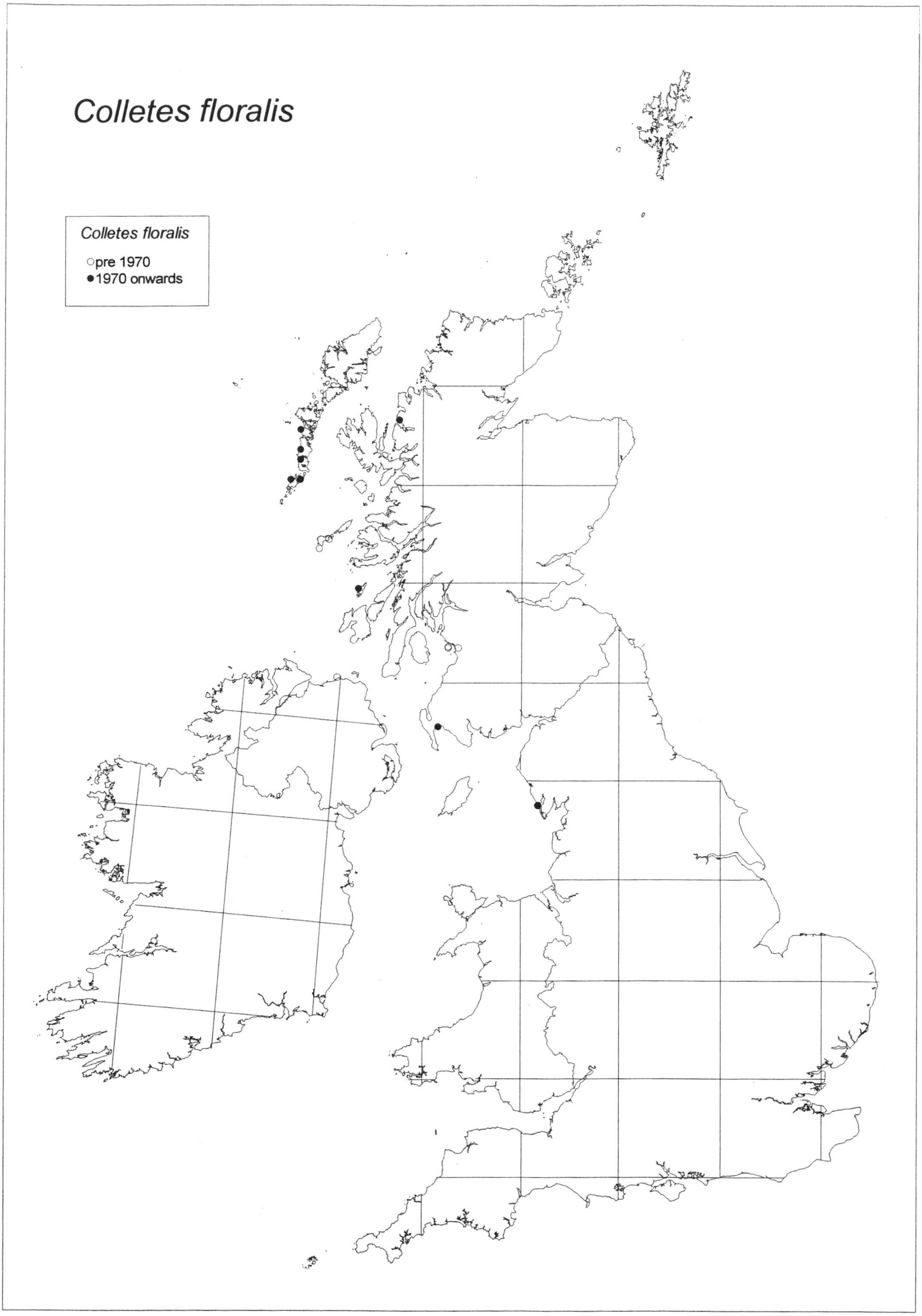

Distribution of Colletes floralis - the northern Colletes in Britain and Northern Ireland, by 10km square.
Source: Provisional atlas of aculeate hymenoptera of Britain and Ireland, 1997. Biological Records Centre (ITE) and BWARS Newsletter, Spring 1995.

Scottish wood ant (*Formica aquilonia*)
Action Plan

1. Current status

1.1 The Scottish wood ant can be locally common in undisturbed woodland, including native pine woodland and old birch woodland. It also occurs on the borders and in clearings of forestry plantations. Nests are usually built on well-drained slopes or small ridges. Studies in Finland indicate that the main factors in determining distribution are the availability of suitable nest sites, a favourable microclimate, and a good food supply. Sap-feeding bugs are especially important, both as prey and for the honey-dew that they produce. It has been estimated that 90% of foraging activity by the ants is in the canopy of trees near the nest.

1.2 In Europe this ant is found from the Alps to Siberia and from northern Italy to Arctic Norway. Within the UK it has been recorded as far north as Ross and Sutherland. Its distribution extends west and south of this into the west Highlands and Argyll. Skye and Arran are the only Scottish islands with records. This species is probably under-recorded in the more remote parts of Scotland. A strong population is present at the sole Irish locality for the species in Armagh, Northern Ireland.

1.3 In Great Britain this species is classified as *Nationally Scarce*. It is classified by the IUCN (1996) as globally *Near Threatened*.

2. Current factors causing loss or decline

2.1 Loss of suitable native pine woodland.

2.2 Inappropriate woodland management.

3. Current action

3.1 The Scottish wood ant is included in the SNH Species Action Programme.

3.2 The response of populations of the Scottish wood ant to the regeneration of Caledonian pine forest is being monitored by SNH as a part of the Cairngorms Project.

3.3 Many of the sites where it occurs are SSSIs or NNRs and some are RSPB or FC reserves.

4. Action plan, objectives and targets

4.1 Maintain the natural range of this ant in the UK.

4.2 Maintain populations at all known sites.

5. Proposed action with lead agencies

The prime actions for the Scottish wood ant are to determine its status in the UK, and to instigate sympathetic woodland management to maintain and enhance populations. It will be necessary to undertake autecological research in order to develop management advice. Studies of the response of this species to the regeneration of Caledonian pine forest and birch woodlands will also need to be continued.

5.1 Policy and legislation

5.1.1 Include specific targets and management for the Scottish wood ant in Forest Design Plans across the species' current and former range. (ACTION: FE)

5.1.2 Take account of the requirements of this ant when considering woodland grant scheme applications. (ACTION: DANI, EHS, FC, SNH)

5.2 Site safeguard and management

5.2.1 Where possible, ensure that all occupied habitat is appropriately managed by 2008, for example through site management agreements. (ACTION: EHS, FC, SNH)

5.2.2 Where possible, increase the available habitat at known sites and adjacent areas, and attempt to link up existing fragments of habitat, through native pinewood expansion policies in Indicative Forestry Strategies. (ACTION: FC, SNH)

5.2.3 Incorporate the requirements of this species in relevant development policies, plans and proposals. (ACTION: EHS, LAs, SNH)

5.2.4 Ensure that this ant is included in all site management documents for relevant SSSIs/ ASSIs, and management plans for RSPB and FC reserves. (ACTION: EHS, FC, SNH)

5.3 Species management and protection

5.3.1 None proposed.

5.4 Advisory

5.4.1 Advise landowners and managers of the presence of this species and the importance of beneficial management for its conservation. (ACTION: EHS, FC, SNH)

5.5 Future research and monitoring

5.5.1 Undertake surveys to determine the range and status of this ant in the UK. (ACTION: EHS, FC, SNH)

5.5.2 Undertake ecological research to establish the habitat requirements of this species. (ACTION: EHS, FC, SNH)

5.5.3 Monitor the response of the Scottish wood ant to the regeneration of Caledonian pine forest and birch woodland. (ACTION: SNH)

5.5.4 Pass information gathered during survey and monitoring of this species to a central database for incorporation in national and international databases. (ACTION: EHS, SNH)

5.6 Communications and publicity

5.6.1 Promote opportunities for the appreciation of the Scottish wood ant and the conservation issues associated with its habitats. This should be achieved through articles within appropriate journals, as well as by publicity leaflets. (ACTION: EHS, FC, SNH)

5.7 Links with other action plans

5.7.1 Implementation of this action plan could benefit other species of the habitat, including the spider *Clubiona subsultans* and twinflower *Linnaea borealis*.

5.7.2 This plan should be considered in conjunction with that for native pine woodland.

Formica aquilonia

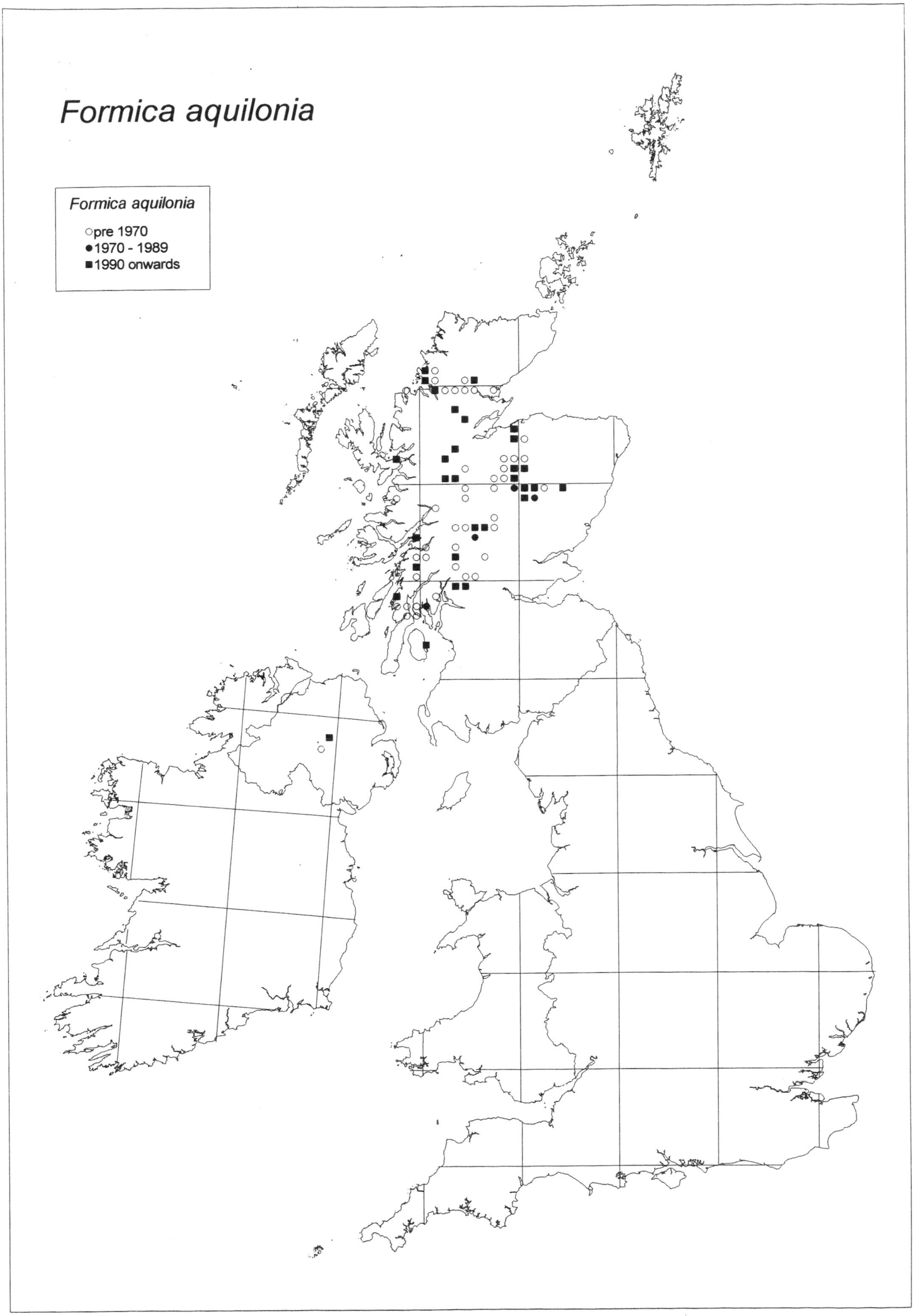

Distribution of Formica aquilonia - Scottish wood ant in Britain and Northern Ireland, by 10km square.
Source: Scottish Natural Heritage records and S.P. Hoy & S.P.M. Roberts - BWARS Newsletter, Autumn 1998.

Red barbed ant (*Formica rufibarbis*)
Action Plan

1. Current status

1.1 The red barbed ant is one of the most thermophilous species of the *Formica* genus; it requires an open habitat in order to obtain sufficient warmth through insolation. In Britain, the species nests in short, lowland grass and heather or maritime heath overlying loose or sandy soils. Nests are excavated in the ground or under stones; a small solarium of soil and vegetation fragments may be raised around a supporting grass tussock. Each nest may contain a colony of a few thousand workers along with one or more queens plus brood. In mature and healthy colonies a new sexual generation containing gynes and/or males is usually produced each year, with mating flights most commonly occuring in July. The workers usually forage singly for invertebrate prey or carrion; they will also take nectar and aphid honey-dew.

1.2 The red barbed ant has been considered a rare species since it was first found in Britain in 1896. It was previously recorded from six mainland British sites and one in the Scilly Isles on Chapel Down, St Martins. All of the mainland sites are (or were formerly) Surrey heathlands. The known distribution of the species is now restricted to two sites in Surrey, Chobham Common and the Bisley ranges, supporting as few as seven and two colonies respectively. The species was still present on St Martins in 1997. The red barbed ant ranges across the Palearctic and is present in southern and central Europe as far north as 62° latitude.

1.3 In Great Britain this species is classified as *Endangered*.

2 Current factors causing loss or decline

2.1 Loss of suitable heathland habitat through urban or industrial development, agricultural improvement and afforestation.

2.2 Inappropriate heathland management.

2.3 Excessive or untimely disturbance of nests through, for example, trampling, off-road vehicles, digging, and inappropriate mechanised scrub or heather clearance.

2.4 Frequent, untimely or intensive heathland fires (although appropriate light burning may be beneficial).

3. Current action

3.1 Both Chobham Common and Bisley ranges are SSSIs; Chobham Common is an NNR.

3.2 Management action at Chobham Common rests with EN, the Surrey Wildlife Trust, and Surrey County Council. Some management of vegetation immediately around nests, and positioning of roofing tiles to encourage nest building, has occurred.

3.3 The red barbed ant is the subject of an EN Species Recovery Programme, for which an action plan was prepared in 1996.

4. Action plan objectives and targets

4.1 Maintain populations at all known sites.

4.2 Enhance the population size at all known sites by 2005.

4.3 Restore populations to suitable sites in order to maintain five viable populations within the historic range by 2010.

5. Proposed action with lead agencies

The conservation of the red barbed ant in the UK is dependent initially on the sympathetic management of the few surviving colonies. Ecological research will be necessary in order to refine management advice. Captive breeding techniques will need to be developed, followed by a programme of (re)introduction to ensure that five viable populations are established.

5.1 Policy and legislation

5.1.1 Where appropriate, include the requirements of the species when preparing or revising prescriptions for agri-environment schemes. (ACTION: EN, MAFF)

5.2 Site safeguard and management

5.2.1 Where possible, ensure that all occupied and nearby potential habitat is appropriately managed, in particular that nests are not shaded by over-hanging vegetation or subjected to excessive disturbance. (ACTION: EN, MAFF)

5.2.2 Ensure that the species is included in site management documents for all relevant SSSIs. (ACTION: EN)

5.3 **Species management and protection**

5.3.1 Reintroduce the red barbed ant to a series of sites within the former range in order to ensure that there is a total of five viable populations by 2010. (ACTION: EN)

5.4 **Advisory**

5.4.1 Advise landowners and managers of the presence of the species and the importance of beneficial management for its conservation. (ACTION: EN)

5.5 **Future research and monitoring**

5.5.1 Conduct targeted autecological research to inform habitat management. (ACTION: EN)

5.5.2 Develop a methodology for captive rearing. (ACTION: EN)

5.5.3 Establish a regular monitoring programme for this species. (ACTION: EN)

5.5.4 Pass information gathered during survey and monitoring of this species to a central database for incorporation in national and international databases. (ACTION: EN)

5.5.5 Encourage research into the ecology and conservation of this species on an international level, and use the experience gained towards its conservation in the UK. (ACTION: EN, JNCC)

5.6 **Communication and publicity**

5.6.1 Promote opportunities for the appreciation of the species and the conservation issues associated with its habitat. This should be achieved through articles within appropriate journals, as well as by a publicity leaflet. (ACTION: EN)

5.7 **Links with other action plans**

5.7.1 Implementation of this action plan could benefit other species of lowland heaths, including *Bombylius minor* and *Cicindela sylvatica*.

5.7.2 This plan should be considered in conjunction with that for lowland heathland.

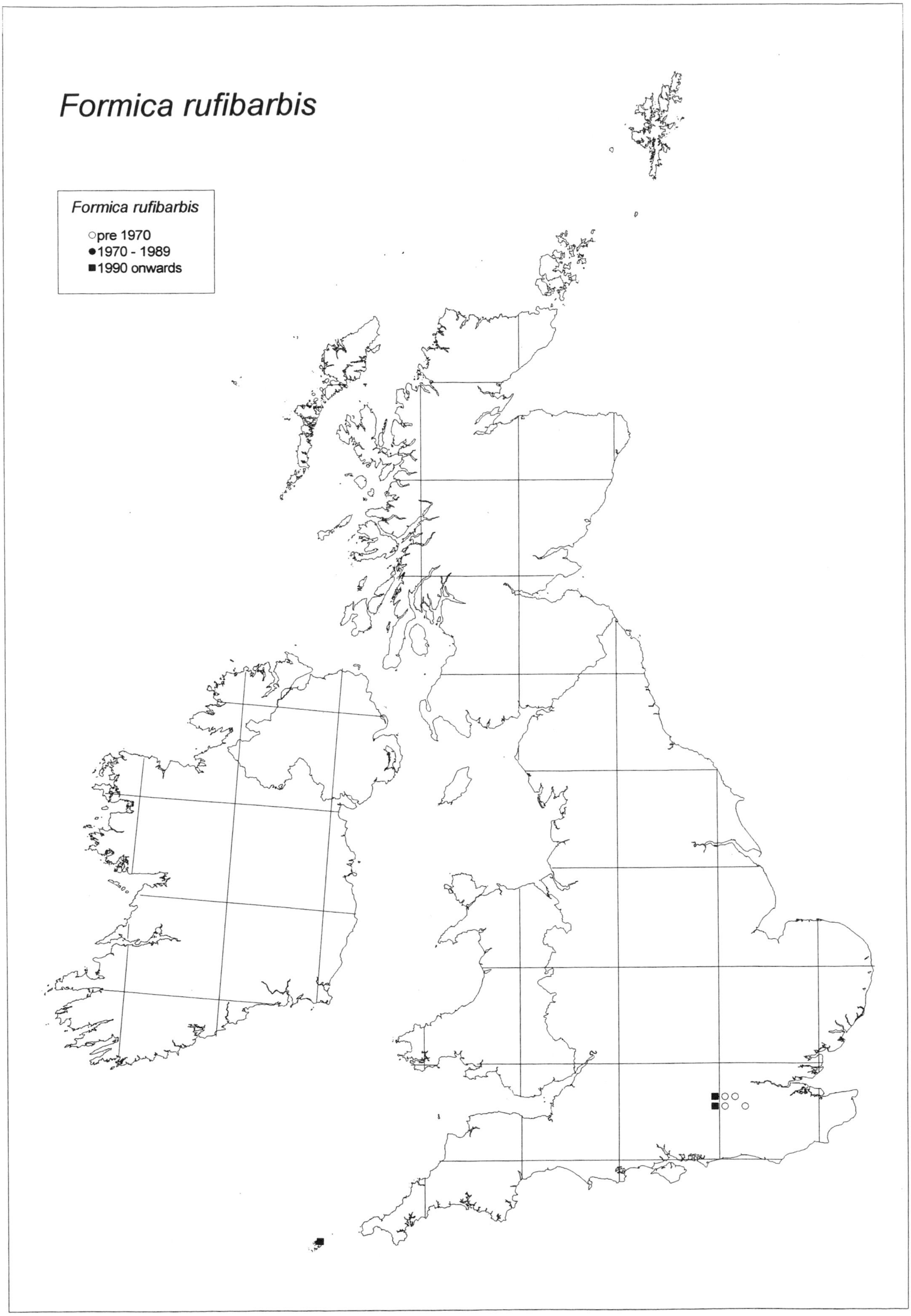

Distribution of Formica rufibarbis - red barbed ant in Britain, by 10km square.
Source: English Nature - Invertebrate Site Register.

Homonotus sanguinolentus (a spider-hunting wasp)
Action Plan

1. Current status

1.1 *Homonotus sanguinolentus* is a predator of spiders of the clubionid genus *Cheiracantheum*. These spiders construct conspicuous retreats in a number of aerial locations, including grass flower heads and heather inflorescences. The wasp enters the egg-laying retreat of gravid female spiders and lays an egg on the front of the spider's abdomen. The spider remains alive in the retreat whilst the wasp larva feeds on its body fluids. After about 10 days the wasp larva kills the spider and consumes the remains. A greyish cocoon is spun up inside the retreat and the prepupa overwinters inside this.

1.2 This spider-hunting wasp has always been erratically and rarely found. There are eight records from lowland heathland in Dorset, Hampshire and Surrey, spanning the years 1900 to 1962. Since then the only record is of a single male taken on Cranes Moor in the New Forest in 1990. It is widespread, but rarely found, throughout southern and central Europe, but is highly thermophilous in the northern part of its range.

1.3 In Great Britain this species is classified as *Endangered*.

2. Current factors causing loss or decline

2.1 Loss of southern heathland, especially grass-heath.

2.2 Scrub and bracken development.

3. Current action

3.1 Most of the localities where this species has been recorded are SSSIs. The New Forest is a proposed SAC.

3.2 This species is the subject of an EN Pre-Recovery Programme.

4. Action plan objectives and targets

4.1 Maintain populations at all known sites.

4.2 Enhance the population size at all known sites by 2010.

4.3 Restore populations to suitable sites to maintain 10 viable populations within the historic range by 2010.

5. Proposed action with lead agencies

This species is under threat due to loss of open, warm grasslands and heathland, with slightly damp areas present. The priority action necessary to halt or reverse the decline of this species is to continue the Species Recovery Programme of autecological research, investigating the prey (including the prey autecology) and nesting requirements of the species, together with its dispersal ability. This will need to be followed by a programme of informed habitat management.

5.1 Policy and legislation

5.1.1 Where appropriate, include the requirements of the species when preparing or revising prescriptions for agri-environment schemes. (ACTION: EN, MAFF)

5.2 Site safeguard and management

5.2.1 Where possible, ensure that all occupied and nearby potential habitat is appropriately managed by 2008, for example through agri-environment scheme management agreements. (ACTION: EN, MAFF)

5.2.2 Ensure that the habitat requirements of *Homonotus sanguinolentus* are taken into account in relevant development policies, plans and proposals. (ACTION: EN, LAs)

5.2.3 Ensure that this species is included in site management documents for all relevant SSSIs. (ACTION: EN)

5.2.4 Consider notifying sites supporting viable populations of *Homonotus sanguinolentus* as SSSIs, where this is necessary to secure their long-term protection and appropriate management. (ACTION: EN)

5.3 Species management and protection

5.3.1 If necessary to maintain 10 viable populations, undertake habitat restoration and/or re-introductions at suitable former or potential sites. (ACTION: EN)

5.4 Advisory

5.4.1 Advise landowners and managers of the presence of the species and the importance of beneficial management for its conservation. (ACTION: EN)

5.5 Future research and monitoring

5.5.1 Undertake surveys to determine the status of the wasp by 2005. (ACTION: EN)

5.5.2 Promote ecological research to establish the habitat requirements of this species, the factors limiting breeding success at existing sites, and its dispersal ability. (ACTION: EN)

5.5.3 Establish a regular monitoring programme for the species. (ACTION: EN)

5.5.4 Pass information gathered during survey and monitoring of this species to a central database for incorporation into national and international databases. (ACTION: EN)

5.6 Communications and publicity

5.6.1 Promote opportunities for the appreciation of this species and the conservation issues associated with its habitat. This should be achieved through articles within appropriate journals, as well as by a publicity leaflet. (ACTION: EN)

5.7 Links with other action plans

5.7.1 Implementation of this action plan could benefit other species of lowland heathland, including: the ground beetles *Amara famelica*, *Cicindela sylvatica* and *Pterostichus kugellani*; the aculeate wasps *Chrysis fulgida* and *Pseudepipona herrichii;* and the flies *Bombylius minor* and *Chrysotoxum octomaculatum*.

5.7.2 This plan should be considered in conjunction with that for lowland heathland.

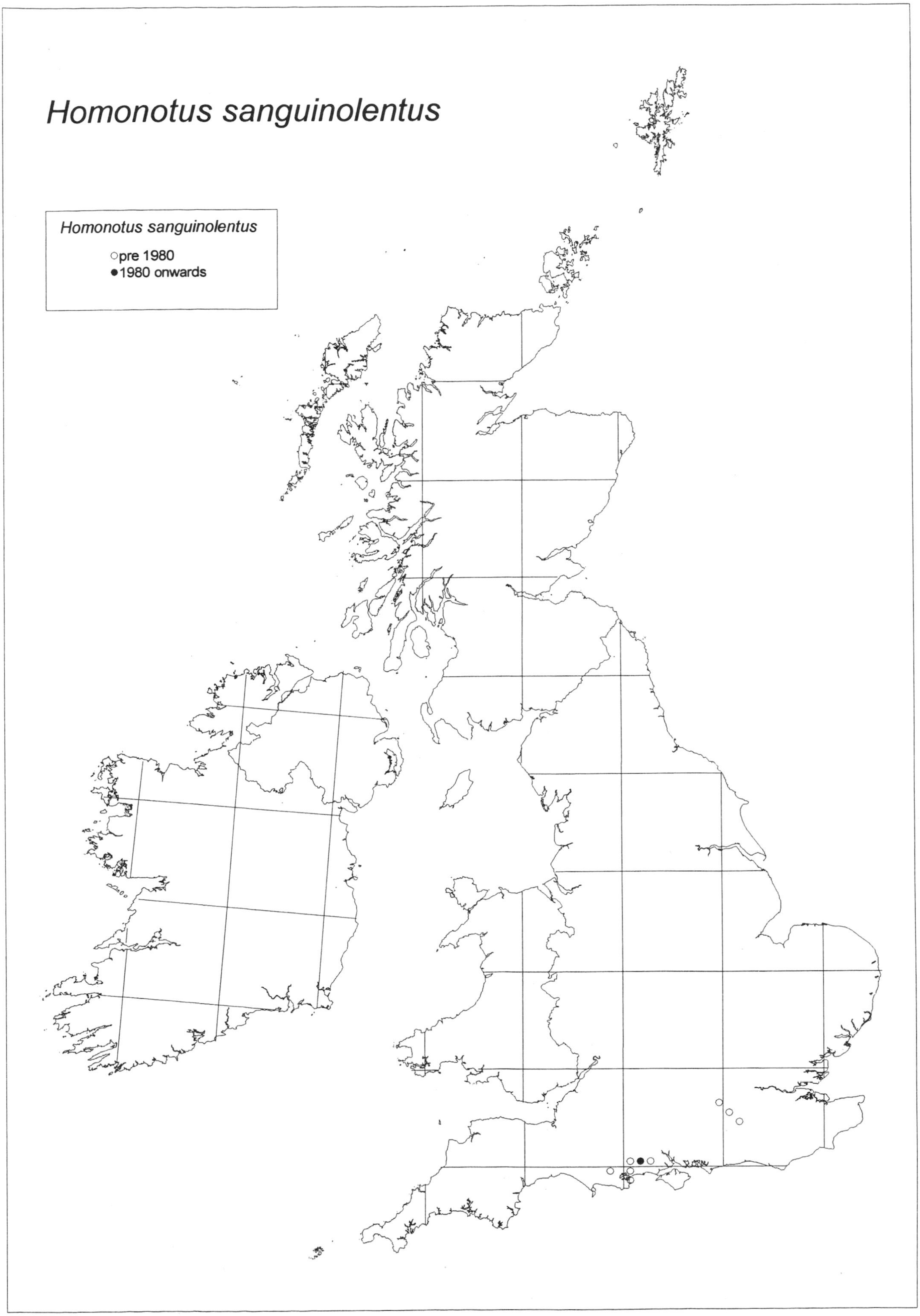

Distribution of Homonotus sanguinolentus - a spider hunting wasp in Britain, by 10km square.
Source: Provisional atlas of aculeate hymenoptera of Britain and Ireland, 1997. Biological Records Centre (ITE) and BWARS records.

Nomada armata (a cuckoo bee) Action Plan

1. Current status

1.1 *Nomada armata* is a large, red cuckoo bee which lays its eggs in the nests of the mining bee *Andrena hattorfiana*. The host bee is closely associated with flowers of field scabious where it forages for the pollen with which to provision its nest. *Nomada armata* is also most often found on the flowers of the scabious. However, it uses these flowers for nectar supplies only. The host bee nests singly within grassland, sometimes in areas of exposed soil. Both *Nomada armata* and *Andrena hattorfiana* fly between June and early August.

1.2 There are confirmed records of *Nomada armata* from much of southern England and a single record from southern Wales. However, the majority of these records are from the 19th and early 20th centuries. There are six localities where this species has been found since 1990, all within the Salisbury Plain area of Wiltshire. These sites all have a calcareous soil, although they comprise both extensive chalk grasslands and marginal grassland areas along the edges of arable fields. The bee is widespread, but uncommon, in Europe as a whole.

1.3 In Great Britain this species is classified as *Vulnerable*.

2. Current factors causing loss or decline

2.1 Loss of calcareous grasslands due to agricultural improvement.

2.2 Inappropriate grazing management.

3. Current action

3.1 All recent localities are within the Salisbury Plain SSSI, some on MoD property.

4. Action plan objectives and targets

4.1 Maintain populations at all known sites.

4.2 Enhance the population size at all known sites by 2010.

4.3 Restore populations to suitable sites to maintain 10 viable populations within the historic range by 2010.

5. Proposed action with lead agencies

This cuckoo bee is under threat due to loss of open grasslands with stands of field scabious, which support populations of its host bee. The priority action necessary to halt or reverse the decline of this species is to establish a programme of autecological research, investigating the nectar, pollen and nesting requirements, together with the dispersal ability, of both species. This will need to be followed by a programme of informed habitat management.

5.1 Policy and legislation

5.1.1 Where appropriate, include the requirements of the species when preparing or revising prescriptions for agri-environment schemes. (ACTION: EN, MAFF)

5.2 Site safeguard and management

5.2.1 Where possible, ensure that all occupied and potential habitat is appropriately managed by 2008, for example through SSSI or agri-environment scheme management agreements. (ACTION: EN, MAFF, MoD)

5.2.2 Ensure that the habitat requirements of *Nomada armata* are taken into account in relevant development policies, plans and proposals. (ACTION: EN, LAs)

5.2.3 Ensure that this species is included in site management documents for all relevant SSSIs. (ACTION: EN)

5.2.4 Consider notifying sites supporting viable populations of *Nomada armata* as SSSIs, where this is necessary to secure their long-term protection and appropriate management. (ACTION: EN)

5.3 Species management and protection

5.3.1 If necessary to maintain 10 viable populations, undertake habitat restoration and/or re-introductions at suitable former or potential sites. (ACTION: CCW, EN)

5.4 Advisory

5.4.1 Advise landowners and managers of the presence of the species and the importance of beneficial management for its conservation. (ACTION: EN, MAFF)

5.4.2 As far as possible, ensure that all relevant agri-environment project officers, and members of regional agri-environment consultation groups, are advised of locations of this species, its importance, and the management needed for its conservation. (ACTION: EN, MAFF)

5.5 **Future research and monitoring**

5.5.1 Undertake surveys to determine the status of the bee by 2005. (ACTION: CCW, EN)

5.5.2 Promote ecological research to establish the habitat requirements of this species, the factors limiting breeding success at existing sites, and its dispersal ability. (ACTION: EN)

5.5.3 Establish a regular monitoring programme for the species. (ACTION: EN)

5.5.4 Pass information gathered during survey and monitoring of this species to a central database for incorporation into national and international databases. (ACTION: CCW, EN)

5.6 **Communications and publicity**

5.6.1 Promote opportunities for the appreciation of this species and the conservation issues associated with its habitat. This should be achieved through articles within appropriate journals, as well as by a publicity leaflet. (ACTION: EN)

5.7 **Links with other action plans**

5.7.1 Implementation of this action plan could benefit the bumblebees *Bombus humilis, B. ruderatus, B. subterraneus* and *B. sylvarum*.

5.7.2 This plan should be considered in conjunction with that for lowland calcareous grassland.

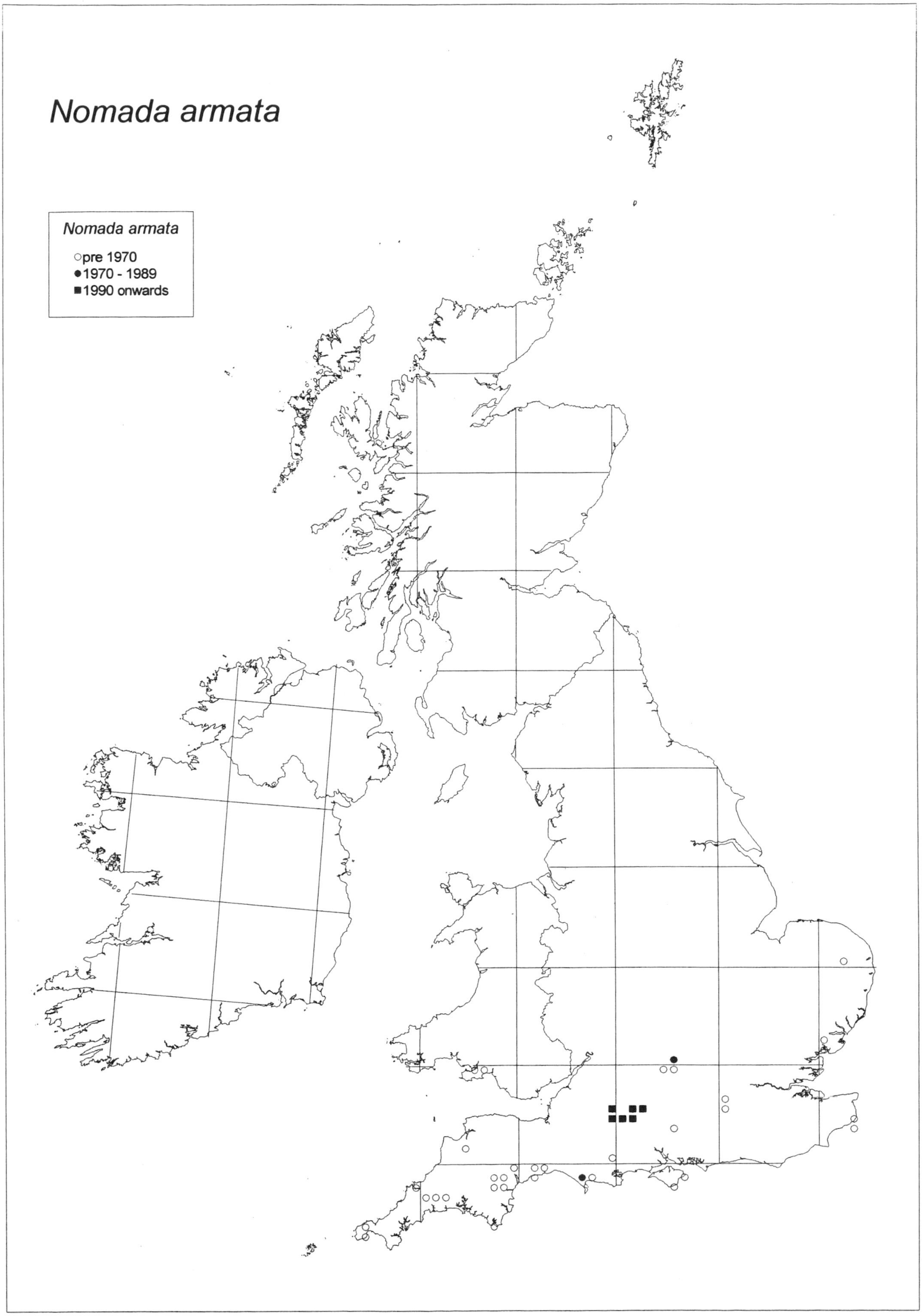

Distribution of Nomada armata - a cuckoo bee in Britain, by 10km square.
Source: G.R. Else & S.P.M. Roberts - BWARS Newsletter, Autumn 1998 and English Nature - Invertebrate Site Register.

Nomada errans (a cuckoo bee) Action Plan

1. Current status

1.1 *Nomada errans is* a species of cuckoo bee that is presumed to be the special cleptoparasite of the mining bee *Andrena nitidiusculus*. The host bee is widespread, but local, in southern England, being found in grassland habitats on both chalk and sand. It collects its pollen from various plant species in the family Apiaceae, notably wild carrot and hogweed, and nests solitarily or in small aggregations on patches of bare ground.

1.2 *Nomada errans* is known in the UK from 1 ten km square only, comprising the rough limestone grasslands and landslips in the area around Durlston Head, Dorset. This is despite the host bee's widespread distribution along the south coast of England. The cuckoo bee has apparently never been common, and only 19 specimens have ever been caught, nearly all of which are known to be extant in collections. The most recent capture is of a female at Anvil Point on 26 July 1982. Recent investigations at the site have failed to rediscover the species. The bee is apparently on the extreme northern edge of its European range, where it is predominantly a southern species, occurring as far north as Poland and Germany.

1.3 In Great Britain this species is classified as *Endangered*.

2. Current factors causing loss or decline

2.1 Coastal cliff stabilisation

2.2 Scrub encroachment.

3. Current action

3.1 The solitary population is at the eastern extremity of the South Dorset Coast SSSI.

4. Action plan objectives and targets

4.1 Maintain the population at its known site.

4.2 Enhance the population size at its known site by 2010.

5. Proposed action with lead agencies

This cuckoo bee is under threat due to loss of open grasslands with stands of umbelliferous flowers, which support populations of its host bee. The priority action necessary to halt or reverse the decline of this species is to establish a programme of autecological research, investigating the nectar, pollen and nesting requirements, together with dispersal ability, of both species. This will need to be followed by a programme of informed habitat management.

5.1 Policy and legislation

5.1.1 Where appropriate, include the requirements of the species when preparing or revising prescriptions for agri-environment schemes. (ACTION: EN, MAFF)

5.2 Site safeguard and management

5.2.1 Where possible, ensure that all occupied and nearby potential habitat is appropriately managed by 2008, for example through agri-environment scheme management agreements. (ACTION: EN, MAFF)

5.2.2 Ensure that the habitat requirements of *Nomada errans* are taken into account in relevant development policies, plans and proposals. (ACTION: EN, LAs)

5.2.3 Ensure that this species is included in site management documents for the South Dorset Coast SSSI. (ACTION: EN)

5.3 Species management and protection

5.3.1 None proposed.

5.4 Advisory

5.4.1 Advise landowners and managers of the presence of the species and the importance of beneficial management for its conservation. (ACTION: EN)

5.5 Future research and monitoring

5.5.1 Promote ecological research to establish the habitat requirements of this species and its host, the factors limiting breeding success at existing sites, and its dispersal ability. (ACTION: EN)

5.5.2 Establish a regular monitoring programme for the species. (ACTION: EN)

5.5.3 Pass information gathered during survey and monitoring of this species to a central database for incorporation into national and international databases. (ACTION: EN)

5.6 Communications and publicity

5.6.1 Promote opportunities for the appreciation of this species and the conservation issues associated with its habitat. This should be achieved through articles within appropriate journals, as well as by a publicity leaflet. (ACTION: EN)

5.7 Links with other action plans

5.7.1 This action plan should be considered in conjunction with those for lowland calcareous grassland, and maritime cliffs and slopes.

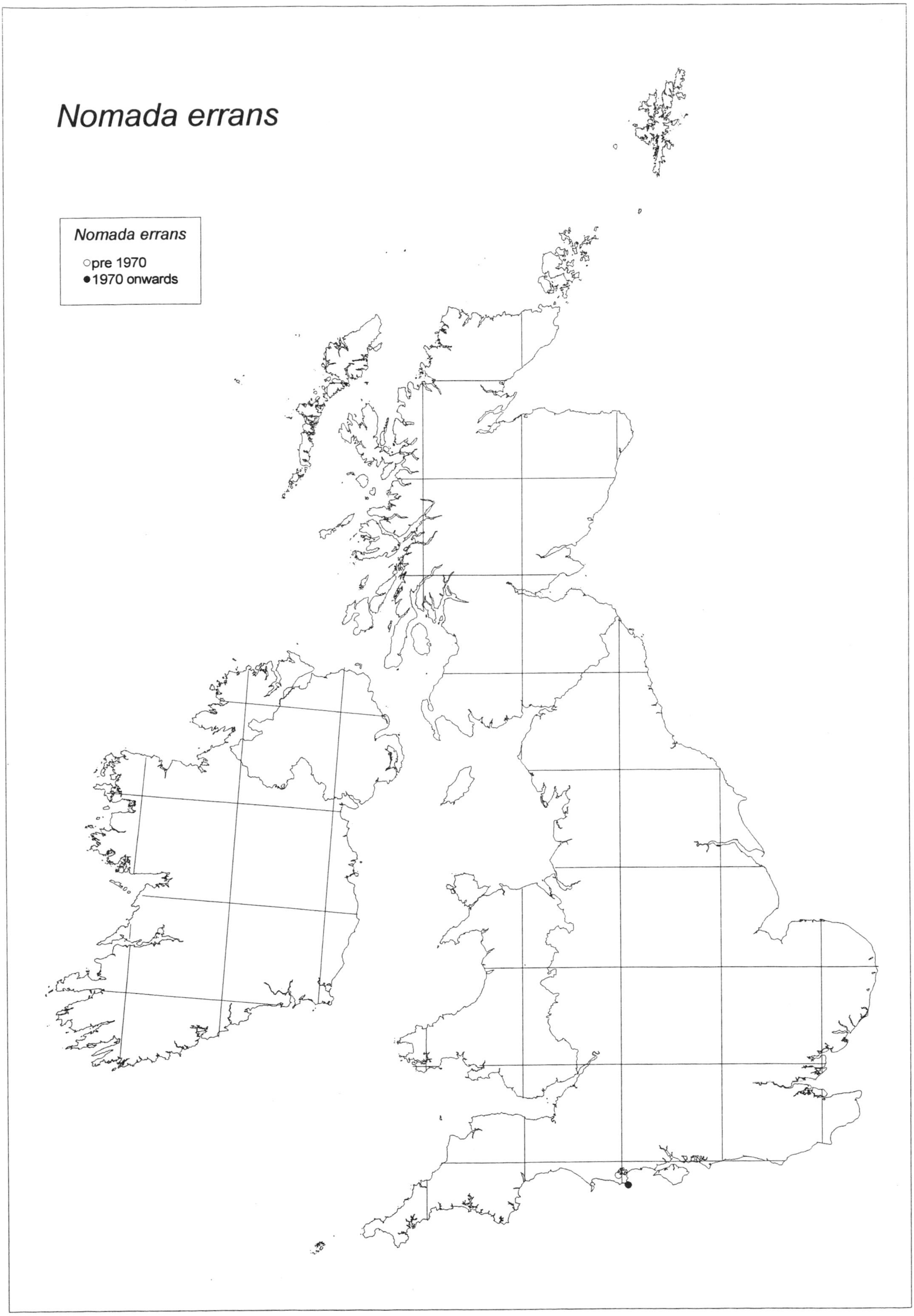

Distribution of Nomada errans - a cuckoo bee in Britain, by 10km square.
Source: S.P.M. Roberts records and English Nature - Invertebrate Site Register.

Osmia inermis (a mason bee) Action Plan

1. Current status

1.1 *Osmia inermis* is one of a small group of boreo-alpine species of bee found in the UK. All nesting sites found in Scotland have been in the altitude range 300 to 600 m, although there are some earlier records from lower areas. Nests have been found in calcareous areas in short, dry, heathery turf which was closely grazed and had a high proportion of lichens present. The surrounding vegetation included numerous plants of bird's-foot trefoil, on which the females forage for pollen. Nests, which may be the work of several bees, are built under stones lying on the surface of the ground, and probably in narrow crevices in rock. All nesting sites need to be in full exposure to the sun. The cuckoo wasp *Chrysura hirsuta* is known to be a parasitoid on the larvae of this bee.

1.2 This bee has a circumpolar distribution, being found at low altitudes north of the Arctic circle and in montane locations farther south. All UK records of *O. inermis* are from the north of the central lowland belt of Scotland. There are old records from Speyside but more recent records are confined to Perthshire.

1.3 In Great Britain this species is classified as *Vulnerable*.

2. Current factors causing loss or decline

2.1 Loss of herb-rich grasslands with short swards through agricultural intensification, commercial afforestation or cessation of grazing.

2.2 As a species with a boreo-alpine distribution, it could be negatively affected by warming of the UK climate.

3. Current action

3.1 Some of the sites are on SSSIs.

4. Action plan objectives and targets

4.1 Maintain populations at all known sites.

5. Proposed action with lead agencies

This bee is under threat from the loss of suitable habitat, especially on upland calcareous grasslands. The priority action necessary to halt or reverse the decline of this species is to establish a programme of autecological research, investigating the nectar, pollen, nesting, mating and overwintering requirements of the species. This will need to be followed by a programme of informed habitat management.

5.1 Policy and legislation

5.1.1 Where appropriate, include the requirements of *Osmia inermis* when preparing or revising prescriptions for agri-environment schemes. (ACTION: SNH, SOAEFD)

5.1.2 Take account of the requirements of *Osmia inermis* when considering Woodland Grant Scheme, and other forestry scheme, applications. (ACTION: FC, SNH)

5.2 Site safeguard and management

5.2.1 Ensure that the species is included management documents for all relevant SSSIs. (ACTION: SNH)

5.2.2 Consider notifying as SSSIs sites supporting viable populations of *Osmia inermis*, where this is necessary to secure their long-term protection and appropriate management. (ACTION: SNH)

5.3 Species management and protection

5.3.1 None proposed.

5.4 Advisory

5.4.1 Advise landowners and managers of the presence and this bee and the importance of beneficial management for its conservation. (ACTION SNH)

5.5 Future research and monitoring

5.5.1 Undertake surveys to determine the current status of the bee by 2005. (ACTION: SNH)

5.5.3 Conduct targeted autecological research to inform habitat management. (ACTION: SNH)

5.5.3 Pass information gathered during survey and monitoring of this species to a central database for incorporation in national and international databases. (ACTION: SNH)

5.6 Communications and publicity

5.6.1 Promote opportunities for the appreciation of this bee and the conservation issues associated with its habitat. This should be achieved through articles within appropriate journals, as well as by publicity leaflets. (ACTION: SNH)

5.7 Links with other action plans

5.7.1 Implementation of this action plan could benefit other species of the habitat, including the wasp *Chrysura hirsuta,* and the bee *Osmia parietina.*

5.7.2 This plan should be considered in conjunction with that for upland calcareous grassland.

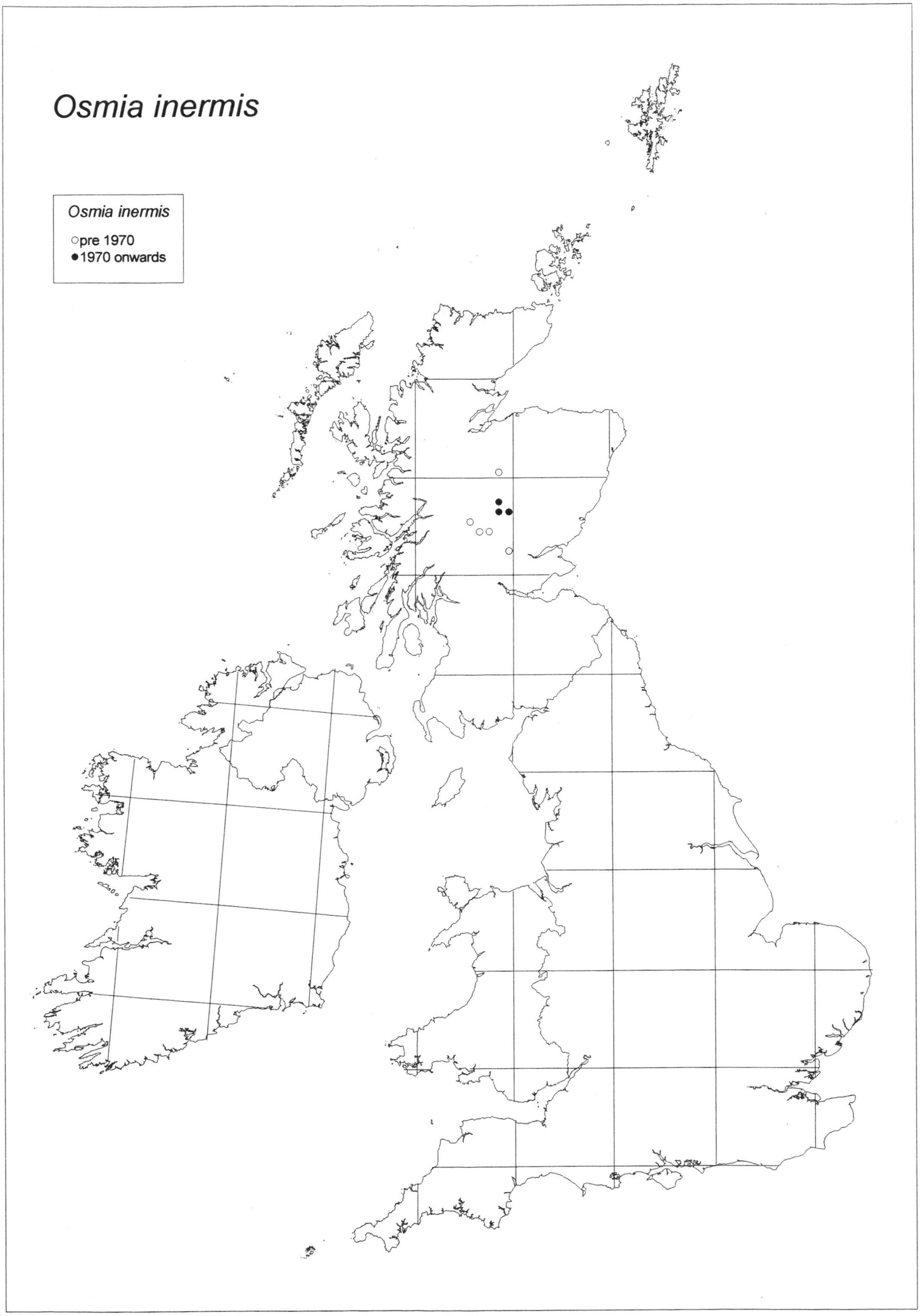

Distribution of Osmia inermis - a mason bee in Britain, by 10km square.
Source: Provisional atlas of aculeate hymenoptera of Britain and Ireland, 1997. Biological Records Centre (ITE).

Osmia parietina (a mason bee) Action Plan

1. Current status

1.1 *Osmia parietina* is one of a small group of boreo-alpine species of bee found in the UK. It nests in cavities within a variety of substrates, including dry-stone walls and holes in dead wood. There is a close association with bird's-foot trefoil, which is probably the main source of pollen. All nesting sites need to be in full exposure to the sun. The cuckoo wasp *Chrysura hirsuta* is known to be parasitic upon this bee on the continent, and it is likely that this is also true in the UK.

1.2 *O. parietina* is widespread in Eurasia, but with a markedly boreo-alpine distribution. Within Britain it is the most widespread of the three northern *Osmia* species. There are widely scattered records from the west and north of Britain, although there are no records from Northern Ireland. Adults were seen at two sites on the Lleyn Peninsula, Caernarvonshire in 1998, and there are several records from Merionethshire in North Wales during the 1970s and one from Pembrokeshire in 1979. Otherwise, one specimen was found at Killiecrankie, Perthshire, during the 1980s and two populations are currently known in northern England at Gait Barrows NNR and Carnforth Iron Works.

1.3 In Great Britain *O. parietina* is classified as *Rare.*

2. Current factors causing loss or decline

2.1 Agricultural intensification of upland herb-rich pastures.

2.2 Destruction of dry-stone walls.

2.3 Inappropriate management of pasture woodlands.

3. Current action

3.1 There are populations on the Gait Barrows NNR and RSPB reserve at Killicrankie.

4. Action plan objectives and targets

4.1 Enhance the population size at all known sites by 2010

4.2 Ensure that there are 20 viable populations within the historic range by 2010.

5. Proposed action with lead agencies

The priority action necessary to halt or reverse the decline of this species is to establish a programme of autecological research, investigating the nectar, pollen and nesting requirements of the species, together with its dispersal ability. This will need to be followed by a programme of informed habitat management of existing and potential sites.

5.1 Policy and legislation

5.1.1 Where appropriate, include the requirements of the species when preparing or revising prescriptions for agri-environment schemes, including the sympathetic maintenance of dry-stone walls. (ACTION: CCW, EN, MAFF, SNH, SOAEFD, WOAD)

5.2 Site safeguard and management

5.2.1 Where possible, ensure that occupied and nearby potential habitat is appropriately managed by 2008, for example through SSSI or agri-environment scheme management agreements. (ACTION: CCW, EN, MAFF, SNH, SOAEFD, WOAD)

5.2.2 Ensure that the habitat requirements of the species are taken into account in relevant development policies, plans and proposals. (ACTION: CCW, EN, LAs, SNH)

5.2.3 Ensure that this species is included in site management documents for all relevant SSSIs. (ACTION: CCW, EN, SNH)

5.2.4 Consider notifying as SSSI sites supporting viable populations of *Osmia parietina,* where this is necessary to secure their long-term protection and appropriate management. (ACTION: CCW, EN, SNH)

5.3 Species management and protection

5.3.1 If necessary to ensure that there are 20 viable populations, undertake habitat restoration and/or reintroductions at suitable former or potential sites. (ACTION: CCW, EN, SNH)

5.4 Advisory

5.4.1 Advise landowners and managers of the presence of the species and the importance of beneficial management for its conservation. (ACTION: CCW, EN, SNH)

5.5 Future research and monitoring

5.5.1 Undertake surveys to determine the current status of the bee by 2005. (ACTION: CCW, EN, SNH)

5.5.2 Promote autecological research targeted to inform habitat management. (ACTION: CCW, EN, SNH)

5.5.3 Establish a regular monitoring programme for the species. (ACTION: CCW, EN, SNH)

5.5.4 Pass information gathered during survey and monitoring of this species to a central database for incorporation in national and international databases. (ACTION: CCW, EN, SNH)

5.6 Communications and publicity

5.6.1 Promote opportunities for the appreciation of this bee and the conservation issues associated with its habitat. This should be achieved through articles within appropriate journals, as well as by publicity leaflets. (ACTION: CCW, EN, SNH)

5.7 Links with other action plans

5.7.1 Implementation of this action plan could benefit the cuckoo wasp *Chrysura hirsuta,* and the mason bees *Osmia inermis* and *Osmia uncinata.*

5.7.2 This plan should be considered in conjunction with those for upland oak woods, limestone pavement, and upland calcareous grassland.

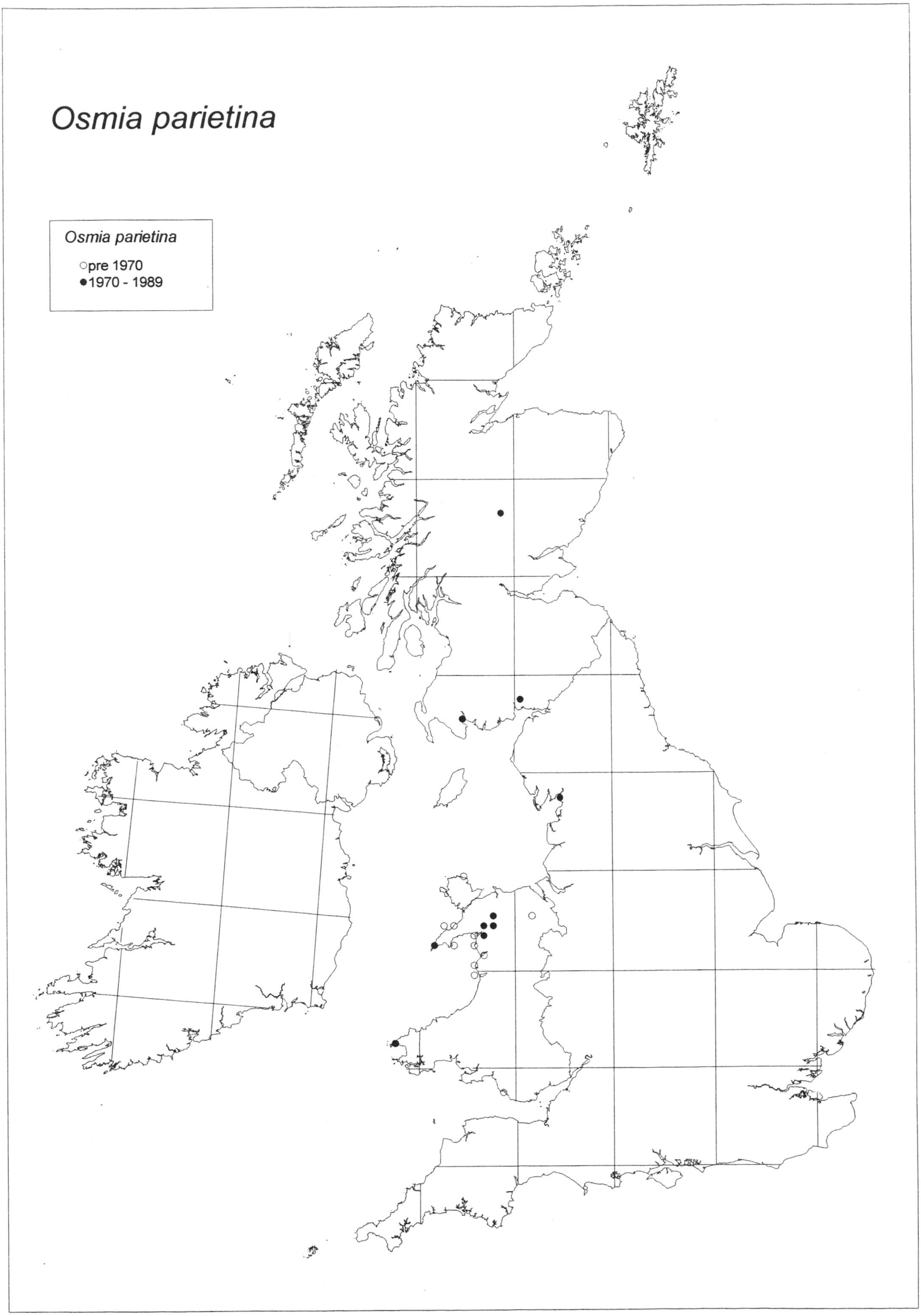

Distribution of Osmia parietina - a mason bee in Britain, by 10km square.
Source: Countryside Council for Wales records and English Nature - Invertebrate Site Register.

Osmia uncinata (a mason bee) Action Plan

1. Current status

1.1 *Osmia uncinata* is one of a small group of boreo-alpine bees found in the UK. All records have come from areas of high forest, with open glades and dead wood present. Although primarily associated with areas of Caledonian pine forest, old plantation areas with a similar high forest structure are also suitable where they have a varied ground flora. No nests have been found in the UK, but elsewhere nesting is reported to be under pine bark on standing and fallen timber. All nesting sites are likely to need full exposure to the sun. The females forage for pollen on bird's-foot trefoil and nectar from other plants, including bilberry and broom. The cuckoo wasp *Chrysura hirsuta* has been found in areas where *O. uncinata* is present, and is probably a parasitoid of the larvae of this species.

1.2 This bee has a boreo-alpine distribution in the Western Palearctic and is associated with coniferous forests. All records of this bee are from the north of the central lowland belt of Scotland. The bee has been recorded from 9 ten km squares since 1904. There are post-1980 records from four of these ten km squares.

1.3 In Great Britain this bee is classified as *Vulnerable*.

2. Current factors causing loss or decline

2.1 Loss of sites with dead pine wood and suitable open glades.

2.2 As a species with a boreo-alpine distribution, it could to be negatively affected by warming of the UK climate.

3. Current action

3.1 Some of the recent records are from SSSIs. The bee is also present on the RSPB reserve at Abernethy Forest.

4. Action plan objectives and targets

4.1 Maintain populations at all known sites.

5. Proposed action with lead agencies

This bee is under threat from the loss of suitable habitat in coniferous woodland. The priority action necessary to halt or reverse the decline of this species is to establish a programme of autecological research, investigating the nectar, pollen, nesting, mating and overwintering requirements of the species. This will need to be followed by a programme of informed habitat management.

5.1 Policy and legislation

5.1.1 Include specific targets and management for *Osmia uncinata* in Forest Design Plans across the species' current and former range. (ACTION: FE)

5.1.2 Take account of the requirements of *Osmia uncinata* when considering grant scheme (eg Woodland Grant Scheme) applications for woodland planting, natural regeneration, and changes in grazing on or near occupied sites. (ACTION: FC, SNH)

5.2 Site safeguard and management

5.2.1 Ensure that the species is included in site management documents for all relevant SSSIs and NNRs, including Abernethy. (ACTION: SNH)

5.2.2 Consider notifying as SSSI sites supporting viable populations of *Osmia uncinata*, where this is necessary to secure their long-term protection and appropriate management. (ACTION: SNH)

5.3 Species management and protection

5.3.1 None proposed.

5.4 Advisory

5.4.1 Advise landowners and managers of the presence of the species and the importance of beneficial management for its conservation. (ACTION SNH)

5.4.2 Develop and disseminate guidelines to protect *Osmia uncinata* for use with landowners; local authority, RSPB and SNH area staff. (ACTION: LAs, FC, SNH)

5.5 Future research and monitoring

5.5.1 Undertake surveys to determine the current status of the bee by 2005. (ACTION: SNH)

5.5.2 Conduct autecological research targeted to inform habitat management. (ACTION: SNH)

5.5.3 Pass information gathered during survey and monitoring of this species to a central database for incorporation in national and international databases. (ACTION: SNH)

5.6 Communications and publicity

5.6.1 Promote opportunities for the appreciation of *Osmia uncinata* and the conservation issues associated with its habitat. This should be achieved through articles within appropriate journals, as well as by publicity leaflets. (ACTION: FC, SNH)

5.7 Links with other action plans

5.7.1 Implementation of this action plan could benefit other species of the habitat, including the cuckoo wasp *Chrysura hirsuta,* the hoverfly *Blera fallax,* and the spider *Clubiona subsultans.*

5.7.2 This plan should be considered in conjunction with that for native pine woodland.

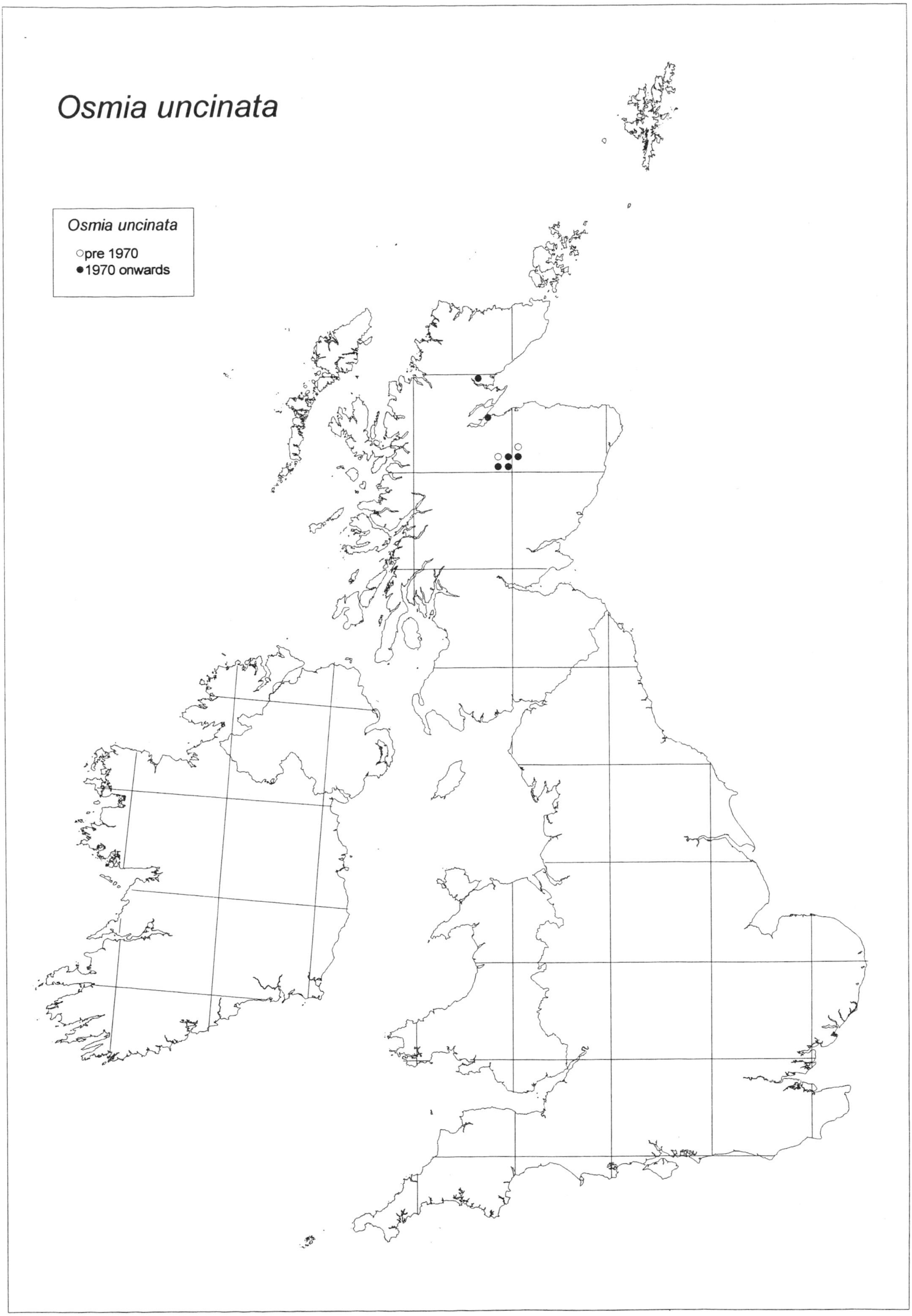

Distribution of Osmia uncinata - a mason bee in Britain, by 10km square.
Source: Provisional atlas of aculeate hymenoptera of Britain and Ireland, 1997. Biological Records Centre (ITE).

Osmia xanthomelana (a mason bee) Action Plan

1. Current status

1.1 *Osmia xanthomelana* is a large mason bee with a conspicuous covering of tawny hair. It builds its nest cells from mud pellets which it gathers at seepage areas on cliffs and banks. The nest is constructed either at the base of grass tussocks or in ready-made cavities. The cells are provisioned with pollen gathered from bird's-foot trefoil or horseshoe vetch. The flight period is from May to July. This species is typical of a number of insect species which are closely associated with the south-facing, soft-rock cliffs of southern England.

1.2 *Osmia xanthomelana* is probably our rarest solitary bee, there being post-1970 records from only 3 ten km squares. Two localities are on soft-rock coastal cliffs in the Isle of Wight and the third is on soft-rock coastal cliffs of the Lleyn Peninsula in North Wales. Even at its main location on the Isle of Wight it is difficult to find, with an estimated population of fewer than 50 individuals in any one year. It was formerly distributed widely in England and Wales, with a total of 21 ten km squares recorded, although most records are from the 19th and early 20th centuries. It has never been considered a common species. It is rare and sporadic in southern and central Europe.

1.3 In Great Britain this species is classified as *Endangered*.

2. Current factors causing loss or decline

2.1 Cliff stabilisation.

2.2 Intensification of agricultural systems at the top of soft-rock cliffs, leading to increased nutrient input to the cliff faces as fertilised agricultural land makes its way down the cliff. This increased input of nutrients results in a coarsening of the vegetation, and rapid shading out of both nesting areas and forage plants.

2.3 Scrub encroachment.

3. Current action

3.1 This species has been the subject of an EN Species Pre-Recovery Project which has led to limited habitat management at its major known site on the Isle of Wight.

3.2 CCW commissioned a survey of former localities and suitable habitat on the Lleyn Peninsula in 1995.

4. Action plan objectives and targets

4.1 Maintain populations at all known sites.

4.2 Enhance the population size at all known sites by 2010.

4.3 Restore populations to suitable sites to maintain five viable populations within the historic range by 2010 and 20 viable populations in the long term.

5. Proposed action with lead agencies

This species is under threat due to loss of open, south-facing, soft-rock cliffs on the coast of southern Britain. The priority action necessary to halt or reverse the decline of this species is to establish a programme of autecological research, investigating the nectar, pollen and nesting requirements of the species, together with its dispersal ability. This will need to be followed by a programme of informed habitat management.

5.1 Policy and legislation

5.1.1 Incorporate the requirements of *Osmia xanthomelana* in relevant Shoreline Management Plans. (ACTION: LAs, MAFF)

5.1.2 Where appropriate, include the requirements of the species when preparing or revising prescriptions for relevant agri-environment schemes. (ACTION: CCW, EN, MAFF, WOAD)

5.2 Site safeguard and management

5.2.1 Where possible, ensure that all occupied and nearby potential habitat is appropriately managed by 2008, for example through agri-environment scheme management agreements. (ACTION: CCW, EN, MAFF, WOAD)

5.2.2 Ensure that the habitat requirements of *Osmia xanthomelana* are taken into account in relevant coastal protection and development policies, plans and proposals. (ACTION: CCW, EN, LAs)

5.2.3 Ensure that this species is included in site management documents for any relevant SSSIs. (ACTION: CCW, EN)

5.2.4 Consider notifying sites supporting viable populations of *Osmia xanthomelana* as SSSIs, where this is necessary to secure their long-term protection and appropriate management. (ACTION: CCW, EN)

5.3 Species management and protection

5.3.1 If necessary to maintain five viable populations, undertake habitat restoration and/or re-introductions at suitable former or potential sites. (ACTION: CCW, EN)

5.4 Advisory

5.4.1 Advise landowners and managers of the presence of the species and the importance of beneficial management for its conservation. (ACTION: CCW, EN)

5.5 Future research and monitoring

5.5.1 Undertake further surveys to determine the status of the bee by 2005. (ACTION: CCW, EN)

5.5.2 Promote ecological research to establish the habitat requirements of this species, the factors limiting breeding success at existing sites, its dispersal ability, and appropriate reintroduction methods. (ACTION: CCW, EN)

5.5.3 Establish a regular monitoring programme for the species. (ACTION: CCW, EN)

5.5.4 Pass information gathered during survey and monitoring of this species to a central database for incorporation into national and international databases. (ACTION: CCW, EN)

5.6 Communications and publicity

5.6.1 Promote opportunities for the appreciation of this species and the conservation issues associated with its habitat. This should be achieved through articles within appropriate journals, as well as by a publicity leaflet. (ACTION: CCW, EN)

5.7 Links with other action plans

5.7.1 Implementation of this action plan could benefit other species of coastal soft-rock cliffs, including the solitary bee *Lasioglossum angusticeps*, and the tiger beetle *Cicindela germanica*.

5.7.2 This plan should be considered in conjunction with that for maritime cliffs and slopes.

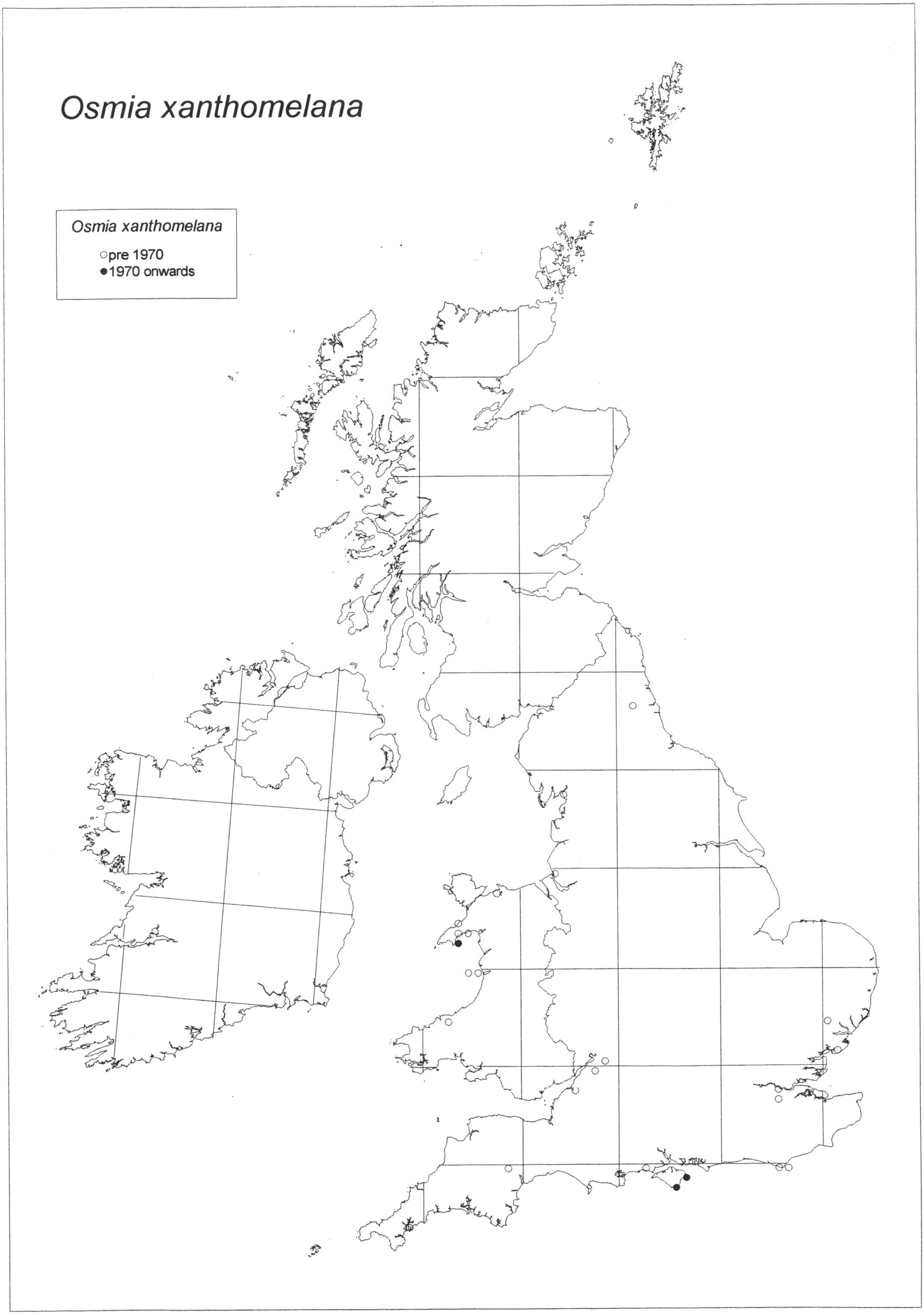

Distribution of Osmia xanthomelana - a mason bee in Britain, by 10km square.
Source: Provisional atlas of aculeate hymenoptera of Britain and Ireland, 1997. Biological Records Centre (ITE), and Countryside Council for Wales records.

Purbeck mason wasp (*Pseudepipona herrichii*) Action Plan

1. Current status

1.1 The Purbeck mason wasp is a large, red, black-and-yellow mason wasp which provisions its nest with the caterpillars of a tortricid moth which feeds on heathers. The host caterpillar is commonest on plants of bell heather *Erica cinerea* in early- to mid-successional heathland. The flowers of bell heather are also the major nectar source for the adult wasps. The nest of the Purbeck mason wasp is dug in areas of bare, clayey ground within heathlands. The wasp flies between May and July.

1.2 This mason wasp has long been known to be restricted to a few lowland heathland sites in the Poole Basin area of Dorset. By the outbreak of the Second World War, it was known from seven different heathlands. Since the late 1940s, the range has contracted and, after the loss of the Stoborough Heath population in about 1980, the only remaining site appeared to be on Godlingston Heath NNR. A survey of clay exposures on Dorset heathlands carried out in 1995 and 1996 failed to find any further breeding sites for the species. In 1997, the monitoring programme revealed that the population size on Godlingston Heath had reached a very high level and, at the same time, new nesting aggregations were discovered on six other heathlands, all within the historic range of the species. The wasp is reported to be widespread in Europe. Although recent records from the near continent are lacking, it is not uncommonly found in the Mediterranean region (Turkey, Greek islands, France, Spain and Morocco). It is also reported from Canada, but the true status of this taxon remains uncertain.

1.3 In Great Britain this species is classified as *Vulnerable*.

2. Current factors causing loss or decline

2.1 Succession on heathland.

3. Current action

3.1 The wasp became part of EN's Species Recovery Programme in 1996.

3.2 Six of the seven colonies recorded in 1997 are on SSSIs; the seventh is just outside one.

4. Action plan objectives and targets

4.1 Maintain populations at all known sites.

4.2 Enhance the population size at all known sites by 2010.

4.3 Restore populations to suitable sites to maintain ten viable populations within the historic range by 2010.

5. Proposed action with lead agencies

This species is under threat due to loss of heathland. Losses in the past have been due to succession, commercial forestry plantation and agricultural intensification. Of these causes, only succession is likely to be a current threat to six of the extant colonies which are on SSSIs, and a priority for the species is to adopt management practices to address this potential threat on occupied or potential sites. Research into the management techniques required to attain the desired composition and height of bell heather is required.

5.1 Policy and legislation

5.1.1 Where appropriate, include the requirements of the species when preparing or revising prescriptions for agri-environment schemes. (ACTION: EN, MAFF)

5.2 Site safeguard and management

5.2.1 Where possible, ensure that all occupied and nearby potential habitat is appropriately managed by 2008, for example through SSSI or agri-environment scheme management agreements. (ACTION: EN, MAFF)

5.2.2 Ensure that the habitat requirements of the Purbeck mason wasp are taken into account in relevant development policies, plans and proposals. (ACTION: EN, LAs)

5.2.3 Ensure that this species is included in site management documents for all relevant SSSIs. (ACTION: EN)

5.2.4 Consider notifying sites supporting viable populations of the Purbeck mason wasp as SSSIs, where this is necessary to secure their long term protection and appropriate management. (ACTION: EN)

5.3 Species management and protection

5.3.1 If necessary to maintain ten viable populations, undertake habitat restoration and/or re-introductions at suitable former or potential sites. (ACTION: EN)

5.4 Advisory

5.4.1 Advise landowners and managers of the presence of the species and the importance of beneficial management for its conservation. (ACTION: EN)

5.5 Future research and monitoring

5.5.1 Continue ecological research to establish the habitat requirements of this species and its prey, the factors limiting breeding success at existing sites, and its dispersal ability. (ACTION: EN)

5.5.2 Continue the current regular monitoring programme. (ACTION: EN)

5.5.3 Pass information gathered during survey and monitoring of this species to a central database for incorporation into national and international databases. (ACTION: EN)

5.6 Communications and publicity

5.6.1 Promote opportunities for the appreciation of this species and the conservation issues associated with its habitat. This should be achieved through articles within appropriate journals, as well as by a publicity leaflet. (ACTION: EN)

5.7 Links with other action plans

5.7.1 Implementation of this action plan could benefit for other species of lowland heath, including: the ground beetles *Amara famelica, Cicindela sylvatica* and *Pterostichus kugellani*; the aculeate wasps *Chrysis fulgida* and *Homonotus sanguinolentus*; and the flies *Bombylius minor* and *Chrysotoxum octomaculatum*.

5.7.2 This plan should be considered in conjunction with that for lowland heathland.

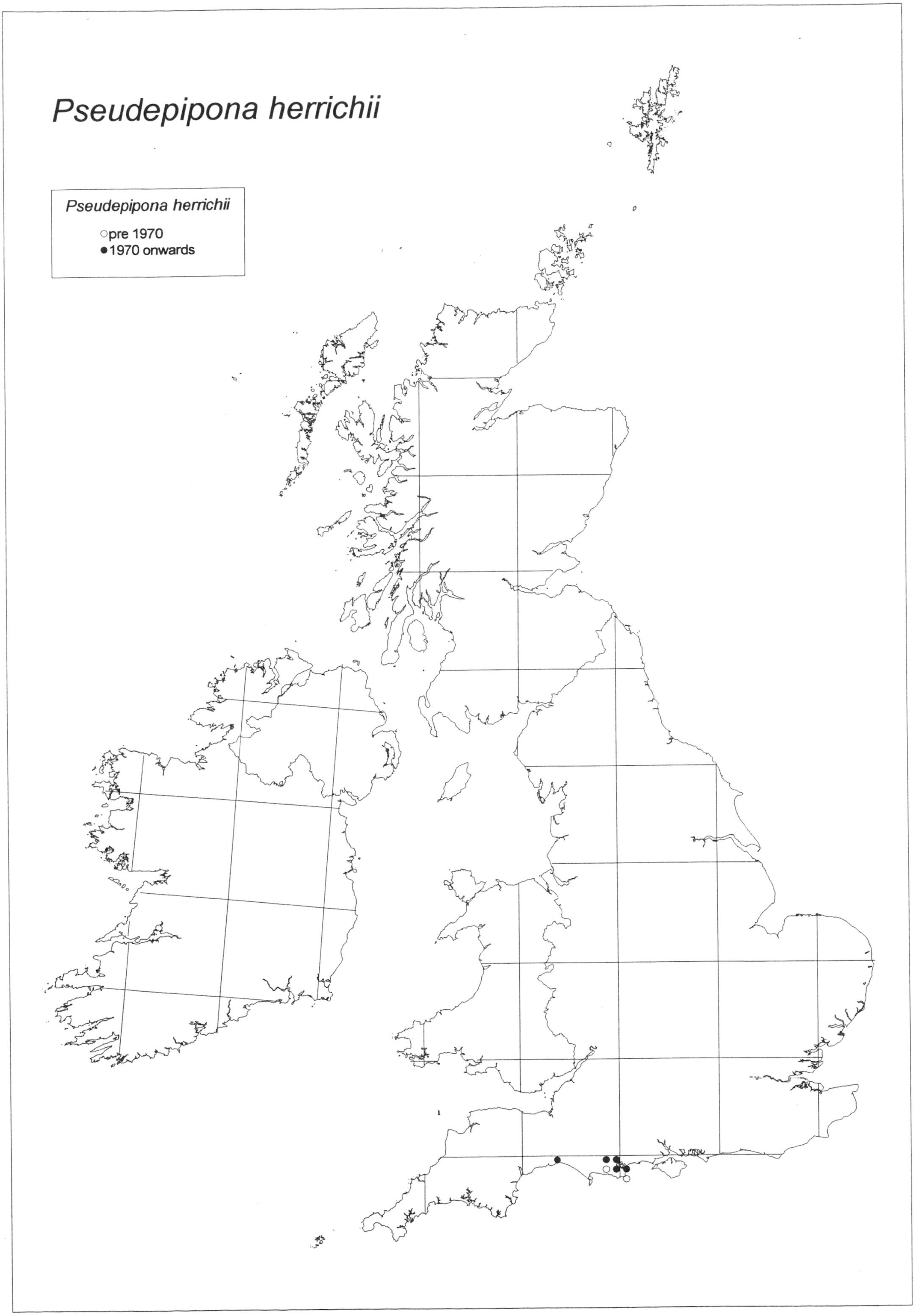

Distribution of Pseudepipona herrichii - Purbeck mason wasp in Britain, by 10km square.
Source: English Nature - Invertebrate Site Register and S.P.M. Roberts - BWARS Newsletter, Spring 1998.

Chrysura hirsuta (a cuckoo wasp) Species Statement

1. Current status

1.1 The wasp *Chrysura hirsuta* is one of a small group of boreo-alpine species of aculeate Hymenoptera found in the UK. This wasp is a specialist parasitoid of the larvae of mason bees of the family Megachilidae. It is known to parasitise *Osmia inermis* in Scotland, whilst elsewhere in Europe it has also been recorded as a parasite of *Osmia uncinata*. In Scotland the hosts occur in upland base-rich grassland and Caledonian pine woodland respectively. It is possible that *Osmia parietina*, the third northern megachilid bee found in the UK, is also a host of this wasp in Scotland.

1.2 This wasp has a boreo-alpine distribution in the Palearctic. Since 1849 this wasp has been recorded from three widely separated areas of Scotland: Blair Atholl (Perthshire), Whithorn (Kirkcudbrightshire) and from Strathspey. There are modern (post-1970) records for all three areas.

1.3 In Great Britain this wasp is now classified as *Rare*.

2. Current factors causing loss or decline

2.1 Loss of herb-rich grasslands with short swards through agricultural intensification, commercial afforestation or cessation of grazing.

2.2 Loss of dead wood and suitable open glades in Caledonian pine woods.

2.3 As a species with a boreo-alpine distribution, it could be negatively affected by warming of the UK climate.

3. Current action

3.1 Some of the records are from SSSIs and it also occurs on the RSPB reserve at Abernethy Forest.

4. Objective for the species

4.1 Maintain the range of *Chrysura hirsuta*.

5. Proposed action

5.1 Monitoring only. The species could benefit from the action plans for its host bees *Osmia inermis*, *O. uncinata* and, probably, *O. parietina*. Its requirements should be considered in the implementation of the upland calcareous grassland and native pine woodland action plans.

Evagetes pectinipes (a spider-hunting wasp) Species Statement

1 Current status

1.1 *Evagetes pectinipes* is a spider-hunting wasp which is presumed to steal spiders from other spider-hunting wasps, most probably *Episyron rufipes*, which is a common species of open dunes and sandy heaths.

1.2 The wasp is known in Britain from only 2 ten km squares on the extensive Deal to Sandwich sand-dune systems of eastern Kent. It was first recognised as a British species from a female taken at Deal in 1966, and has been recorded at the same site on a number of occasions since. The absence of the species in extensive old collections from the current site has led to a suggestion that the species may be a recent colonist from continental mainland Europe. *Evagetes pectinipes* is not uncommon in the Channel Islands (Jersey and Guernsey) and is widespread in mainland Europe (except the south), its range extending eastwards to the Middle East.

1.3 In Great Britain this species is classified as *Endangered*.

2. Current factors causing loss or decline

2.1 Not known.

3. Current action

3.1 At least part of the British population occurs on the Sandwich Bay to Hacklinge Marshes SSSI.

4. Objective for the species

4.1 Maintain existing populations of *Evagetes pectinipes*.

5. Proposed action

5.1 Monitoring only. It is likely that the species may benefit from the action plans for other species of coastal sand dunes, including the click beetle *Melanotus punctolineatus*. The requirements of the species should be considered in the implementation of the coastal sand dunes action plan.

Lasioglossum angusticeps (a solitary bee) Species Statement

1. Current status

1.1 *Lasioglossum angusticeps* is a small, black mining bee which is difficult to separate from its close relative, *L. punctatissimum*. Males are required for reliable identification. Circumstantial evidence suggests that females provision their nests with pollen from bird's-foot trefoil. The bee nests gregariously in open situations exposed to the sun, particularly on areas of clay which have slumped at the base of cliffs. It is typical of a number of insect species which are closely associated with the south-facing, soft-rock cliffs of southern England. This habitat is prone to constant local changes through natural land slippage and cliff falls, providing a dynamic matrix of bare ground and pioneer vegetation which is open to the heating influence of the sun. *Lasioglossum angusticeps* flies between late May to September.

1.2 The species has a very restricted distribution in the UK. It is found only along the soft-rock coastal cliffs between the Isle of Wight (Niton) and eastern Devon (Sidmouth). Where found, it may be locally common. It is rare and sporadic in southern and central Europe.

1.3 In Great Britain this species is classified as *Rare*.

2. Current factors causing loss or decline

2.1 Cliff stabilisation.

2.2 Intensification of agricultural systems at the top of soft-rock cliffs, leading to increased nutrient input to the cliff faces as fertilised agricultural land makes its way down the cliff. This increased input of nutrients results in a coarsening of the vegetation and rapid shading out of both nesting areas and forage plants.

2.3 Scrub encroachment.

3. Current action

3.1 Some populations occur on SSSIs.

4. Objective for the species

4.1 Maintain the range of *Lasioglossum angusticeps*.

5. Proposed action

5.1 Monitoring only. It is likely that the species will benefit from the action plans for other species of coastal soft-rock cliffs, including the solitary bee *Osmia xanthomelana* and the tiger beetle *Cicindela germanica*. The requirements of the species should be considered in the implementation of the maritime cliffs and slopes action plan.

Nomada ferruginata (= *N. xanthosticta*) (a cuckoo bee) Species Statement

1. Current status

1.1 *Nomada ferruginata* is a species of cuckoo bee that is the special cleptoparasite of the early spring mining bee *Andrena praecox*. The host bee is strongly associated with the male flowers of sallows, which provide the only pollen source for provisioning the nest cells. Nest burrows of the host bee are constructed, usually singly, in patches of bare ground.

1.2 *Nomada ferruginata* is known to be widely distributed throughout southern England, with 21 confirmed ten km squares, of which nine are post 1970. Old records from Manchester, Northumberland and eastern Scotland may be misidentifications. Despite the continued relative abundance of the host bee, *Nomada ferruginata* appears to have declined significantly since 1945. There has, however, been an increase in the number of records since the mid 1980s, with populations being found in Wiltshire, Hampshire, Suffolk, Essex, Kent and Warwickshire. It is a northern and central European species, becoming more sparsely distributed in the south.

1.3 In Great Britain this species is classified as *Endangered*.

2. Current factors causing loss or decline

2.1 Not known.

3. Current action

3.1 Some populations are on SSSIs.

4. Objective for the species

4.1 Maintain the range of *Nomada ferruginata*.

5. Proposed action

5.1 Monitoring only.

Lepidoptera

Reddish buff (*Acosmetia caliginosa*)
Action Plan

1. Current status

1.1 The reddish buff is a moth whose sole larval foodplant is saw-wort *Serratula tinctoria*. Its preferred breeding habitat is open grassy, often heathy, swards rich in saw-wort, but neither strongly acidic nor strongly alkaline. Most larvae have been found in sward heights of 5-15 cm.

1.2 This moth has been recorded from several sites in Hampshire and on the Isle of Wight. In Hampshire it had been lost from the New Forest by the 1930s, and from the county as a whole in the 1960s. On the Isle of Wight three sites had been lost by 1980, another was lost during the 1980s, and now a single native population remains. The reddish buff has a very local but scattered distribution in Europe which extends eastwards into Asia.

1.3 In Great Britain this moth is classified as *Endangered*. It is given full protection under Schedule 5 of the Wildlife and Countryside Act 1981.

2. Current factors causing loss or decline

2.1 Establishment of conifer plantations on open heathland.

2.2 Scrub encroachment due to insufficient browsing, grazing and clearance.

3. Current action

3.1 The species has been the subject of an EN Species Recovery Programme project since 1992.

3.2 A captive breeding programme with the Federation of Zoological Gardens has been underway since 1993.

3.3 A species action plan, commissioned by EN, was prepared in 1995.

4. Action plan objectives and targets

4.1 Maintain the sole natural population and any newly discovered or naturally re-established populations.

4.2 Restore the species to at least 10 viable populations within its former range in Britain by 2005.

5. Proposed action with lead agencies

The objectives of the plan will be achieved by encouraging beneficial land management on existing sites, surveying all available habitat for undiscovered populations, and restoring a network of habitat (if necessary with introductions of the species) to combat potential isolation effects. Research should focus on the ecological requirements of the species, monitoring the effects of habitat management designed to meet these needs, and detection of any changes in the population which may be due to isolation.

5.1 Policy and legislation

5.1.1 Where appropriate, include the requirements of the reddish buff when preparing or revising prescriptions for agri-environment and woodland grant schemes. (ACTION: EN, FC, MAFF)

5.2 Site safeguard and management

5.2.1 Where possible, ensure that all occupied and nearby potential habitat is appropriately managed by 2003, for example through SSSI or agri-environment scheme management agreements. (EN, MAFF)

5.2.2 Ensure that the habitat requirements of the reddish buff are taken into account in relevant development policies, plans and proposals. (ACTION: EN, LAs)

5.2.3 Where possible, increase the available habitat at known sites and in adjacent areas, and attempt to link up existing fragments of habitat. At least 5 ha of suitable habitat at each established population of the moth should be restored by 2010. (ACTION: FC, EN)

5.2.4 Consider notifying as SSSIs sites holding key populations of the species, where this is necessary to secure their long-term protection and appropriate management. (ACTION: EN)

5.3 Species management and protection

5.3.1 Continue the cooperative captive breeding project with the Federation of Zoological Gardens to produce sufficient captive stock for establishment trials. (ACTION: EN)

5.3.3 Consider (re)introducing the reddish buff to former or potential sites if necessary to restore 10 viable populations by 2005. (ACTION: EN)

5.4 Advisory

5.4.1 Advise landowners and managers of the presence of the species and the importance of beneficial management for its conservation. (ACTION: EN)

5.5 Future research and monitoring

5.5.1 Undertake surveys of all potential habitat in order to locate any surviving colonies by 2005. (ACTION: EN)

5.5.2 Conduct autecological research on the moth's population biology and requirements, including the effects of habitat management. (ACTION: EN)

5.5.3 Establish a regular monitoring programme for the species. (ACTION: EN)

5.5.4 Pass information gathered during survey and monitoring of this moth to a central database for incorporation in national and international databases. (ACTION: EN)

5.5.5 Encourage research on the status, autecology, conservation and genetics of this species throughout its international range and share the results to further its conservation. (ACTION: EN, JNCC)

5.6 Communications and publicity

5.6.1 Promote opportunities for the appreciation of this species and the conservation issues associated with its habitat. This should be achieved through articles within appropriate journals, as well as by a publicity leaflet. (ACTION: EN)

5.7 Links with other action plans

5.7.1 This plan should be considered in conjunction with that for lowland heathland.

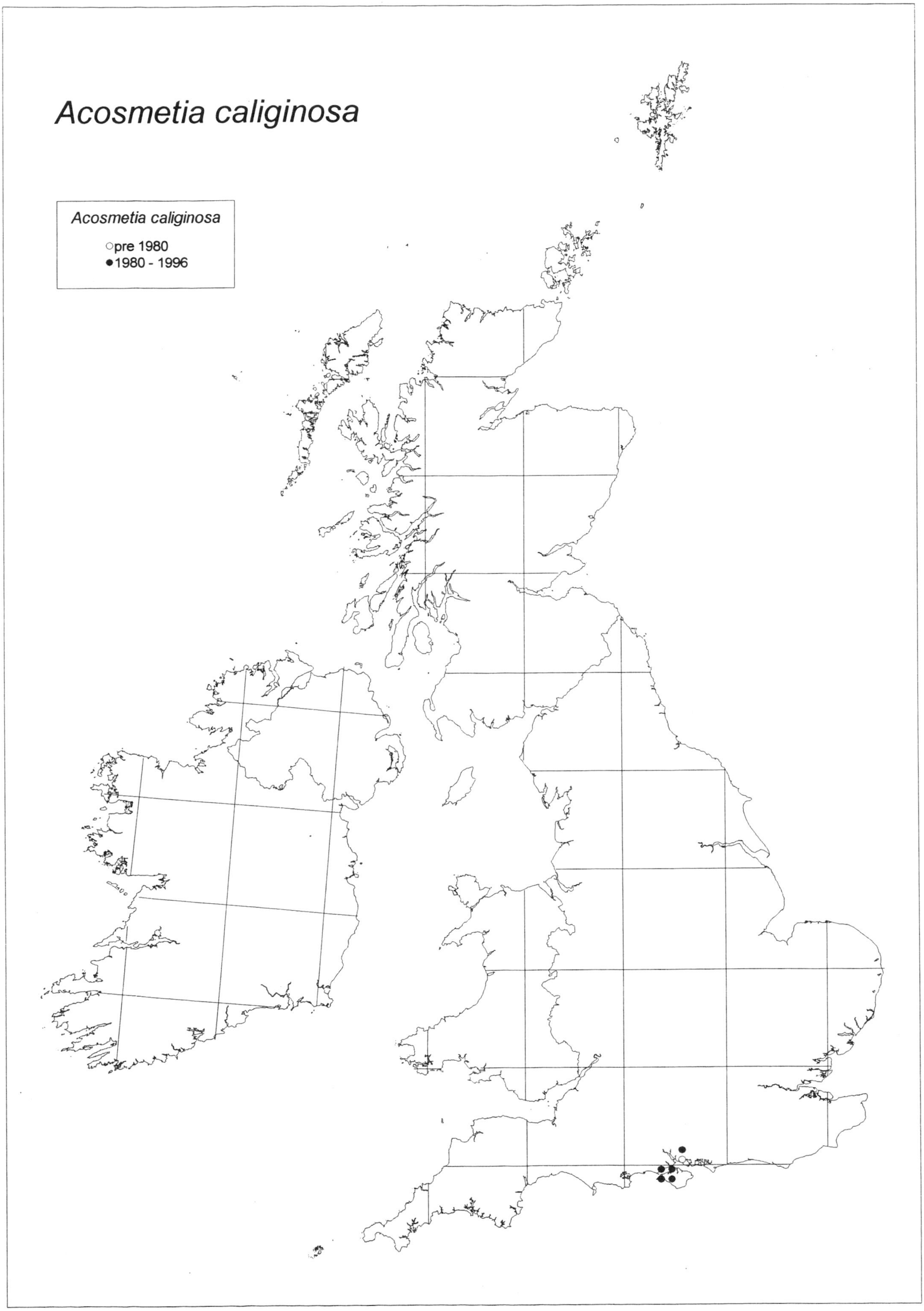

Distribution of Acosmetia caliginosa - reddish buff in Britain, by 10km square.
Source: P. Waring - Joint Nature Conservation Committee/Butterfly Conservation Rare Moth Project.

Straw belle (*Aspitates gilvaria*)
Action Plan

1. Current status

1.1 The straw belle is a moth of chalk grasslands, where the larva feeds on various low-growing herbs.

1.2 The moth has declined severely and is now confined to small fragments of the North Downs of Surrey and Kent. Formerly the moth has been reported from Devon, Somerset, Gloucestershire, Hampshire, the Isle of Wight, Sussex, Middlesex and Cheshire. Some of these records are of suspected migrants, but others are of colonies which are now extinct. This moth has been recorded locally from most of the countries in Europe, but it reaches its northern limit in Fenno-Scandia. Its range extends across Asia to Mongolia.

1.3 In Great Britain this species is classified as *Rare*.

2. Current factors causing loss or decline

2.1 Habitat loss due to road construction, development, and agricultural improvement of unimproved calcareous grassland.

2.2 Inappropriate grazing management.

2.3 Accidental and deliberate burning of grasslands supporting this species.

3. Current action

3.1 Most remaining sites are on SSSIs.

4. Action plan objectives and targets

4.1 Maintain all existing populations.

4.2 Restore five populations within its former range by 2005.

5. Proposed action with lead agencies

The objectives of the plan will be achieved by encouraging beneficial land management on existing sites, surveying all available habitat for undiscovered populations, and restoring a network of habitat (if necessary with introductions of the species) to combat potential isolation effects. Research should focus on the ecological requirements of the species, monitoring the effects of habitat management designed to meet these needs, and detection of any changes in the population which may be due to isolation.

5.1 Policy and legislation

5.1.1 Where appropriate, include the requirements of the species when preparing or revising prescriptions for agri-environment schemes. (ACTION: EN, MAFF)

5.2 Site safeguard and management

5.2.1 Ensure that all occupied habitat is appropriately managed by the year 2005, for example through SSSI or agri-environment scheme management agreements. (ACTION: EN, MAFF)

5.2.2 Ensure that the habitat requirements of the straw belle are taken into account in relevant development policies, plans and proposals. (ACTION: LAs)

5.2.3 Encourage an increase in suitable habitat on occupied sites and attempt to link up existing fragments by restoring sites throughout the former range of the moth. (ACTION: EN)

5.2.4 Ensure that the straw belle is included in site management documents for all relevant SSSIs. (ACTION: EN)

5.2.5 Consider notification of breeding sites as SSSIs, where this is considered necessary to secure their long-term protection and appropriate management. (ACTION: EN)

5.3 Species management and protection

5.3.1 Consider (re)introducing to a series of sites within the former range if necessary to restore five populations by 2005. (ACTION: EN)

5.4 Advisory

5.4.1 Advise landowners and managers of the presence of the species and the importance of beneficial management for its conservation. (ACTION: EN, MAFF)

5.4.2 As far as possible, ensure that all relevant agri-environment project officers, and members of regional agri-environment consultation groups, are advised of locations of this species, its importance and the management needed for its conservation. (ACTION: EN, MAFF)

5.5 Future research and monitoring

5.5.1 Undertake surveys of occupied and potential sites by 2005. (ACTION: EN)

5.5.2 Conduct autecological research to determine the precise habitat requirements of the species by 2005. (ACTION: EN)

5.5.3 Establish a regular monitoring programme for the species. (ACTION: EN)

5.5.4 Pass information gathered during survey and monitoring of this species to a central database for incorporation in national and international databases. (ACTION: EN)

5.6 Communications and publicity

5.6.1 Promote opportunities for the appreciation of this species and the conservation issues associated with its habitat. This should be achieved through articles within appropriate journals, as well as by a publicity leaflet. (ACTION: EN)

5.7 Links with other action plans

5.7.1 This action plan should be considered in conjunction with that for lowland calcareous grassland.

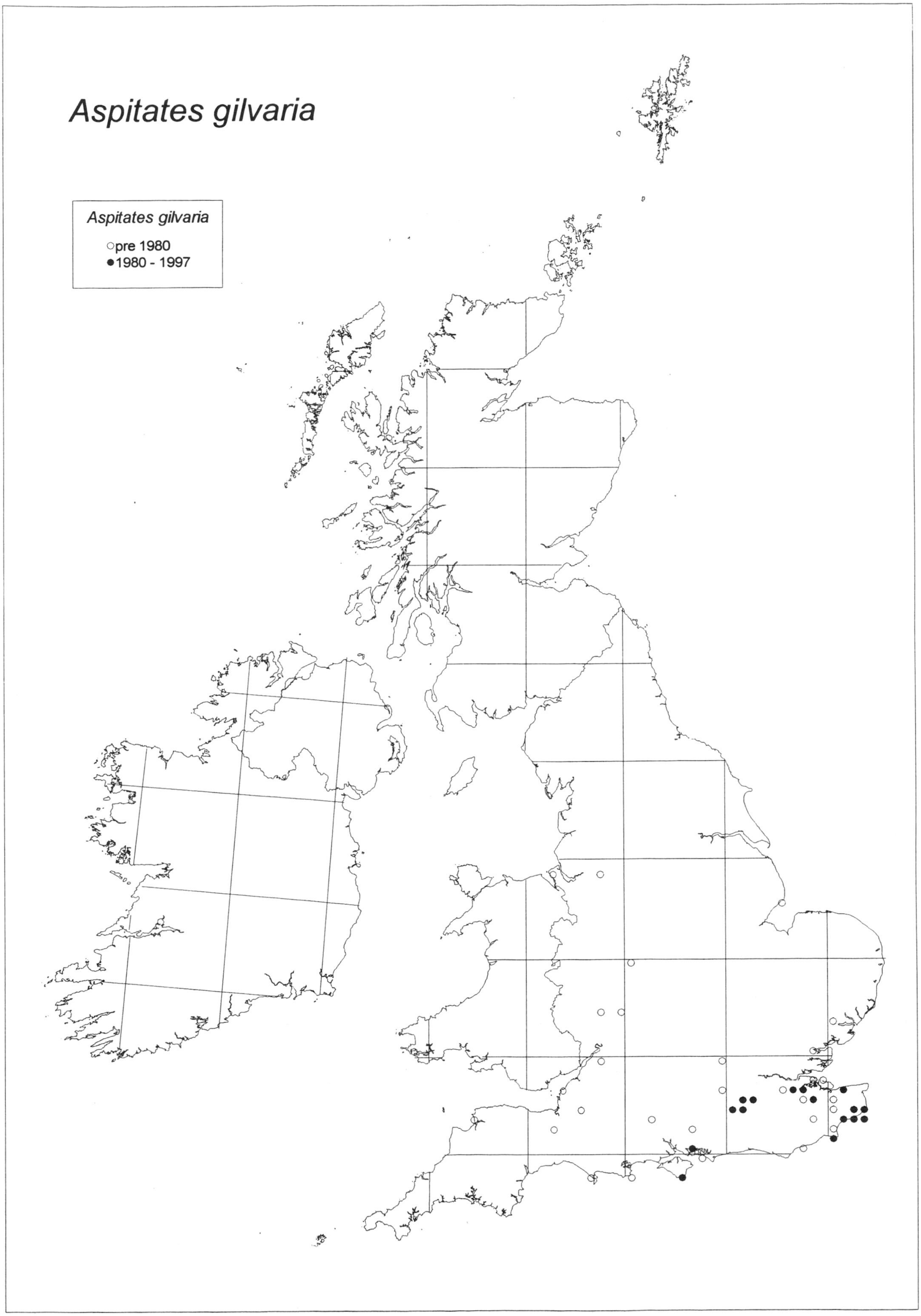

Distribution of Aspitates gilvaria - straw belle in Britain, by 10km square.
Source: P. Waring - Joint Nature Conservation Committee/Butterfly Conservation Rare Moth Project.

Marsh moth (*Athetis pallustris*) Action Plan

1. Current status

1.1 The marsh moth is a species of unimproved grassland on frequently waterlogged ground. The larvae feed on plantains *Plantago* spp.

1.2 Formerly there were populations of the marsh moth in Huntingdonshire, Cambridgeshire, Norfolk, Suffolk, Yorkshire and Cumbria, with a single record in Hampshire, but the moth has not been seen in any of these counties since 1970. It is now confined to the coastal belt of Lincolnshire where it occurs on two nature reserves and possibly two additional sites. This moth has been reported as local from most European countries from Spain to the Balkans, and reaches its northern limit at the Arctic circle in Lapland. Its range extends to southern Russia, the Urals, Siberia and Mongolia.

1.3 In Great Britain this species is classified as *Rare*.

2. Current factors causing loss or decline

2.1 Changes in land use including drainage and development.

2.2 Heavy grazing.

3. Current action

3.1 Both of the main populations are on SSSIs which are also nature reserves.

3.2 There is a Species Recovery Project at one of the Lincolnshire sites which is jointly funded by EN and the Lincolnshire Trust for Nature Conservation.

4. Action plan objectives and targets

4.1 Maintain populations at all known sites.

4.2 Enhance the population size at all known sites by 2010.

4.3 Restore a self-sustaining population to at least one site (Woodwalton Fen) by 2010.

4.4 Establish an *ex situ* programme to provide material for ecological research and, where necessary, for introduction to suitable sites.

5. Proposed action with lead agencies

The objectives of the plan will be achieved by encouraging beneficial land management on existing sites, surveying all available habitat for undiscovered populations and restoring a network of habitat, if necessary with introductions of the species, to combat potential isolation effects. Research should focus on the ecological requirements of the species, monitoring the effects of habitat management designed to meet these needs, and detection of any changes in the population which may be due to isolation.

5.1 Policy and legislation

5.1.1 Where appropriate, include the requirements of the species when preparing or revising prescriptions for agri-environment schemes. (ACTION: EN, MAFF)

5.2 Site safeguard and management

5.2.1 Ensure that all occupied and nearby potential habitat is appropriately managed by the year 2005, for example through uptake of agri-environment schemes. (ACTION: EN, MAFF)

5.2.2 Ensure that the habitat requirements of the marsh moth are taken into account in relevant development policies, plans and proposals. (ACTION: LAs)

5.2.3 Where possible, increase the available habitat on known sites and in adjacent sites, and attempt to link up existing fragments of habitat. (ACTION: EN)

5.2.4 Ensure that the marsh moth is included in site management documents for all relevant SSSIs. (ACTION: EN)

5.3 Species management and protection

5.3.1 Undertake an establishment trial at Woodwalton Fen. (ACTION: EN)

5.3.2 Consider the advisability of establishment trials elsewhere in the Huntingdonshire and Cambridgeshire fens, once former sites have been adequately surveyed, and provided that the causes of loss are no longer operating. (ACTION: EN)

5.4 Advisory

5.4.1 Advise landowners and managers of the presence of the species and the importance of beneficial management for its conservation. (ACTION: EN)

5.5 Future research and monitoring

5.5.1 Undertake surveys to determine the status of this species. (ACTION: EN)

5.5.2 Conduct targeted autecological research to inform habitat management. (ACTION: EN)

5.5.3 Establish a monitoring programme for the species on all occupied sites by 2005. (ACTION: EN)

5.5.4 Regularly assess potential sites to monitor the effectiveness of management agreements. (ACTION: EN)

5.5.5 Pass information gathered during survey and monitoring of this species to a central database for incorporation in national and international databases. (ACTION: EN)

5.6 Communications and publicity

5.6.1 Promote opportunities for the appreciation of this species and the conservation issues associated with its habitat. This should be achieved through articles within appropriate journals, as well as by a publicity leaflet. (ACTION: EN)

5.7 Links with other action plans

5.7.1 This action plan should be considered in conjunction with that for coastal and floodplain grazing marsh.

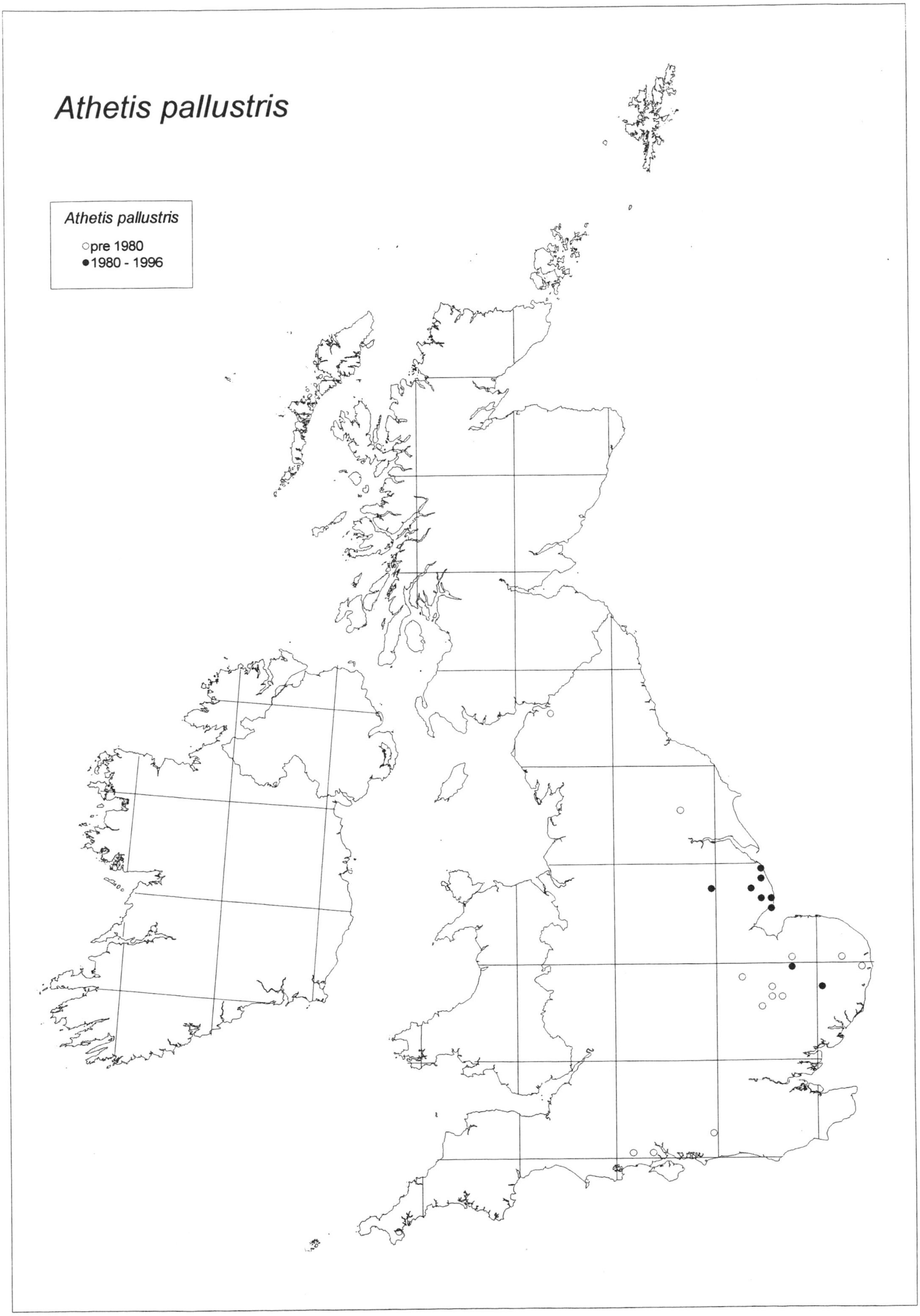

Distribution of Athetis pallustris - marsh moth in Britain, by 10km square.
Source: P. Warring - Joint Nature Conservation Committee/Butterfly Conservation Rare Moth Project.

Fiery clearwing (*Bembecia chrysidiformis*) Action Plan

1. Current status

1.1 The fiery clearwing is restricted to warm south-facing slopes where the larvae feed in the roots of curled dock *Rumex crispus* and common sorrel *R. acetosa*, probably preferring larger, older plants. The adults visit flowers by day and rest on bare soil.

1.2 This moth is at the northern edge of its range and currently breeds only on the coast between Folkestone and Dover in Kent. It was formerly found in Essex (until about 1860), Hampshire and Sussex, with occasional records elsewhere on the south coast. It is a central and southern species in Europe, occurring from the Mediterranean countries north to Belgium.

1.3 In Great Britain this species is classified as *Endangered*. It is given full protection under Schedule 5 of the Wildlife and Countryside Act 1981.

2. Current factors causing loss or decline

2.1 Collecting, chiefly by uprooting the foodplant, is a major cause of decline of the remaining population.

2.2 Scrub invasion.

2.3 Spraying, cutting and clearance of stands of the foodplants.

3. Current action

3.1 The moth has been the subject of an EN Species Recovery Project since 1995.

4. Action plan objectives and targets

4.1 Maintain populations at all known sites.

4.2 Enhance the population size at all known sites by 2010.

5. Proposed action with lead agencies

The objectives of the plan will be achieved by encouraging beneficial land management on existing sites, surveying all available habitat for undiscovered populations, and restoring a network of habitat to combat potential isolation effects. Research should focus on the ecological requirements of the species, monitoring the effects of habitat management designed to meet these needs, and detection of any changes in the population which may be due to isolation.

5.1 Policy and legislation

5.1.1 Where appropriate, include the requirements of the species when preparing or revising prescriptions for environment schemes. (ACTION: EN, MAFF)

5.1.2 Address the requirements of the fiery clearwing in relevant Shoreline Management Plans. (ACTION: LAs, MAFF)

5.2 Site safeguard and management

5.2.1 Increase the available habitat on the known sites and in adjacent sites, and attempt to link up existing fragments of habitat. (ACTION: EN)

5.2.2 Where possible, ensure that all occupied and potential nearby habitat is appropriately managed by 2001, for example through agri-environment scheme management agreements. (ACTION: EN, MAFF)

5.2.3 Ensure that the habitat requirements of the fiery clearwing are taken into account in relevant development policies, plans and proposals. (ACTION: LAs)

5.2.4 Ensure that existing populations do not become fragmented by management practices or development. (ACTION: EN, LAs)

5.3 Species management and protection

5.3.1 None proposed.

5.4 Advisory

5.4.1 Advise landowners and managers of the presence of the species and the importance of beneficial management for its conservation. (ACTION: EN)

5.5 Future research and monitoring

5.5.1 Map the precise areas of occupancy of the fiery clearwing and monitor the populations annually. (ACTION: EN)

5.5.2 Investigate all new records of the species occurrence within the UK and all reports of potentially suitable habitat to locate any overlooked colonies of the moth. (ACTION: EN)

5.5.3 Regularly assess potential sites to monitor the effectiveness of management agreements. (ACTION: EN)

5.5.4 Conduct targeted autecological research to inform habitat management. (ACTION: EN)

5.5.5 Pass information gathered during survey and monitoring of this species to a central database for incorporation in national and international databases. (ACTION: EN)

5.5.6 Encourage research on the ecology and conservation of this species on an international level, and use the experience gained towards its conservation in the UK. (ACTION: EN, JNCC)

5.6 Communications and publicity

5.6.1 Promote opportunities for the appreciation of the species and the conservation issues associated with its habitat. The need to protect species such as the fiery clearwing from irresponsible collecting should be emphasised. This should be achieved through articles within appropriate journals, as well as by a publicity leaflet. (ACTION: EN)

5.7 Links with other action plans

5.7.1 This action plan should be considered in conjunction with that for maritime cliffs and slopes.

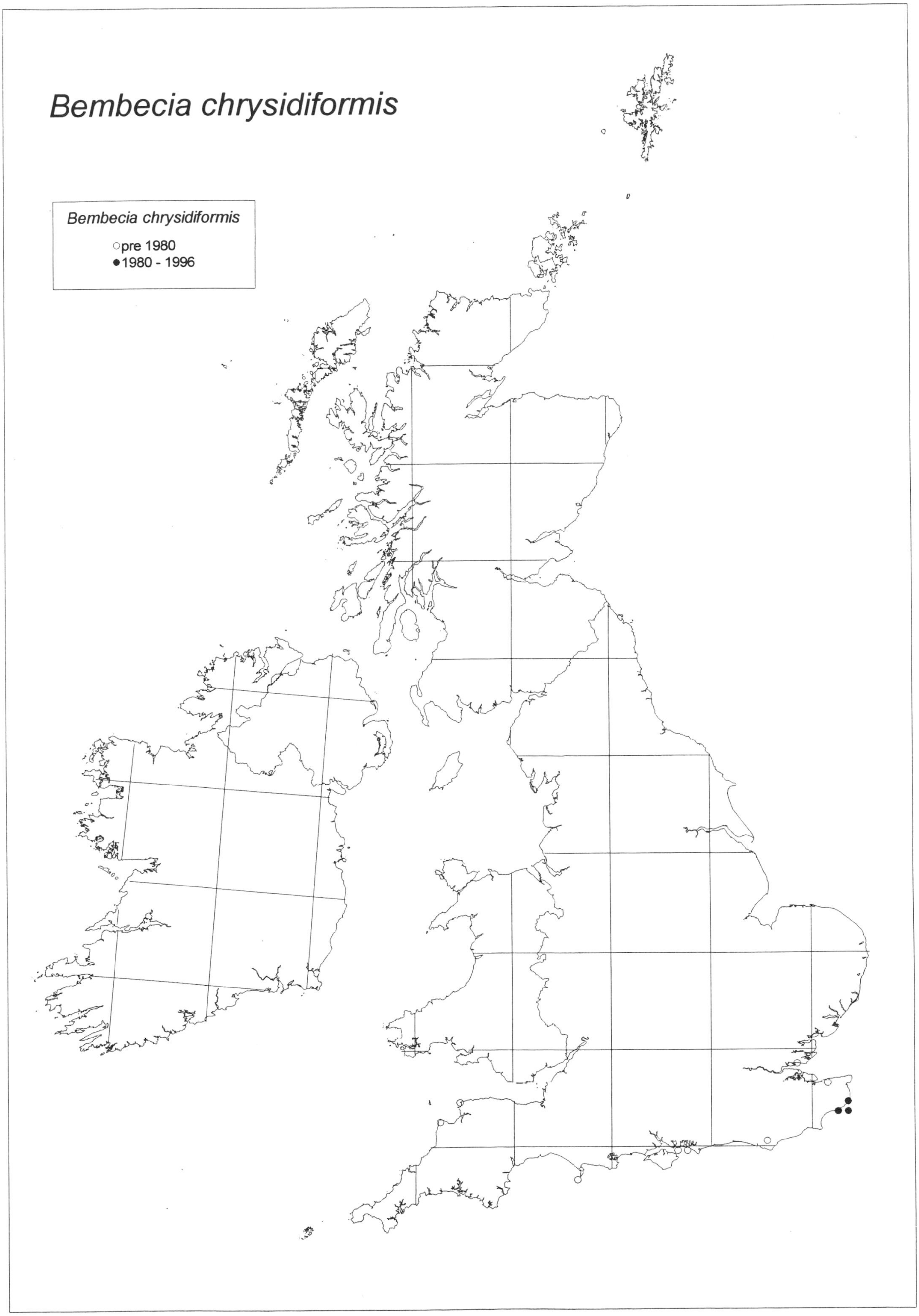

Distribution of Bembecia chrysidiformis - fiery clearwing in Britain, by 10km square.
Source: P. Waring - Joint Nature Conservation Committee/Butterfly Conservation Rare Moth Project.

Chequered skipper (*Carterocephalus palaemon*) Action Plan

1. Current status

1.1 In Scotland, the chequered skipper is primarily a species of woodland edge and scrub. It occurs in areas of lightly grazed or ungrazed grassland, scrub and marsh around open broadleaved woodland, on wet but well-aerated soils. These areas are dominated by the larval foodplant, purple moor-grass. Nectaring occurs in glades with bluebells and bugle. Males defend territories, usually located in warm, sheltered areas. Females may move several kilometres and can be widely scattered towards the end of the flight period.

1.2 The chequered skipper is a boreal species that occurs across Europe, Asia and North America. It is declining in several European countries and is extinct in Denmark. It is endangered in some countries outside Europe (eg Japan). In England the chequered skipper was once fairly common in the East Midlands, but it became extinct there in the 1970s. The British populations are now restricted to about 50 sites in a small area of western Scotland. The known history of the species in Scotland is short as it was not documented here until 1942.

1.3 In Great Britain the chequered skipper is classified as *Out of Danger*. It is protected under Schedule 5 of the Wildlife and Countryside Act 1981, with respect to sale only.

2. Current factors causing loss or decline

2.1 Inappropriate grazing management of wood pasture.

2.2 Loss of open areas within woodland.

3. Current action

3.1 Many populations are on SSSIs or NNRs. One colony is on a Scottish Wildlife Trust Reserve.

3.2 Three populations of the chequered skipper in Scotland are monitored as a part of the National Butterfly Monitoring Scheme.

3.3 A species action plan, grant-aided by EN, CCW, SNH and WWF, was published by Butterfly Conservation in 1996.

3.4 Butterfly Conservation has produced a comprehensive site inventory, identifying 10 core areas in Scotland.

3.5 A booklet describing conservation measures for the species was published jointly by Butterfly Conservation and SNH in 1996.

3.6 Butterfly Conservation initiated a reintroduction in England in 1995, in collaboration with FE, EN, the University of Birmingham, and the French and Belgian authorities.

4. Action plan objectives and targets

4.1 Maintain populations at all known sites.

4.2 Restore a viable population in England by 2005.

4.3 If suitable habitat can be restored, re-establish a further five populations in England by 2010.

5. Proposed action with lead agencies

In Scotland there will need to be regular surveys of all populations and monitoring of adult numbers on key sites. Beneficial management will be needed on key sites, including sites associated with commercial activities such as forestry plantations. Research is needed on the responses of populations to management of the woodland sites where it occurs. In England the objectives will be achieved by continuing the re-establishment programme with appropriate monitoring and research. Opportunities for re-establishing viable populations in England are limited by lack of suitable habitat in its former sites.

5.1 Policy and legislation

5.1.1 Take account of the requirements of the chequered skipper when considering grant applications (eg Woodland Grant Scheme, Countryside Premium Scheme, Farm Woodland Premium Scheme) for woodland planting, natural regeneration, and changes in grazing on or near chequered skipper sites. (ACTION: FC, SNH, SOAEFD)

5.1.2 Encourage financial incentives for coppice restoration and beneficial woodland management in the recent former range in the East Midlands. (ACTION: EN, FC)

5.2 Site safeguard and management

5.2.1 Discourage detrimental development proposals affecting known breeding areas. (ACTION: LAs, SNH)

5.2.2 In areas with populations of the butterfly, encourage positive management of forestry plantations and wayleaves associated with broadleaved woodland and incorporate requirements of the chequered skipper into Forest Design Plans and other management plans. (ACTION: FC, SNH)

5.2.3 Where possible, increase the available habitat at known sites and adjacent areas, and attempt to link up existing fragments of habitat. (ACTION: FC, SNH)

5.2.4 Where there is realistic potential for re-establishment of this butterfly, promote restoration of potential habitats in the former range in England. (ACTION: EN, FC)

5.2.5 Ensure that the butterfly is included in site management documents for all relevant SSSIs and NNRs. (ACTION: SNH)

5.2.6 Consider notifying as SSSIs sites supporting viable populations of the chequered skipper, where this is necessary to secure their long-term protection and appropriate management. (ACTION: SNH)

5.3 Species management and protection

5.3.1 Continue the re-establishment programme at the FE site in eastern England, with monitoring of the butterfly and its habitat. (ACTION: EN, FE)

5.3.2 If suitable, appropriately managed, extensive habitats can be found or restored, conduct five further strategic reintroductions to England. (ACTION: EN, FC)

5.3.3 Discourage collection of chequered skippers at all sites. (ACTION: EN, FE, SNH)

5.4 Advisory

5.4.1 Advise landowners and managers of the presence of this butterfly and the importance of beneficial management for its conservation. (ACTION: EN, FC, SNH).

5.5 Future research and monitoring

5.5.1 Monitor key populations in Scotland, either by standard transects or timed counts, and collate data annually to compare trends with changes in site condition. (ACTION: SNH)

5.5.2 Undertake regular surveys in Scotland to confirm the status of all known breeding areas and to confirm the range of the species. (ACTION: SNH)

5.5.3 Conduct targeted autecological research to inform habitat management. (ACTION: EN, FC, SNH)

5.5.4 Pass information gathered during survey and monitoring of this species to a central database for incorporation into national and international databases. (ACTION: EN, SNH)

5.6 Communications and publicity

5.6.1 Promote opportunities for the appreciation of the chequered skipper and the conservation issues associated with its habitat. This should be achieved through articles within appropriate journals, as well as by publicity leaflets. (ACTION: EN, FC, SNH)

5.7 Links with other action plans

5.7.1 Implementation of this action plan could benefit other species of the habitat, including the pearl-bordered fritillary *Boloria euphrosyne*.

5.7.2 This plan should be considered in conjunction with those for purple moor-grass and rush pastures, and upland oak woods.

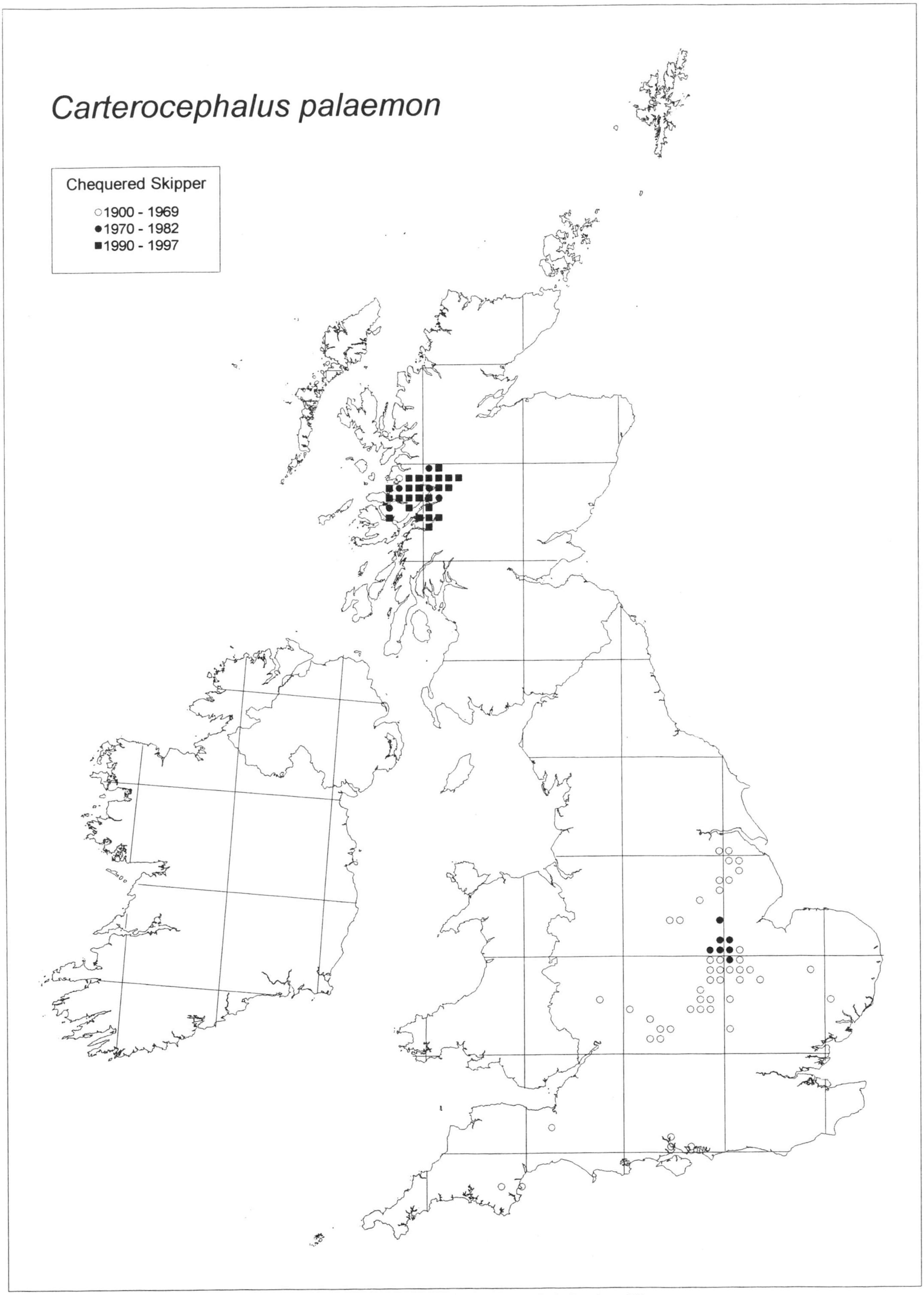

Distribution of Carterocephalus palaemon - Chequered Skipper in Britain, by 10km ssquare.
Source: Buttefly Conservation and Biological Records Centre (ITE). The 1990 - 1997 records are provisional data from the ongoing Butterflies for the New Millennium project. The Chequered Skipper has been extinct in England since 1975.

Light crimson underwing (*Catocala promissa*) Action Plan

1. Current status

1.1 The light crimson underwing requires large areas of mature oak woodland. The larva is dependent on oak (*Quercus* spp).

1.2 This moth is now confined to the New Forest and two large woodlands in north Hampshire and south Wiltshire. Formerly there were populations northwards to Buckinghamshire and eastwards to Huntingdonshire and Sussex, some surviving into the 1950s or later. The moth has been reported from every country in Europe except Ireland, Malta and Albania. It is locally widespread in southern and central Europe, becoming increasingly local and rare northwards. Its range extends eastwards to Siberia and southwards to Iran and North Africa.

1.3 In Great Britain this species is classified as *Rare*.

2. Current factors causing loss or decline

2.1 The felling of large stands of mature oak, which is damaging even when replanting with oak.

2.2 Replanting woodland with species other than oak, and the fragmentation of large blocks of oak woodland.

3. Current action

3.1 Almost all of the surviving colonies are within the New Forest boundary or on nearby SSSIs. The New Forest is a candidate SAC.

4. Action plan objectives and targets

4.1 Maintain populations at all known sites.

4.2 Enhance the population size at all known sites by 2010.

4.3 Initiate restoration of populations to three suitable sites within the historic range by 2010.

5. Proposed action with lead agencies

The objectives of the plan will be achieved by encouraging beneficial land management on existing sites, surveying all available habitat for undiscovered populations, and restoring a network of habitat, if necessary with introductions of the species, to combat potential isolation effects. Progress towards the restoration of populations may be limited by the rate of tree growth at the sites chosen. Research will focus on the ecological requirements of the species, monitoring the effects of habitat management designed to meet these needs, and detection of any changes in the population which may be due to isolation.

5.1 Policy and legislation

5.1.1 Where appropriate, include the requirements of the species when preparing or revising prescriptions for agri-environment (farm woodland) and woodland grant schemes. (ACTION: EN, FC, MAFF)

5.2 Site safeguard and management

5.2.1 Where possible, ensure that all occupied and nearby potential habitat is appropriately managed by 2005, for example through SSSI or agri-environment/woodland grant scheme management agreements. (ACTION: EN, FC, MAFF)

5.2.2 Ensure that existing populations do not become fragmented by management practices or development. (ACTION: EN)

5.2.3 Increase the available habitat on the known sites and in adjacent woodland, and attempt to link up existing fragments of habitat, for example by replanting with oaks. (ACTION: EN, FE)

5.2.4 Ensure that the habitat requirements of the species are taken into account in relevant development policies, plans and proposals. (ACTION: LAs)

5.2.5 Ensure that the light crimson underwing is included in site management documents for all relevant SSSIs. (ACTION: EN)

5.3 Species management and protection

5.3.1 Undertake reintroductions into suitably restored former sites in South East and central England by 2010. (ACTION: EN)

5.4 Advisory

5.4.1 Advise landowners and managers of the presence of the species and the importance of beneficial management for its conservation. (ACTION: EN)

5.5 Future research and monitoring

5.5.1 Undertake surveys to determine the status of the species. (ACTION: EN)

5.5.2 Conduct targeted autecological research to establish the requirements necessary to maintain viable populations of the light crimson underwing in the long term. (ACTION: EN)

5.5.3 Establish a regular monitoring programme for the species. (ACTION: EN)

5.5.4 Pass information gathered during survey and monitoring of this species to a central database for incorporation in national and international databases. (ACTION: EN)

5.6 Communications and publicity

5.6.1 Promote opportunities for the appreciation of this species and the conservation issues associated with its habitat. This should be achieved through articles within appropriate journals, as well as by a publicity leaflet. (ACTION: EN)

5.7 Links with other action plans

5.7.1 Implementation of this action plan could benefit other species of lowland oak woodlands, including the dark crimson underwing *Catocala sponsa*.

5.7.2 This plan should be considered in conjunction with that for lowland wood pastures and parklands.

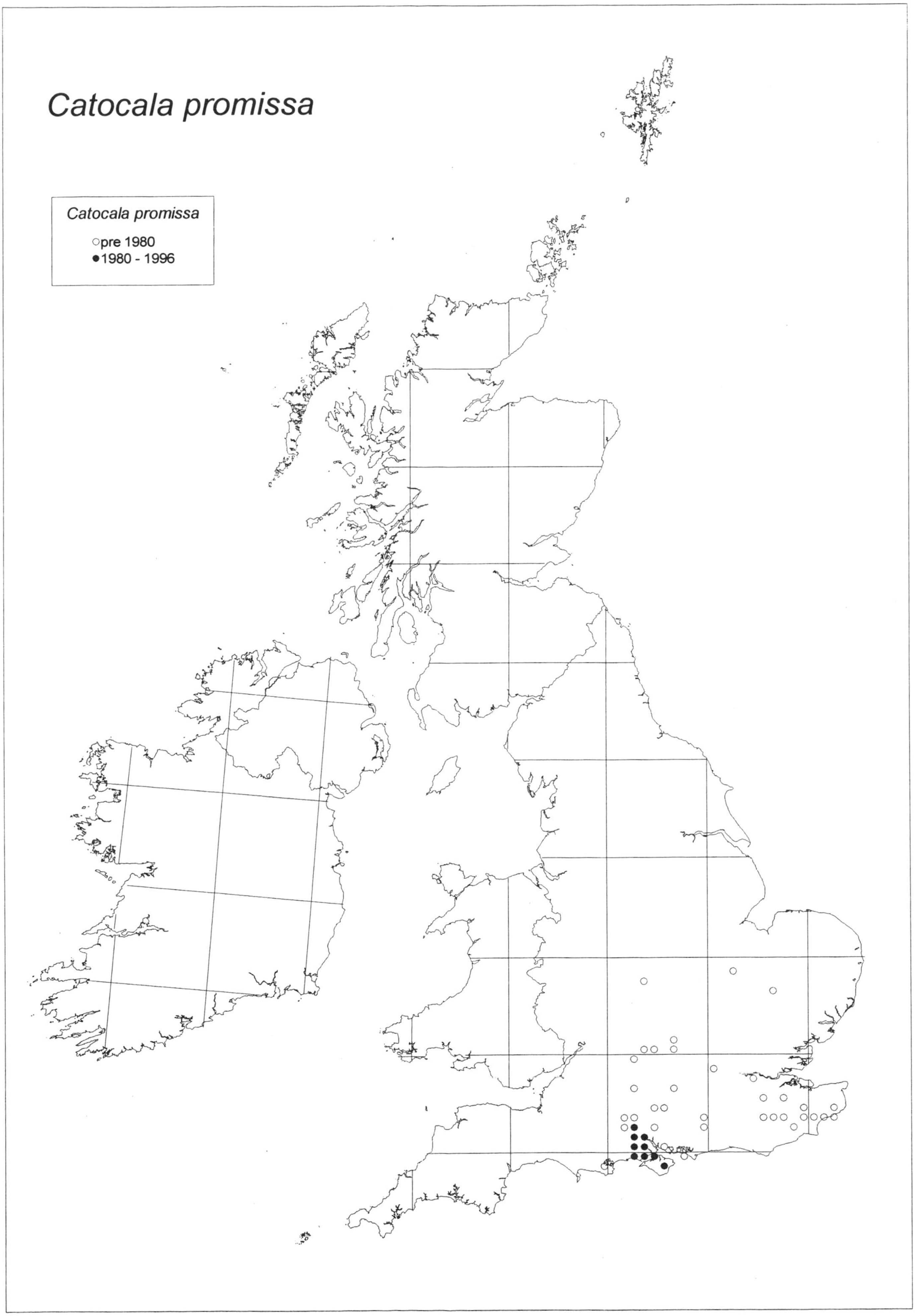

Distribution of Catocala promissa - light crimson underwing in Britain, by 10km square.
Source: P. Waring - Joint Nature Conservation Committee/Butterfly Conservation Rare Moth Project.

Dark crimson underwing (*Catocala sponsa*) Action Plan

1. Current status

1.1 The dark crimson underwing requires large areas of mature oak woodland. The larva is dependent on oak *Quercus* spp.

1.2 The dark crimson underwing is confined as a breeding species to the New Forest, Hampshire. Formerly there were colonies in south Wiltshire (until at least 1949) and the London area (in the 19th century). The species declined in the New Forest in the 1970s, but there was some resurgence in the mid 1980s and in 1995. Long-term fluctuations in the abundance of this species have been noted in the past. This moth has been recorded in virtually every country in Europe, but is often local and sometimes rare. It reaches Siberia in the north and occurs south to North Africa.

1.3 In Great Britain this species is classified as *Rare*.

2. Current factors causing loss or decline

2.1 The felling of large stands of mature oak, which is damaging even when replanting with oak.

2.2 Replanting woodland with species other than oak, and the fragmentation of large blocks of oak woodland.

3. Current action

3.1 The surviving colonies are on SSSIs within the New Forest. The New Forest is a candidate SAC.

4. Action plan objectives and targets

4.1 Maintain populations at all known sites.

4.2 Enhance the population size at all known sites by 2010.

4.3 Restore populations to two additional sites within the historic range by 2010.

5. Proposed action with lead agencies

The objectives of the plan will be achieved by encouraging beneficial land management on existing sites, surveying all available habitat for undiscovered populations, and restoring a network of habitat, if necessary with introductions of the species, to combat potential isolation effects. Research should focus on the ecological requirements of the species, monitoring the effects of habitat management designed to meet these needs, and detection of any changes in the population which may be due to isolation.

5.1 Policy and legislation

5.1.1 Where appropriate, include the requirements of the species when preparing or revising prescriptions for woodland grant schemes. (ACTION: EN, FC)

5.2 Site safeguard and management

5.2.1 Where possible, ensure that all occupied and potential nearby habitat is appropriately managed by 2005, for example through site management agreements. (ACTION: EN)

5.2.2 Increase the available habitat on the known sites and in adjacent woodland, and attempt to link up existing fragments of habitat, for example by replanting with oaks. (ACTION: EN, FE)

5.2.3 Ensure that the habitat requirements of the species are taken into account in relevant development policies, plans and proposals, ensuring in particular that existing populations do not become fragmented. (ACTION: LAs)

5.2.4 Ensure that the dark crimson underwing moth is included in site management documents on all relevant SSSIs. (ACTION: EN)

5.3 Species management and protection

5.3.1 Reintroduce the dark crimson underwing to two former sites by 2010. (ACTION: EN)

5.4 Advisory

5.4.1 Advise landowners and managers of the presence of the species and the importance of beneficial management for its conservation. (ACTION: EN)

5.5 Future research and monitoring

5.5.1 Undertake surveys to determine the status of the species. (ACTION: EN)

5.5.2 Conduct targeted autecological research to discover the species' precise requirements, particularly the minimum area of habitat required to maintain populations in the long term. (ACTION: EN)

5.5.3 Establish a regular monitoring programme for the species on all its known sites, including an assessment of potential sites, to monitor the effectiveness of management agreements. (ACTION: EN)

5.5.4 Pass information gathered during survey and monitoring of this species to a central database for incorporation in national and international databases. (ACTION: EN)

5.5.5 Encourage research on the ecology and conservation of this species on an international level, and use the experience gained towards its conservation in the UK. (ACTION: EN, JNCC)

5.6 Communications and publicity

5.6.1 Promote opportunities for the appreciation of this species and the conservation issues associated with its habitat. This should be achieved through articles within appropriate journals, as well as by a publicity leaflet. (ACTION: EN)

5.7 Links with other action plans

5.7.1 Implementation of this action plan could benefit other species of lowland oak woodlands, including the light crimson underwing *Catocala promissa*.

5.7.2 This plan should be considered in conjunction with that for the lowland wood pastures and parklands.

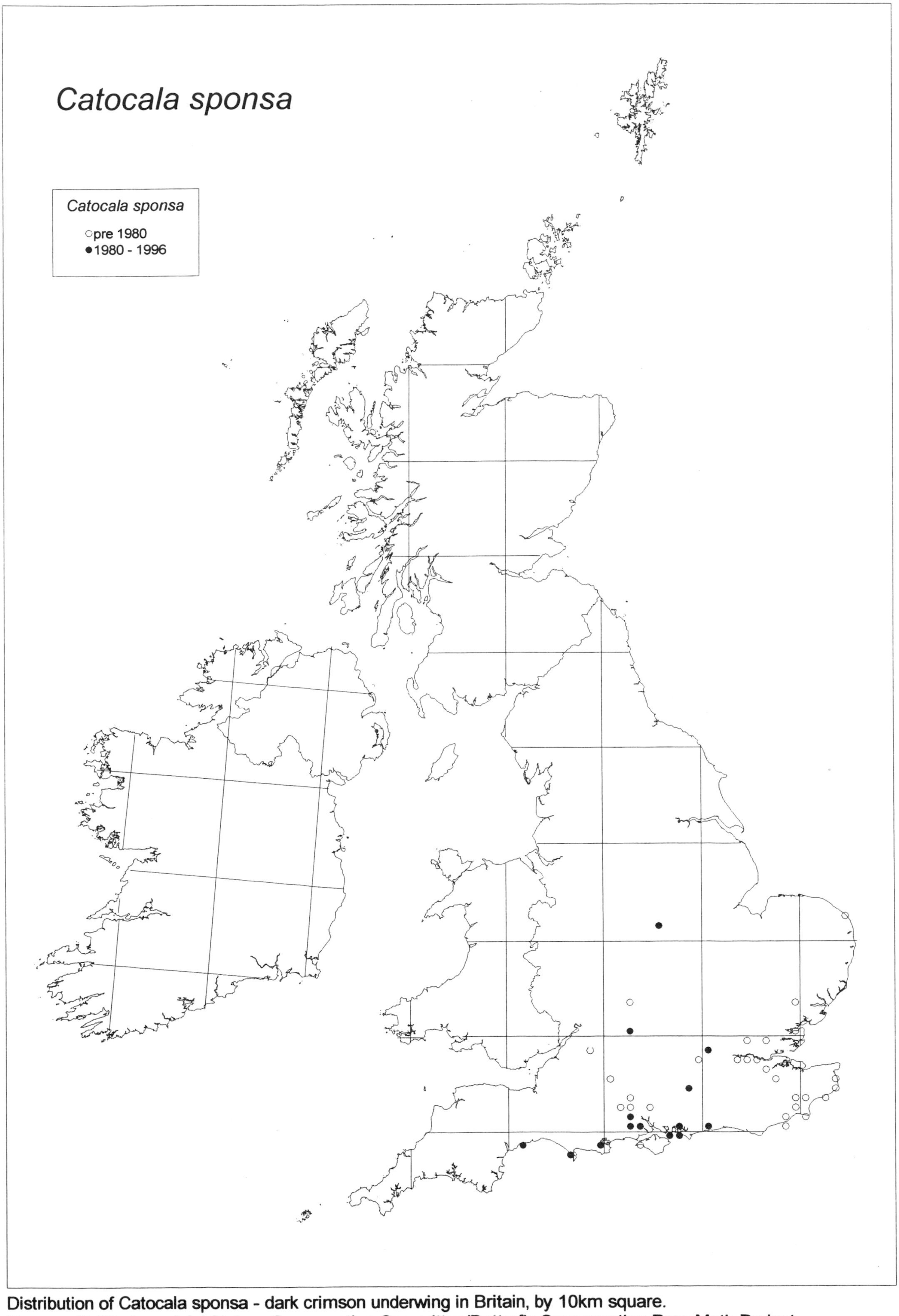

Distribution of Catocala sponsa - dark crimson underwing in Britain, by 10km square.
Source: P. Waring - Joint Nature Conservation Committee/Butterfly Conservation Rare Moth Project.

Basil thyme case-bearer (*Coleophora tricolor*) Action Plan

1. Current status

1.1 The basil thyme case-bearer has been recorded in Britain only from unimproved grassland, including road verges, grazed solely by rabbits. The larvae feed on basil thyme *Acinos arvensis* seedheads in open conditions in early autumn before moving onto grasses on which they overwinter and feed in spring. Adults are on the wing in July and early August. Although there is no direct evidence that this species is in decline, basil thyme has declined in the Brecks and surrounding area. This is thought to be due to a reduction in grazing levels and ground disturbance, particularly that produced by rabbits.

1.2 This species has been recorded only from the Breckland district of Suffolk and Norfolk. Larvae have been recorded at two sites and adults at another. In 1996 the species was recorded in good numbers on a road verge in Suffolk. At one of the sites in Norfolk, owned by the MoD, the moth has not been recorded since the mid 1970s and the habitat there now appears to be unsuitable. Elsewhere in Europe, this species has been recorded at only a single site in Switzerland.

1.3 In Great Britain this species is classified as *Endangered*.

2. Current factors causing loss or decline

2.1 Decline in the abundance of the foodplant due to reductions in grazing intensity, particularly as a result of changes in rabbit populations.

2.2 Loss of unimproved Breck grassland.

3. Current action

3.1 A small number of Breckland sites were surveyed for the species by the Norfolk Moth Survey in 1997.

4. Action plan objectives and targets

4.1 Maintain populations at all known sites.

4.2 Enhance the population size at all known sites by 2010.

4.3 Ensure that 10 viable populations occur within the current range by 2010, using introductions if necessary.

5. Proposed action with lead agencies

The objectives of the plan will be achieved by encouraging beneficial land management on existing sites, surveying all available habitat for undiscovered populations, and restoring a network of habitat (if necessary with introductions of the species) to combat potential isolation effects. Research should focus on the ecological requirements of the species, and monitoring the effects of habitat management designed to meet these needs.

5.1 Policy and legislation

5.1.1 Where appropriate, include the requirements of the species when preparing or revising prescriptions for agri-environment schemes. (ACTION: EN, MAFF)

5.2 Site safeguard and management

5.2.1 Where possible, ensure that all occupied and nearby potential habitat is appropriately managed by 2008. (ACTION: EN, FE, MAFF, MoD)

5.2.2 Ensure that the species is included in site management documents for all relevant SSSIs. (ACTION: EN)

5.2.3 Consider notifying as SSSIs sites holding key populations of the species, where necessary to secure their long-term protection and appropriate management. (ACTION: EN)

5.3 Species management and protection

5.3.1 Introduce the basil thyme case-bearer to a series of sites within the known range, if necessary to achieve 10 viable populations by 2010. (ACTION: EN)

5.4 Advisory

5.4.1 Advise landowners and managers of the presence of the species and the importance of beneficial management for its conservation. (ACTION: EN, MAFF)

5.4.2 As far as possible, ensure that all relevant agri-environment project officers, and members of regional agri-environment consultation groups, are advised of locations of this species, its importance, and the management needed for its conservation. (ACTION: EN, MAFF)

5.5 **Future research and monitoring**

5.5.1 Undertake surveys to determine the status of this species. (ACTION: EN)

5.5.2 Conduct targeted autecological research to inform habitat management. (ACTION: EN)

5.5.3 Establish a regular monitoring programme for the species. (ACTION: EN)

5.5.4 Pass information gathered during survey and monitoring of this species to a central database for incorporation into national and international databases. (ACTION: EN)

5.6 **Communications and publicity**

5.6.1 Promote opportunities for the appreciation of the species and the conservation issues associated with its habitat. This should be achieved through articles within appropriate journals, as well as a publicity leaflet. (ACTION: EN)

5.7 **Links with other action plans**

5.7.1 Implementation of this action plan could benefit other species of Breck grassland, including: starry Breck lichen *Squamarina lentigera*, perennial-knawel *Scleranthus perennis* ssp *prostratus*, the four-spotted moth *Tyta luctuosa*, the ground beetle *Harpalus froehlichi*, and the stone-curlew *Burhinus oedicnemus*.

5.7.2 This plan should be considered in conjunction with those for lowland dry acid grassland and lowland calcareous grassland.

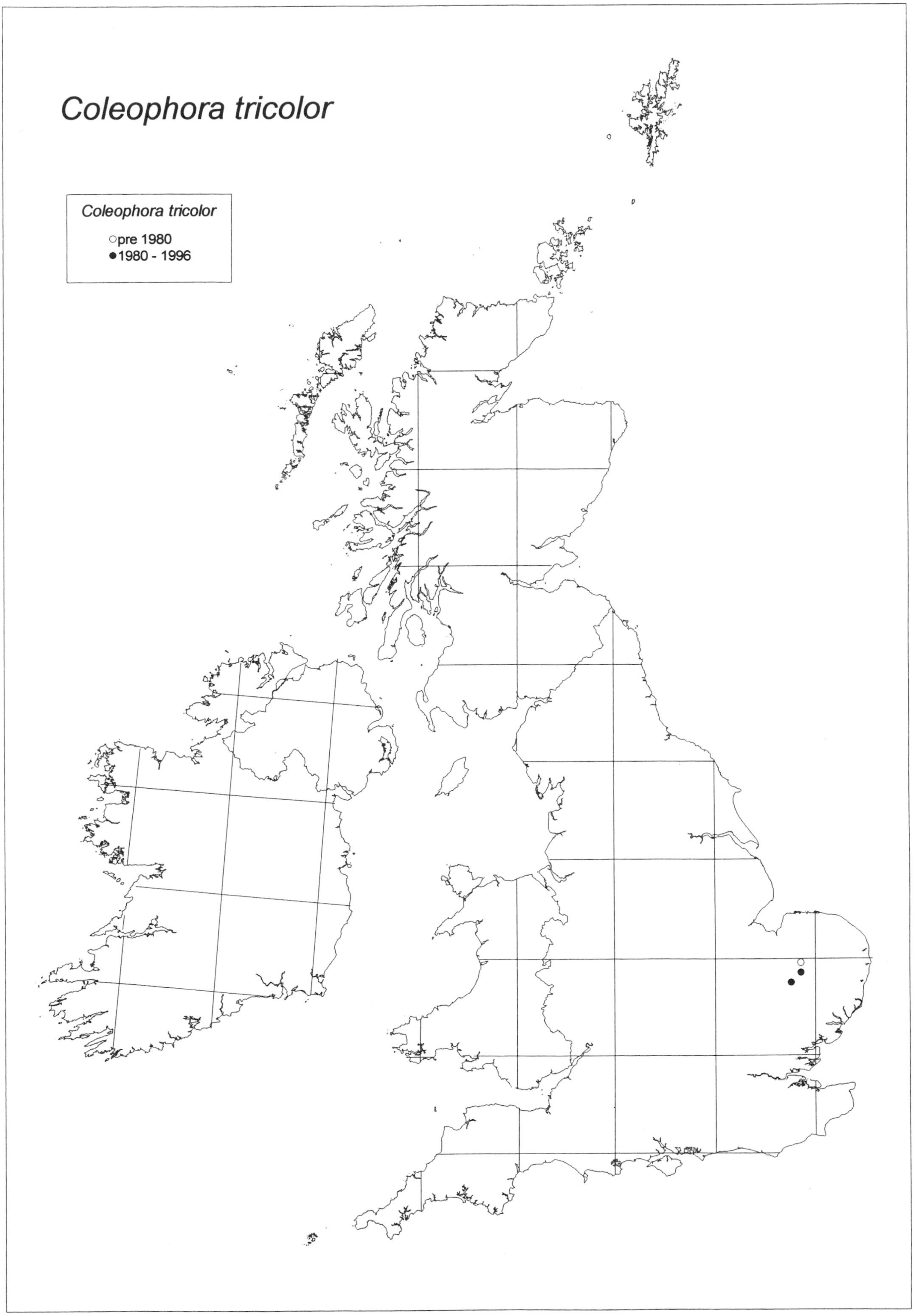

Distribution of Coleophora tricolor - basil thyme case-bearer in Britain, by 10km square.
Source: Butterfly Conservation and English Nature - Invertebrate Site Register.

White-spotted pinion (*Cosmia diffinis*) Action Plan

1. Current status

1.1 The white-spotted pinion is a moth whose larvae feed on the foliage of English elm *Ulmus procera* and wych elm *U. glabra*, possibly preferring the side-shoots (epicormics) of mature trees growing on damp ground.

1.2 This species was widespread and well represented in central and southern England and parts of Wales until the 1970s, since when there has been a massive decline. Huntingdonshire is the only area where it is now reported frequently and in numbers, but occasional records elsewhere indicate that the moth survives at low density in a few other places within its former range. The white-spotted pinion has been recorded from all European countries except Ireland, Norway and Finland, and in many places is local and rare. The range extends at least to Syria in the Middle East.

2. Current factors causing loss or decline

2.1 The white-spotted pinion has declined due to the death of mature elms as a result of Dutch elm disease.

3. Current action

3.1 Some of the surviving colonies of the white-spotted pinion are on SSSIs.

4. Action plan objectives and targets

4.1 Maintain populations at all known sites.

4.2 Enhance populations at all known sites by 2010.

4.3 Restore populations to three suitably managed former localities in England and Wales, using reintroductions if necessary.

5. Proposed action with lead agencies

The objectives of the plan will be achieved by encouraging beneficial land management on existing sites, surveying all available habitat for undiscovered colonies, and restoring a network of habitat, if necessary with strategic reintroductions of the species, to combat potential isolation effects. Research should focus on the ecological requirements of the species, monitoring the effects of habitat management designed to meet these needs, and detection of any changes in the population which may be due to isolation of colonies.

5.1 Policy and legislation

5.1.1 Where appropriate, include the requirements of the species when preparing or revising prescriptions for agri-environment or woodland grant schemes. (ACTION: CCW, EN, FC, MAFF, WOAD)

5.2 Site safeguard and management

5.2.1 Ensure that all occupied and nearby potential habitat is appropriately managed by the year 2005, for example through SSSI or agri-environment/woodland grant scheme management agreements. (ACTION: CCW, EN, FC, MAFF, WOAD)

5.2.2 Increase the available habitat on the known sites and in adjacent sites, and attempt to link up existing fragments of habitat. (ACTION: CCW, EN)

5.2.3 Ensure that the habitat requirements of the species are taken into account in relevant development policies, plans and proposals. There should be a strong presumption against any tree-felling proposals which could adversely affect any significant colonies of the moth. (ACTION: FC, LAs)

5.3 Species management and protection

5.3.1 Initiate a programme of captive breeding. (ACTION: CCW, EN)

5.3.2 Identify a series of potential reintroduction sites in different parts of the former range. (ACTION: CCW, EN)

5.3.3 If further colonies are not found, release the species into a series of sites in different parts of the former range, to establish three new viable populations. (ACTION: CCW, EN)

5.4 Advisory

5.4.1 Advise landowners and managers of the presence of the species and the importance of beneficial management for its conservation. (ACTION: CCW, EN)

5.5 Future research and monitoring

5.5.1 Undertake surveys to determine the status of this species. (ACTION: CCW, EN)

5.5.2 Conduct targeted autecological research to inform habitat management. (ACTION: CCW, EN)

5.5.3 Establish a regular monitoring programme for the species. (ACTION: CCW, EN)

5.5.4 Pass information gathered during survey and monitoring of this species to a central database for incorporation in national and international databases. (ACTION: CCW, EN)

5.5.5 Encourage research on the ecology and conservation of this species on an international level, and use the experience gained towards its conservation in the UK. (ACTION: CCW, EN, JNCC)

5.6 Communications and publicity

5.6.1 Promote opportunities for the appreciation of white-spotted pinion and the issue of wildlife affected by Dutch elm disease. This should be achieved through articles within appropriate journals as well as by a publicity leaflet. (ACTION: CCW, EN, FC)

5.7 Links with other action plans

5.7.1 This action plan should be considered in conjunction with those for lowland wood pastures and parklands, and upland oak woods.

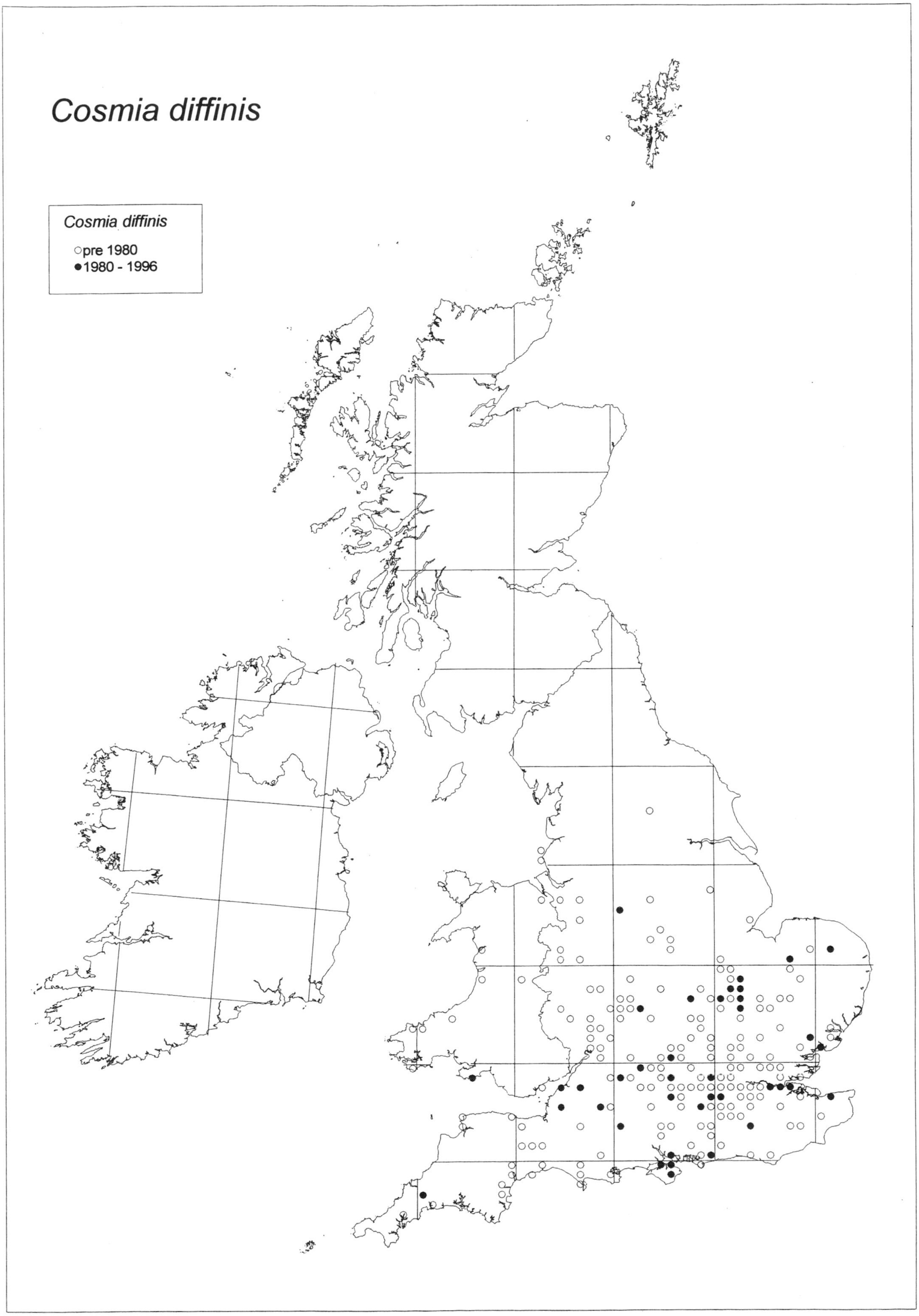

Distribution of Cosmia diffinis - white-spotted pinion in Britain, by 10km square.
Source: P. Waring - Joint Nature Conservation Committee/Butterfly Conservation Rare Moth Project.

Striped lychnis (*Cucullia lychnitis*)
Action Plan

1. Current status

1.1 Striped lychnis larvae feed on the flowers of dark mullein *Verbascum nigrum* (which is mostly found on soft limestone) and occasionally other *Verbascum* and *Scrophularia* species, preferring sunny open sites.

1.2 This moth was found in scattered sites in 23 ten km squares between 1980 and 1996, in Buckinghamshire, Oxfordshire, Berkshire, north Hampshire and West Sussex. Its range has declined greatly, and within the last 25 years or so it has been lost from half of its range, including all of Wiltshire, Dorset, Surrey, East Anglia and Gloucestershire. In Europe this moth occurs in most countries from the Mediterranean to Denmark and southern Sweden. The range extends to central Asia, the Caucasus, the Urals and Russia.

1.3 In Great Britain this species is classified as *Nationally Scarce*.

2. Current factors causing loss or decline

2.1 Inappropriately timed cutting of the larval foodplant on roadside verges and open grassland.

3. Current action

3.1 Some of the colonies are on SSSIs.

3.2 A national survey was undertaken in 1991 for JNCC.

3.3 Buckinghamshire County Council has funded surveys, and modified the cutting regimes on particular sections of roadside verge for this species.

4. Action plan objectives and targets

4.1 Maintain populations at all known sites.

4.2 Enhance the population size at all known sites by 2010.

4.3 Restore viable populations to one site in Wiltshire, one site in Dorset and one in East Anglia by 2010.

5. Proposed action with lead agencies

The objectives of the plan will be achieved by encouraging beneficial land management on existing sites, surveying all available habitat for undiscovered populations, and restoring a network of habitat, combined with reintroductions, to combat potential isolation effects. Research should focus on the ecological requirements of the species, monitoring the effects of habitat management designed to meet these needs, and detection of any changes in the population which may be due to isolation.

5.1 Policy and legislation

5.1.1 Where appropriate, include the requirements of the species when preparing or revising prescriptions for agri-environment and woodland grant schemes. (ACTION: EN, FC, MAFF)

5.2 Site safeguard and management

5.2.1 Where possible, ensure that all occupied and nearby potential habitat is appropriately managed by 2005, including encouraging a wider adoption of appropriate roadside verge cutting regimes. (ACTION: EN, LAs)

5.2.2 Ensure that the habitat requirements of the striped lychnis are taken into account in relevant development policies, plans and proposals. (ACTION: LAs)

5.2.3 Increase the available habitat on known sites and in adjacent sites, and attempt to link up existing fragments of habitat. (ACTION: EN, FC, LAs)

5.2.4 Ensure that the striped lychnis is listed in site management documents for all relevant SSSIs. (ACTION: EN)

5.3 Species management and protection

5.3.1 (Re)introduce populations to three former sites, in Dorset, Wiltshire and East Anglia, once apparently unoccupied potential sites have been adequately surveyed. (ACTION: EN)

5.4 Advisory

5.4.1 Advise landowners and managers of the presence of the species and the importance of beneficial management for its conservation. (ACTION: EN)

5.5 Future research and monitoring

5.5.1 Undertake further surveys to determine current distribution. (ACTION: EN)

5.5.2 Conduct targeted autecological research to elucidate further the causes of the species' decline and inform habitat management. (ACTION: EN)

5.5.3 Establish a regular monitoring programme for this species, including an assessment of potential sites, to monitor the effectiveness of management agreements. (ACTION: EN)

5.5.4 Pass the information gathered during the survey and monitoring of this species to a central database for incorporation into national and international databases. (ACTION: EN)

5.5.5 Encourage research on the ecology and conservation of this species on an international level, and use the experience gained towards its conservation in the UK. (ACTION: EN, JNCC)

5.6 Communications and publicity

5.6.1 Promote opportunities for the appreciation of this species and the conservation issues associated with its habitat, including the opportunities for biodiversity provided by appropriate management of roadside verges. This should be achieved through articles within appropriate journals, as well as by a publicity leaflet. (ACTION: EN)

5.7 Links with other action plans

5.7.1 This action plan should be considered in conjunction with that for lowland calcareous grassland.

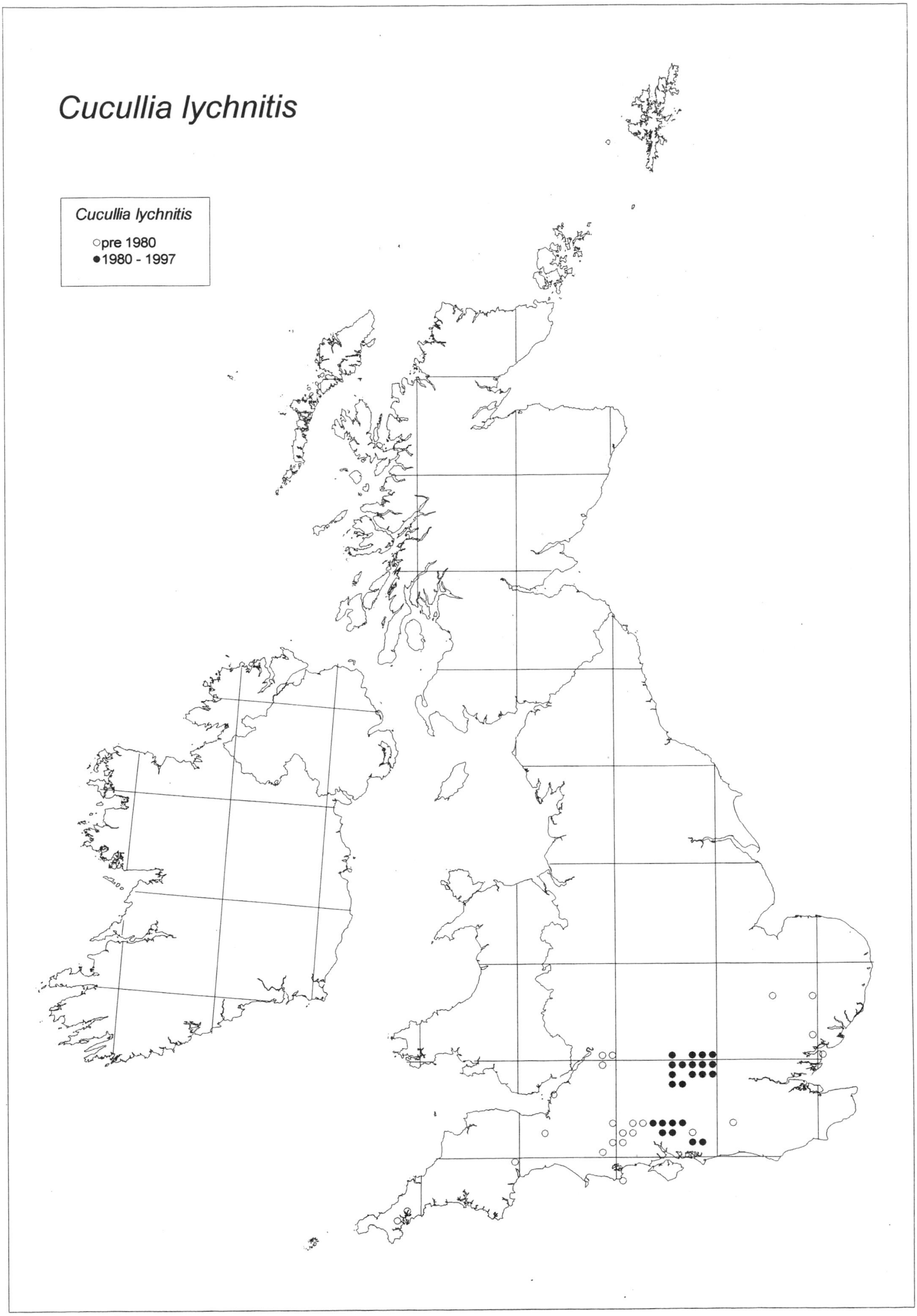

Distribution of Cucullia lychnitis - striped lychnis in Britain, by 10km square.
Source: P. Waring - Joint Nature Conservation Committee/Butterfly Conservation Rare Moth Project.

Dingy mocha (*Cyclophora pendularia*)
Action Plan

1. Current status

1.1 The larvae of the dingy mocha require 1-3 m tall willow bushes, such as *Salix aurita* and *S. cinerea*, in open heathy situations.

1.2 The dingy mocha is a very local species, confined to Dorset and western Hampshire where it occurs on the Purbeck heaths between Studland and Wareham, the Ringwood area of the New Forest, and the Luscombe Valley nature reserve near the east Dorset border. Formerly the moth was reported from heathy areas of South Wiltshire, Surrey, Sussex and Suffolk. There are also old records from Devon, Kent and South Wales. This moth has been reported from most countries in Europe, but is very local and rare in Scandinavia. The range extends to north and central Russia, southern Siberia, China, Mongolia, central Asia and Korea.

1.3 In Great Britain this species is classified as *Rare*.

2. Current factors causing loss or decline

2.1 Loss of heathland to development, forestry, agricultural improvement and road construction.

2.2 Succession to woodland (often from self-sown pine) on unmanaged heathland.

2.3 Extensive, unplanned heathland fires.

2.4 Scrub clearance during heathland restoration.

3. Current action

3.1 Most of the remaining populations are within existing SSSIs.

4. Action plan objectives and targets

4.1 Maintain populations at all known sites.

4.2 Enhance the population size at all known sites by 2010.

4.3 Restore viable populations to five additional sites within the historic range by 2010.

5. Proposed action with lead agencies

The objectives of the plan will be achieved by encouraging beneficial land management on existing sites, surveying all available habitat for undiscovered populations, and restoring a network of habitat, if necessary with introductions of the species, to combat potential isolation effects. Research should focus on the ecological requirements of the species, monitoring the effects of habitat management designed to meet these needs, and detection of any changes in the population which may be due to isolation.

5.1 Policy and legislation

5.1.1 Where appropriate, include the requirements of the species when preparing or revising prescriptions for land management schemes which are targeted at restoring heathland. (ACTION: EN, MAFF)

5.2 Site safeguard and management

5.2.1 Where possible, ensure that all existing habitat within the current range of the moth is appropriately managed by 2005. (ACTION: EN, MAFF)

5.2.2 Encourage an increase in the available habitat on known sites, and link up existing fragments of habitat. (ACTION: EN)

5.2.3 Ensure that the habitat requirements of the dingy mocha are taken into account in relevant development policies, plans and proposals. (ACTION: LAs)

5.2.4 Ensure that the dingy mocha is listed in site management documents for all relevant SSSIs. (ACTION: EN)

5.3 Species management and protection

5.3.1 Reintroduce the dingy mocha to a series of restored sites, if necessary, to establish an additional five populations across the former range by 2010. (ACTION: EN)

5.4 Advisory

5.4.1 Advise landowners and managers of the presence of the species and the importance of beneficial management for its conservation. (ACTION: EN)

5.5 Future research and monitoring

5.5.1 Undertake surveys to determine the status of this species by 2004. (ACTION: EN)

5.5.2 Conduct targeted autecological research by 2004 to inform habitat management. (ACTION: EN)

5.5.3 Establish a regular monitoring programme for the species on a representative selection of sites throughout its range. (ACTION: EN)

5.5.4 Pass information gathered during survey and monitoring of this species to a central database for incorporation in national and international databases. (ACTION: EN)

5.6 Communications and publicity

5.6.1 Promote opportunities for the appreciation of this species and the conservation issues associated with its habitat. This should be achieved through articles within appropriate journals, as well as by a publicity leaflet. (ACTION: EN)

5.7 Links with other action plans

5.7.1 This action plan should be considered in conjunction with that for lowland heathland.

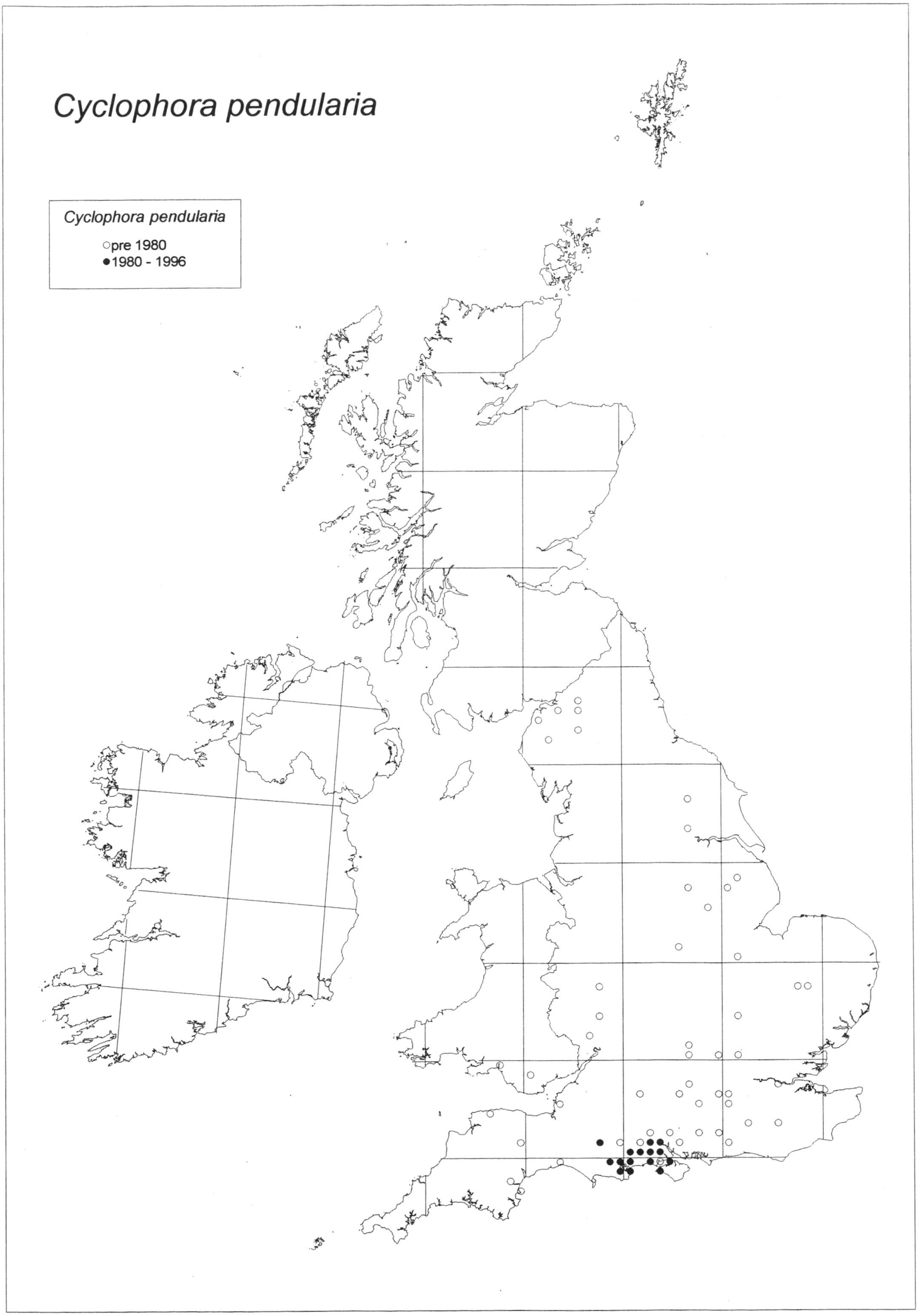

Distribution of Cyclophora pendularia - dingy mocha in Britain, by 10km square.
Source: P. Waring - Joint Nature Conservation Committee/Butterfly Conservation Rare Moth Project.

Heart moth (*Dicycla oo*)
Action Plan

1. Current status

1.1 The heart moth is to be found in parkland and open woodland, where the larvae feed on the foliage of pedunculate oak *Quercus robur* and seem to prefer over-mature trees.

1.2 The moth is now seen in numbers only in parts of Surrey, but it also survives at low density in north-west Kent, Berkshire and Northamptonshire. It has been lost from Buckinghamshire, Essex, Middlesex, Hertfordshire and Hampshire in recent decades. The moth has been reported from most countries in Europe but it is extinct, very rare or localised in many parts of its range, which extends to the Middle East and the Urals.

1.3 In Great Britain this species is classified as *Rare*.

2. Current factors causing loss or decline

2.1 Felling of over-mature oak trees.

3. Current action

3.1 The main population is on Epsom and Ashtead Commons SSSI.

4. Action plan objectives and targets

4.1 Maintain populations at all known sites.

4.2 Enhance the population size at all known sites by 2010.

5. Proposed action with lead agencies

The objectives of the plan will be achieved by encouraging beneficial land management on existing sites, surveying all available habitat for undiscovered populations, and restoring a network of habitat to combat potential isolation effects. Research should focus on the ecological requirements of the species, monitoring the effects of habitat management designed to meet these needs, and detection of any changes in the population which may be due to isolation.

5.1 Policy and legislation

5.1.1 Where appropriate, include the requirements of the species when preparing or revising prescriptions for agri-environment and woodland grant schemes. (ACTION: EN, FC, MAFF)

5.2 Site safeguard and management

5.2.1 Ensure that all occupied and nearby potential habitat is appropriately managed by 2005, for example through SSSI or agri-environment/woodland grant scheme management agreements. (ACTION: EN, FC, MAFF)

5.2.2 Increase the available habitat on known sites and in adjacent sites, and attempt to link up existing fragments of habitat, retaining over-mature oak trees wherever possible. (ACTION: EN)

5.2.3 Ensure that the habitat requirements of this species are taken into account in relevant development policies, plans and proposals. There should be a strong presumption against any tree-felling proposals which could adversely affect significant colonies of the moth. (ACTION: LAs)

5.2.4 Ensure that the heart moth is listed in site management documents for all relevant SSSIs. (ACTION: EN)

5.3 Species management and protection

5.3.1 None proposed

5.4 Advisory

5.4.1 Advise landowners and managers of the presence of the species and importance of beneficial management for its conservation. (ACTION: EN)

5.5 Future research and monitoring

5.5.1 Undertake surveys to determine the status of the heart moth. (ACTION: EN)

5.5.2 Conduct targeted autecological research to inform habitat management. (ACTION: EN, FC)

5.5.3 Establish a regular monitoring programme for the species. (ACTION: EN)

5.5.4 Pass information gathered during survey and monitoring of this species to a central database for incorporation in national and international databases. (ACTION: EN)

5.5.6 Encourage research on the ecology and conservation of this species on an international level, and use the experience gained towards its conservation in the UK. (ACTION: EN, JNCC)

5.6 Communications and publicity

5.6.1 Promote opportunities for the appreciation of this species and the conservation issues associated with its habitat. This should be achieved through articles within appropriate journals, as well as by a publicity leaflet. (ACTION: EN)

5.7 Links with other action plans

5.7.1 Implementation of this action plan could benefit other species of lowland oak woodlands, including the light crimson underwing *Catocala promissa,* and the dark crimson underwing *Catocala sponsa*.

5.7.2 This plan should be considered in conjunction with that for lowland wood pastures and parklands.

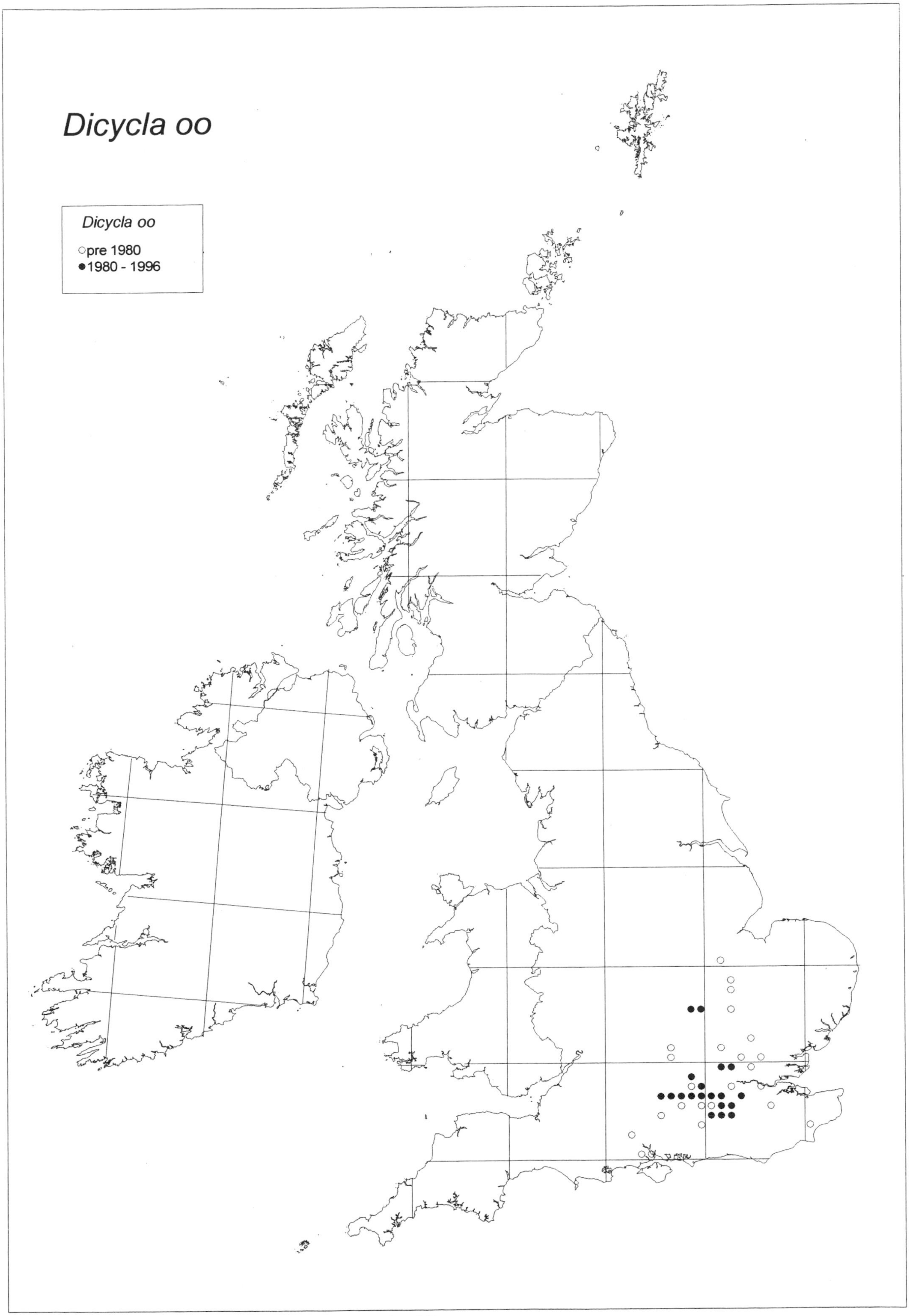

Distribution of Dicycla oo - heart moth in Britain, by 10km square.
Source: P. Waring - Joint Nature Conservation Committee/Butterfly Conservation Rare Moth Project.

Dark-bordered beauty (*Epione parallelaria*) Action Plan

1. Current status

1.1 The dark-bordered beauty is associated with damp places. The larva feeds on creeping willow at the English sites, and on low re-growth of aspen on the sites in Scotland.

1.2 The dark-bordered beauty has been recorded from most countries in Europe, where it is associated with northern or upland habitats. The range extends eastwards through Russia and Siberia to the Amur region. In the UK four small and isolated populations are known: one in north-east Yorkshire, one near Hexham, Northumberland, one near Balmoral (Aberdeenshire) and one in Strathspey (Moray). At one site, in Roxburghshire, its status is unclear as there are no recent records. There are genuine old records from other sites in Northumberland, and many doubtful records from other parts of Britain.

1.3 In Great Britain this moth is classified as *Rare*.

2. Current factors causing loss or decline

2.1 Inappropriate habitat management.

3. Current action

3.1 Both English populations are on SSSIs, one of which is an NNR.

4. Action plan objectives and targets

4.1 Maintain populations at all known sites.

4.2 Enhance the population size at all known sites by 2010.

4.3 Ensure that there are 10 viable populations within the historic range by 2010, by enhancing population sizes at known sites or by re-introducing populations to suitable localities.

5. Proposed actions with lead agencies

The objectives of the plan will be achieved by encouraging beneficial land management on existing sites, surveying for undiscovered colonies, and restoring a network of habitat to combat potential isolation effects. If necessary, reintroductions of the moth may need to be considered. Research should focus on the ecological requirements of the species, monitoring the effects of habitat management designed to meet these needs, and detection of any changes in the population which may be due to isolation of colonies.

5.1 Policy and legislation

5.1.1 Where appropriate, include the requirements of the species when preparing or revising prescriptions for environment schemes (eg ESAs, Countryside Stewardship, Woodland Grant Scheme, Countryside Premium Scheme). (ACTION: EN, FC, MAFF, SNH, SOAEFD)

5.2 Site safeguard and management

5.2.1 Ensure that all occupied is appropriately managed by 2005. (ACTION: EN, LAs, SNH)

5.2.2 Where possible, increase the available habitat at known sites and adjacent areas, and attempt to link up existing fragments of habitat. (ACTION: EN, FC, SNH)

5.2.3 Ensure that the habitat requirements of this species are taken account of in relevant development policies, plans and proposals. (ACTION: EN, LAs, SNH)

5.2.4 Ensure that dark-bordered beauty is included in site management documents within all relevant SSSIs. (ACTION: EN, SNH)

5.2.5 Consider notifying as SSSI sites supporting viable populations of the dark-bordered beauty, where this is necessary to secure their long-term protection and appropriate management. (ACTION: EN, SNH)

5.3 Species management and protection

5.3.1 Consider reintroducing populations of the dark-bordered beauty to former sites, if necessary to maintain 10 viable populations. (ACTION: EN, SNH)

5.4 Advisory

5.4.1 Advise land owners and managers of the presence of this species and the importance of beneficial management for its conservation. (ACTION: EN, SNH)

5.5 Future research and monitoring

5.5.1 Establish a regular monitoring programme for the species. It will be important to monitor the effects of habitat management for this moth, and to detect any changes in the population which may be due to isolation of colonies. (ACTION: EN, SNH)

5.5.2 Undertake surveys to determine the status of the moth. (ACTION: EN, SNH)

5.5.3 Conduct targeted autecological research to inform habitat management. (ACTION: EN, SNH)

5.5.4 Pass information gathered during survey and monitoring of this species to a central database for incorporation into national and international databases. (ACTION: EN, SNH)

5.5.5 Encourage research on the ecology and conservation of this species on an international level, and use the experience gained towards its conservation in the UK. (ACTION: JNCC)

5.6 Communications and publicity

5.6.1 Promote understanding and appreciation of the conservation of this moth and its habitat. This should be achieved through articles within appropriate journals, as well as by a publicity leaflet. (ACTION: EN, SNH)

5.7 Links with other action plans

5.7.1 Implementation of this action plan could benefit other species of aspen woods, including the hoverfly *Hammerschmidtia ferruginea*.

5.7.2 This plan should be considered in conjunction with that for wet woodlands.

Epione parallelaria

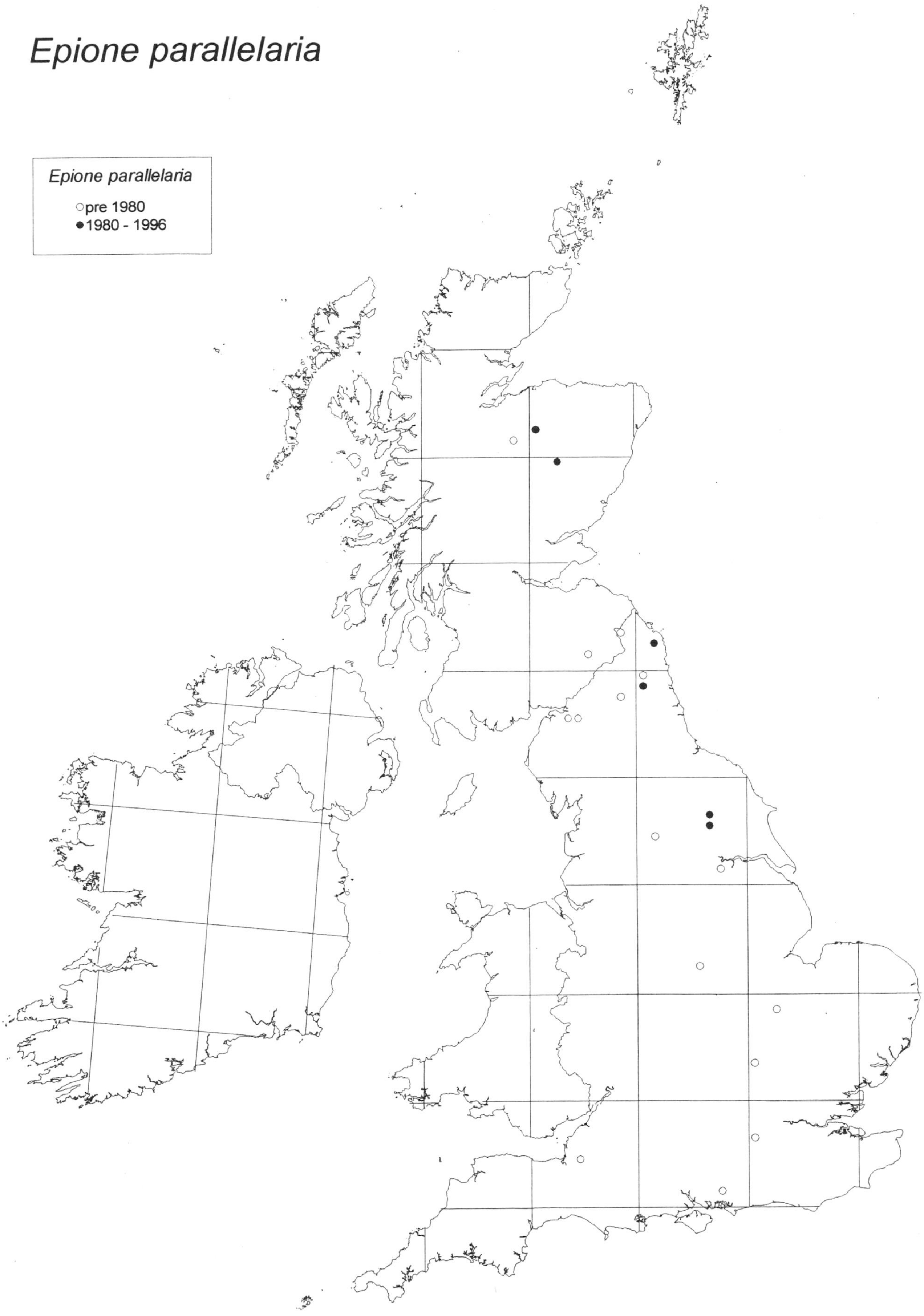

Distribution of Epione parallelaria - dark-bordered beauty in Britain, by 10km square.
Source: P. Waring - Joint Nature Conservation Committee/Butterfly Conservation Rare Moth Project.

Bordered gothic (*Heliophobus reticulata marginosa*) Action Plan

1. Current status

1.1 The bordered gothic is associated with open, mainly calcareous, grassland sites but the larval ecology in the wild is unknown. The seedpods of *Silene* species, such as bladder campion *S. vulgaris,* and possibly soapwort *Saponaria officinalis,* as well as knotgrass *Polygonum aviculare,* are suggested foodplants, based on observations in captivity.

1.2 This moth was widely distributed, but always local, in England and Wales from Yorkshire southwards, but its range has declined substantially since the 1960s; it is now reported mainly from the Portland area of Dorset, from the Breckland of East Anglia (where it has become scarce in the last decade) and from South Wales. The species has been recorded throughout Europe. The range extends to Russia, Siberia, Japan and Asia Minor.

1.3 In Great Britain this species is classified as *Nationally Scarce.*

2. Current factors causing loss or decline

2.1 Not known.

3. Current action

3.1 Some populations are on SSSIs.

4. Action plan objectives and targets

4.1 Maintain populations at all known sites.

4.2 Enhance the population size at all known sites by 2010.

4.3 Restore viable populations to five additional sites within the historic range by 2010.

5. Proposed action with lead agencies

The objectives of the plan will be achieved by encouraging beneficial land management on existing sites, surveying all available habitat for undiscovered populations, and restoring a network of habitat, if necessary with introductions of the species, to combat potential isolation effects. Research should focus on the ecological requirements of the species, monitoring the effects of habitat management designed to meet these needs, and detection of any changes in the population which may be due to isolation.

5.1 Policy and legislation

5.1.1 Where appropriate, include the requirements of the species when preparing or revising prescriptions for agri-environment schemes. (ACTION: CCW, EN, MAFF, WOAD)

5.2 Site safeguard and management

5.2.1 Where possible, ensure that all occupied and nearby potential habitat is appropriately managed, for example through SSSI or agri-environment scheme management agreements. (ACTION: CCW, EN, MAFF, WOAD)

5.2.2 Where possible, increase available habitat on known sites and in adjacent sites, and attempt to link up existing fragments of habitat. (ACTION: CCW, EN)

5.2.3 Ensure that the habitat requirements of the bordered gothic are taken into account in relevant development policies, plans and proposals. (ACTION: LAs)

5.2.4 Ensure that the bordered gothic is listed in site management documents for all relevant SSSIs. (ACTION: CCW, EN)

5.3 Species management and protection

5.3.1 Reintroduce the bordered gothic to a series of sites within the historic range, if necessary to restore five additional viable populations. (ACTION: CCW, EN)

5.4 Advisory

5.4.1 Advise landowners and managers of the presence of the species and the importance of beneficial management for its conservation. (ACTION: CCW, EN, MAFF, WOAD)

5.4.2 As far as possible, ensure that all relevant agri-environment project officers, and members of regional agri-environment consultation groups, are advised of locations of this species, its importance, and the management needed for its conservation. (ACTION: CCW, EN, MAFF, WOAD)

5.5 Future research and monitoring

5.5.1 Undertake surveys to determine current distribution. (ACTION: CCW, EN)

5.5.2 Conduct targeted autecological research to inform habitat management. (ACTION: CCW, EN)

5.5.3 Establish a regular monitoring programme. (ACTION: CCW, EN)

5.5.4 Pass information gathered during survey and monitoring of this species to a central database for incorporation in national and international databases. (ACTION: CCW, EN)

5.6 **Communications and publicity**

5.6.1 Promote opportunities for the appreciation of this species and the conservation issues associated with its habitat. This should be achieved through articles within appropriate journals, as well as by a publicity leaflet. (ACTION: CCW, EN)

5.7 **Links with other action plans**

5.7.1 This action plan should be considered in conjunction with that for lowland calcareous grassland.

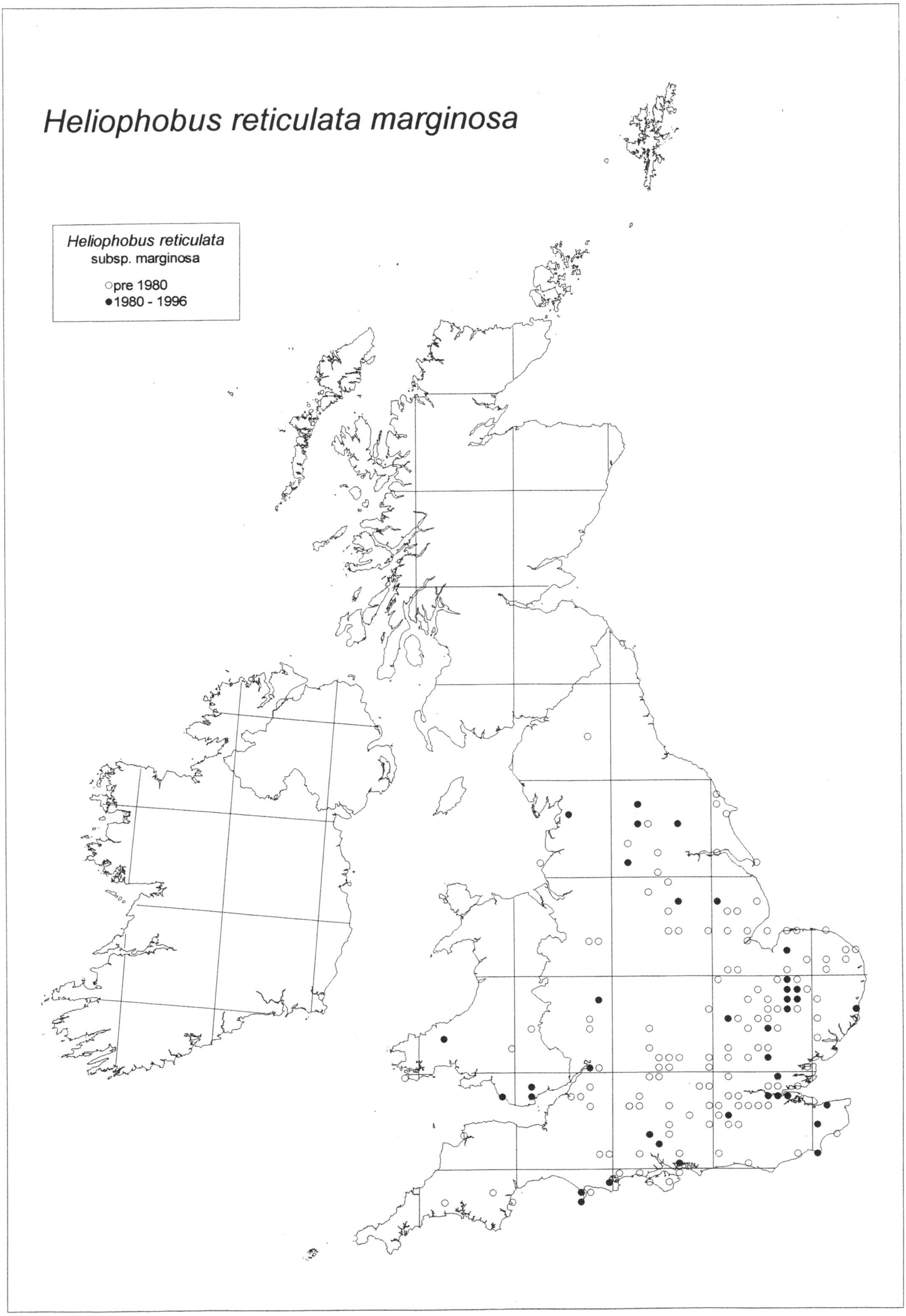

Distribution of Heliophobus reticulata marginosa - bordered gothic in Britain, by 10km square.
Source: P. Waring - Joint Nature Conservation Committee/Butterfly Conservation Rare Moth Project.

Narrow-bordered bee hawk-moth (*Hemaris tityus*) Action Plan

1. Current status

1.1 The narrow-bordered bee hawk-moth occurs on a wide range of unimproved grasslands, including wet, acidic grassland and chalk downland; it is also found on acid bogs, peat cuttings and drier heathland. The larval foodplant is devil's-bit scabious. The adult moth requires a supply of nectar but visits various flower species.

1.2 Formerly widespread in the UK, the narrow-bordered bee hawk-moth has declined severely and now appears to have retreated to western Britain, especially south-west England from Cornwall to Wiltshire. There are also scattered records from west Wales, the west coast of Scotland, Northern Ireland, and a single colony on a nature reserve in Yorkshire. The moth occurs locally across the western Palaearctic, with records from virtually every country in Europe. It reaches Lapland in the north, Iran to the south, extends eastwards into China, and has been reported from Morocco.

1.3 In Great Britain this species is classified as *Nationally Scarce*.

2. Current factors causing loss or decline

2.1 Agricultural improvement of unimproved grassland and heathland.

2.2 Inappropriate management of grassland, heathland and bogs.

3. Current action

3.1 Some of the remaining localities are within existing SSSIs/ASSIs, nature reserves or MoD land, and many are now covered by agri-environment schemes.

3.2 Several grassland areas supporting populations of the narrow-bordered bee hawk-moth have been proposed as candidate SACs.

4. Action plan objectives and targets

4.1 Maintain populations at all known sites.

4.2 Restore populations of the moth to 10 suitable sites within its former range by 2010.

5. Proposed action with lead agencies

The objectives of the plan will be achieved by encouraging beneficial land management on existing sites, undertaking surveys to locate undiscovered colonies, and restoring a network of habitat. Reintroductions of the species to sites within its former range may be necessary. Research will focus on the ecological requirements of the species, and monitoring the effects of habitat management designed to meet these needs.

5.1 Policy and legislation

5.1.1 Where appropriate, include the requirements of the narrow-bordered bee hawk-moth when drawing up or revising prescriptions for agri-environment schemes. (ACTION: CCW, DANI, EHS, EN, MAFF, SNH, SOAEFD, WOAD)

5.2 Site safeguard and management

5.2.1 Where possible, ensure that all occupied habitat is appropriately managed by 2005, for example through SSSI/ASSI or agri-environment scheme management agreements. (ACTION: CCW, DANI, EHS, EN, MAFF, MoD, SNH, SOAEFD, WOAD)

5.2.2 Encourage an increase in the available habitat and attempt to link up existing fragments of habitat. (ACTION: CCW, DANI, EHS, EN, MAFF, MoD, SNH, SOAEFD, WOAD)

5.2.3 Ensure that the habitat requirements of this species are taken account of in relevant development policies, plans and proposals. (ACTION: CCW, EHS, EN, LAs, SNH)

5.2.4 Ensure that the narrow-bordered bee hawk-moth is included in site management documents for all relevant SSSIs/ASSIs. (ACTION: CCW, EHS, EN, SNH)

5.3 Species management and protection

5.3.1 Consider reintroducing populations to a series of sites within the former range, if necessary to restore 10 new populations within the former range by 2010. (ACTION: CCW, EHS, EN, SNH)

5.4 Advisory

5.4.1 Advise landowners and managers about the presence of this species and the importance of beneficial management for its conservation. (ACTION: CCW, DANI, EHS, EN, MAFF, SNH, SOAEFD, WOAD)

5.4.2 As far as possible, ensure that all relevant agri-environment project officers and members of regional agri-environment consultation groups are advised of locations of this species, its importance, and the management needed for its conservation. (ACTION: CCW, DANI, EHS, EN, MAFF, SNH, SOAEFD, WOAD)

5.5 Future research and monitoring

5.5.1 Undertake surveys to determine the current distribution and status of the narrow-bordered bee hawk-moth. (ACTION: CCW, EHS, EN, SNH)

5.5.2 Conduct targeted autecological research to inform habitat management. (ACTION: CCW, EHS, EN, SNH)

5.5.3 Establish a regular monitoring programme for this species. It will be important to monitor the effects of habitat management for this moth. (ACTION: CCW, EHS, EN, MoD, SNH)

5.5.4 Pass information gathered during survey and monitoring of this species to a central database for inclusion in national and international databases. (ACTION: CCW, EHS, EN, SNH)

5.6 Communications and publicity

5.6.1 Promote opportunities for the appreciation of the narrow-bordered bee hawk-moth and the conservation issues associated with its habitat. This should be achieved through articles within appropriate journals, as well as by a publicity leaflet. (ACTION: CCW, EHS, EN, SNH)

5.7 Links with other action plans

5.7.1 Implementation of this action plan could benefit other species of unimproved wet grasslands, including the double-line moth *Mythimna turca,* and the marsh fritillary *Eurodryas aurinia*.

5.7.2 This plan should be considered in conjunction with those for purple moor-grass and rush pastures, lowland heathland, and fens.

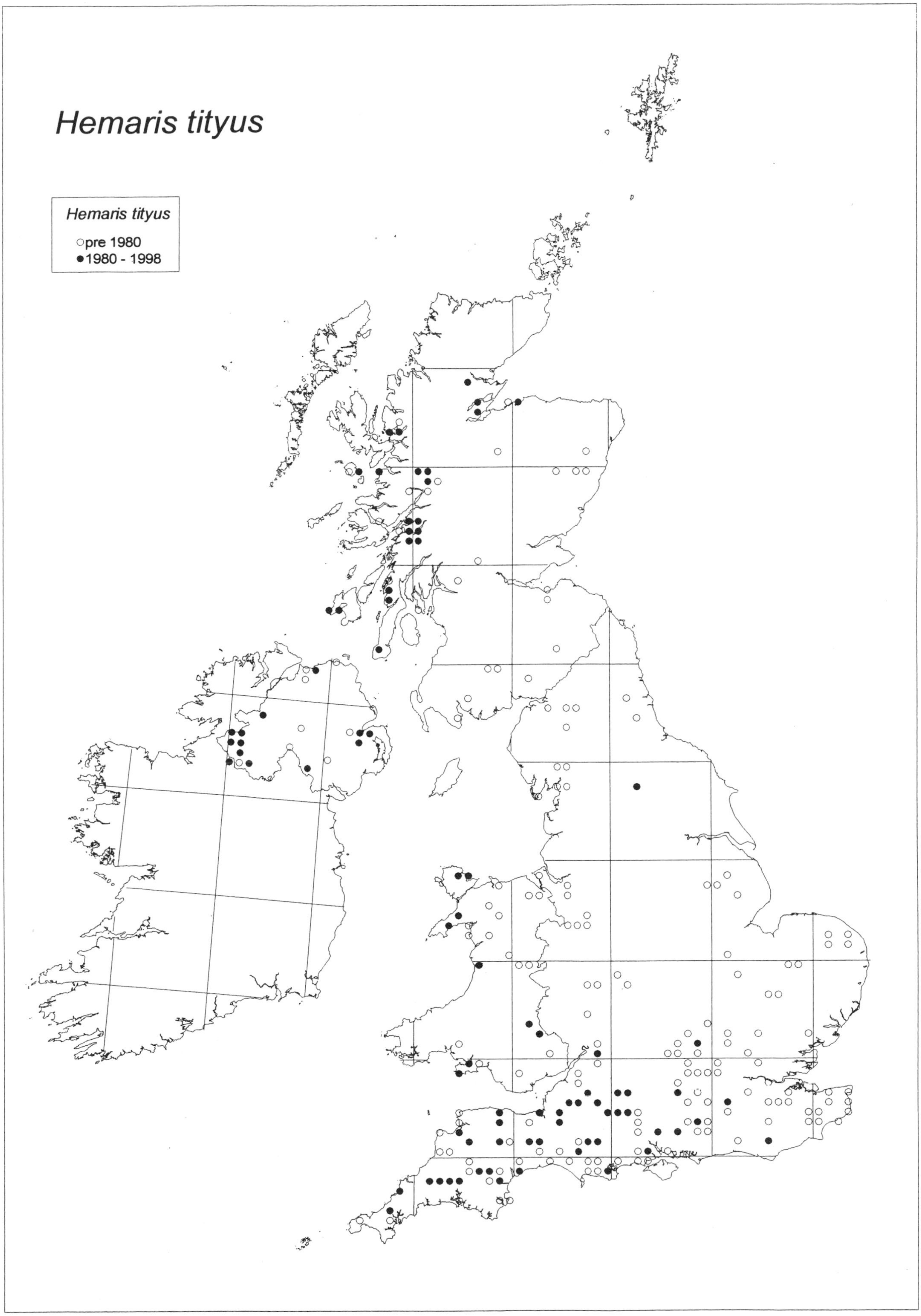

Distribution of Hemaris tityus - narrow-bordered bee hawk-moth in Britain and Northern Ireland, by 10km square.
Source: P. Waring - Joint Nature Conservation Committee/Butterfly Conservation Rare Moth Project and Countryside Council for Wales records.

Buttoned snout (*Hypena rostralis*)
Action Plan

1. Current status

1.1 Buttoned snout larvae feed on hop *Humulus lupulus*, particularly plants sprawling across the ground. The adults hibernate in man-made shelters, outbuildings, etc and in caves.

1.2 This moth was formerly widespread throughout southern Britain north to Lincolnshire and South Wales. It has declined significantly and now occurs mainly in river valleys in south-east England, particularly the Thames basin, and on estuaries and other scattered sites around the coast of England. The species has been reported from every country in Europe except Ireland. The range extends to the Lebanon, southern Russia and Iran.

1.3 In Great Britain this species is classified as *Nationally Scarce*.

2. Current factors causing loss or decline

2.1 Redevelopment of derelict urban sites.

3. Current action

3.1 Some populations are on SSSIs.

4. Action plan objectives and targets

4.1 Maintain populations at all known sites.

4.2 Enhance the population size at all known sites by 2010.

4.3 Restore self-sustaining populations to five additional sites within the historic range by 2010.

5. Proposed action with lead agencies

The objectives of the plan will be achieved by encouraging beneficial land management on existing sites, surveying all available habitat for undiscovered populations, and restoring a network of habitat, if necessary with introductions of the species, to combat potential isolation effects. Research should focus on the ecological requirements of the species, monitoring the effects of habitat management designed to meet these needs, and detection of any changes in the population which may be due to isolation.

5.1 Policy and legislation

5.1.1 Where appropriate, include the requirements of the species when preparing or revising prescriptions for agri-environment schemes. (ACTION: CCW, EN, MAFF, WOAD)

5.2 Site safeguard and management

5.2.1 Where possible, ensure that all occupied and nearby potential habitat is appropriately managed by 2005, for example through SSSI or agri-environment scheme management agreements. (ACTION: CCW, EN, MAFF, WOAD)

5.2.2 Where possible, increase available habitat on known sites and in adjacent sites, and attempt to link up existing fragments of habitat. (ACTION: CCW, EN)

5.2.3 Ensure that the habitat requirements of the buttoned snout are taken into account in relevant development policies, plans and proposals, including the redevelopment of derelict urban sites. (ACTION: LAs)

5.2.4 Ensure that the buttoned snout is included in site management documents for all relevant SSSIs. (ACTION: CCW, EN)

5.3 Species management and protection

5.3.1 Reintroduce the buttoned snout to a series of sites, if necessary to restore an additional five self-sustaining populations by 2010. (ACTION: CCW, EN)

5.4 Advisory

5.4.1 Advise landowners and managers of the presence of the species and the importance of beneficial management for its conservation. (ACTION: CCW, EN, MAFF, WOAD)

5.4.2 As far as possible, ensure that all relevant agri-environment project officers, and members of regional agri-environment consultation groups, are advised of locations of this species, its importance, and the management needed for its conservation. (ACTION: CCW, EN, MAFF, WOAD)

5.5 Future research and monitoring

5.5.1 Undertake surveys to determine the current status of this species. (ACTION: CCW, EN)

5.5.2 Conduct targeted autecological research to inform habitat management. (ACTION: CCW, EN)

5.5.3 Establish a regular monitoring programme for the species. (ACTION: CCW, EN)

5.5.4 Pass information gathered during survey and monitoring of this species to a central database for incorporation in national and international databases. (ACTION: CCW, EN)

5.5.5 Encourage research on the ecology and conservation of this species on an international level, and use the experience gained towards its conservation in the UK. (ACTION: CCW, EN, JNCC)

5.6 Communications and publicity

5.6.1 Promote opportunities for the appreciation of the buttoned snout and the conservation issues associated with its habitat. This should be achieved through articles within appropriate journals, as well as by a publicity leaflet. (ACTION: CCW, EN)

5.7 Links with other action plans

5.7.1 None proposed.

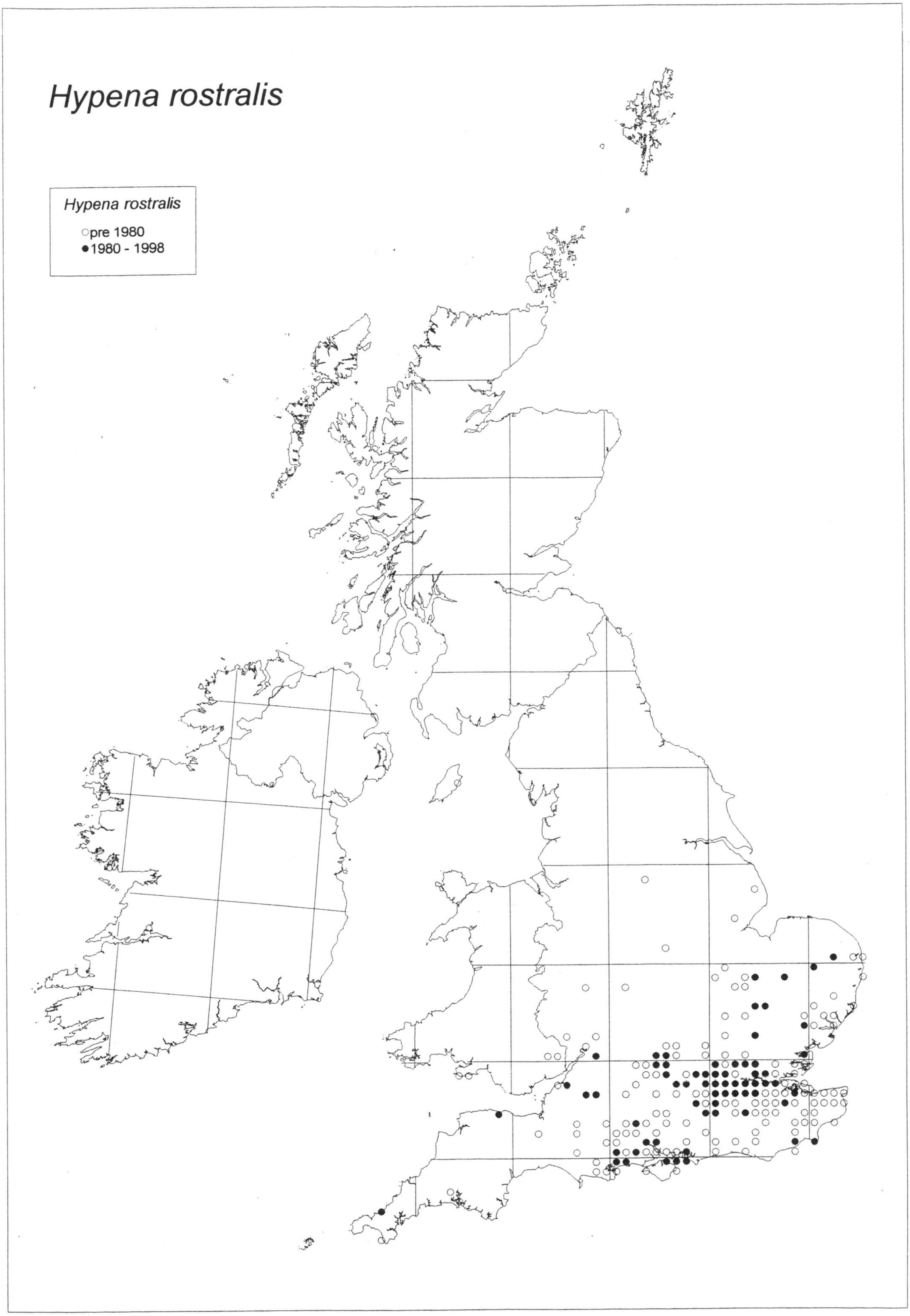

Distribution of Hypena rostralis - buttoned snout in Britain, by 10km square.
Source: P. Waring - Joint Nature Conservation Committee/Butterfly Conservation Rare Moth Project.

Silky wave (*Idaea dilutaria*)
Action Plan

1. Current status

1.1 All of the known sites for the silky wave are steep, south-facing areas of open calcareous grassland, and populations are confined to areas where grazing is light or absent. The recorded larval foodplant is common rock-rose, but the withered leaves of various other herbs and shrubs are reported as foodplants elsewhere in Europe.

1.2 Three populations are known in the UK, one on the Great Orme in North Wales, another near Bristol, and a third on the Gower coast of Glamorgan. Formerly the moth was reported much more widely in England and Wales. Some of the old records are misidentifications or are the result of confusing changes of nomenclature in the past, so the real decline may be less than it appears. However, it is possible that there are still some overlooked populations. The silky wave is well-distributed in central and southern Europe; it extends eastwards into the Balkans and Asia Minor, occurring in a wide range of habitats north to southern Sweden where it is very restricted and confined to south-facing slopes.

1.3 In Great Britain this species is classified as *Rare*.

2. Current factors causing loss or decline

2.1 Inappropriate grassland management.

3. Current action

3.1 All of the known sites are SSSIs and two are candidate SACs.

3.2 Butterfly Conservation, CCW and EN jointly funded a survey of the known sites in 1994.

4. Action plan objectives and targets

4.1 Maintain populations at all known sites.

4.2 Enhance populations size at all known sites by 2005.

4.3 If no further colonies are discovered, reintroduce populations to three former sites by 2010.

5. Proposed action with lead agencies

The objectives of the plan will be achieved by encouraging beneficial land management on existing sites, and undertaking surveys for undiscovered colonies. Reintroductions of populations to former sites will need to be considered if no further colonies are discovered. Research should focus on the ecological requirements of the species, whilst monitoring the effects of habitat management designed to meet these needs.

5.1 Policy and legislation

5.1.1 Where appropriate, include the requirements of the species when preparing or revising prescriptions for agri-environment schemes. (ACTION: CCW, EN, MAFF, WOAD)

5.2 Site safeguard and management

5.2.1 Ensure that all occupied habitat is appropriately managed by 2004, for example through SSSI or agri-environment scheme management agreements. (ACTION: CCW, EN, MAFF, WOAD)

5.2.2 Where possible, increase the area of suitable habitat on known sites and adjacent areas, and attempt to link up existing fragments of habitat. (ACTION: CCW, EN, LAs, MAFF, WOAD)

5.2.3 Ensure that the silky wave is included in site management documents for all relevant SSSIs. (ACTION: CCW, EN)

5.3 Species management and protection

5.3.1 Consider reintroducing populations to three former sites by 2010. (ACTION: CCW, EN)

5.4 Advisory

5.4.1 Advise landowners and managers of the presence of this species and the importance of beneficial management for its conservation. (ACTION: CCW, EN)

5.5 Future research and monitoring

5.5.1 Undertake further surveys to determine the status of this species. (ACTION: CCW, EN)

5.5.2 Conduct targeted autecological research to inform habitat management. (ACTION: CCW, EN)

5.5.3 Establish a regular monitoring programme for the species. (ACTION: CCW, EN)

5.5.4 Pass information gathered during survey and monitoring of this species to a central database for incorporation into national and international databases. (ACTION: CCW, EN)

5.5.5 Encourage research on the ecology and conservation of this species on an international level, and use the experience gained towards its conservation in the UK. (ACTION: CCW, EN, JNCC)

5.6 Communications and publicity

5.6.1 Promote opportunities for the appreciation of the silky wave and the conservation issues associated with its habitat. This should be achieved through articles within appropriate journals, as well as by a publicity leaflet. (ACTION: CCW, EN)

5.7 Links with other action plans

5.7.1 Implementation of this action plan could benefit other species of calcareous grasslands, including the silver-studded blue *Plebejus argus*.

5.7.2 This plan should be considered in conjunction with those for lowland calcareous grassland, and maritime cliffs and slopes.

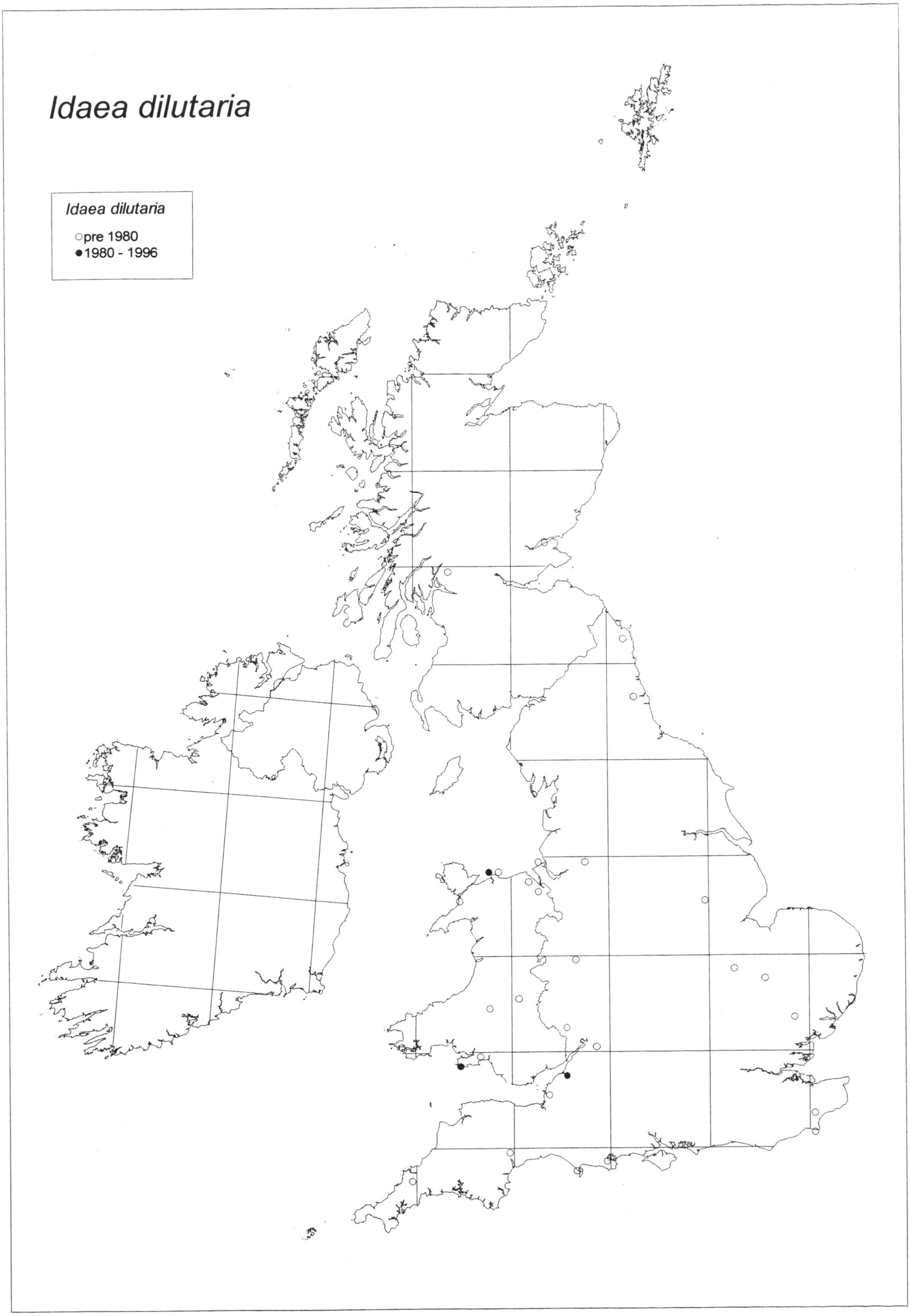

Distribution of Idaea dilutaria - silky wave in Britain, by 10km square.
Source: P. Waring - Joint Nature Conservation Committee/Butterfly Conservation Rare Moth Project.

Orange upperwing (*Jodia croceago*)
Action Plan

1. Current status

1.1 The orange upperwing is an open woodland or woodland-edge species. The larval foodplants are pedunculate oak and sessile oak (*Quercus robur* and *Q. petraea*), both of which are abundant throughout Britain. The moth is particularly associated with small or coppice trees that retain their leaves over winter, as the adult moths overwinter within withered oak leaves which have remained on the tree.

1.2 The orange upperwing has been recorded from central, southern and south-western England, with occasional records from Wales, but by about 1980 it was apparently restricted to Cornwall, Devon, Sussex, Surrey, Shropshire and South Wales. The last definite record was from Sussex in 1984, although there is a recent unconfirmed record from Hampshire. It seems to have disappeared from its main locality in Surrey. There are no populations currently known. The orange upperwing is widely distributed but scarce in Europe and North Africa.

1.3 In Great Britain this species is classified as *Endangered*.

2. Current factors causing loss or decline

2.1 Decline of woodland coppice management.

2.2 Inappropriate ride and woodland management.

3. Current action

3.1 Current searches for the moth centre on former sites, including Yarner Woods NNR and Friday Street in Surrey.

4. Action plan objectives and targets

4.1 If refound in Britain, enhance the population size at known sites by 2010.

4.2 Establish an *ex situ* programme to provide material for reintroductions and ecological research.

4.3 Restore to 1980 status in Wales and southern and south-western England, by reintroductions if necessary.

5. Proposed action with lead agencies

The first priority is to determine whether the orange upperwing is still present in Britain. Suitable land management on former and potential sites will be important, in conjunction with a captive breeding programme and reintroductions to a range of former sites. Liaison with landowners and managers should highlight the importance of a diverse woodland structure.

5.1 Policy and legislation

5.1.1 Where appropriate, include the requirements of the orange upperwing when preparing or revising prescriptions for agri-environment and woodland grant schemes, focussing on the retention of small oak trees within woodlands. (ACTION: CCW, EN, FC, MAFF. WOAD)

5.2 Site safeguard and management

5.2.1 Ensure that all sites where re-establishment is proposed are appropriately managed, for example through uptake of woodland grants. (ACTION: CCW, EN, FC)

5.3 Species management and protection

5.3.1 Initiate a programme of captive breeding to provide material for experimental study and reintroductions. (ACTION: CCW, EN)

5.3.2 Following assessment of the current status of the orange upperwing, undertake reintroductions into suitably restored habitats in a range of former sites across southern and south-western England and in Wales. (ACTION: CCW, EN)

5.4 Advisory

5.4.1 Advise landowners and managers of the presence of the orange upperwing and the importance of beneficial management, aimed at a diverse woodland structure, for its conservation. (ACTION: CCW, EN)

5.5 Future research and monitoring

5.5.1 Undertake surveys to determine the status of the species. (ACTION: CCW, EN)

5.5.2 Conduct targeted autecological research to inform habitat management. (ACTION: CCW, EN, FC)

5.5.3 Pass information gathered during survey and monitoring of this species to a central database for incorporation into national and international databases. (ACTION: CCW, EN)

5.6 Communications and publicity

5.6.1 Promote opportunities for the appreciation of this species and the conservation issues associated with its habitat. This should be achieved through articles within appropriate journals, as well as by a publicity leaflet. (ACTION: CCW, EN)

5.7 Links with other action plans

5.7.1 Implementation of this action plan could benefit other species of lowland oakwoods, including the light crimson underwing *Catocala promissa,* and the dark crimson underwing *Catocala sponsa*.

5.7.2 This plan should be considered in conjunction with those for lowland wood pastures and parklands, and upland oak woods.

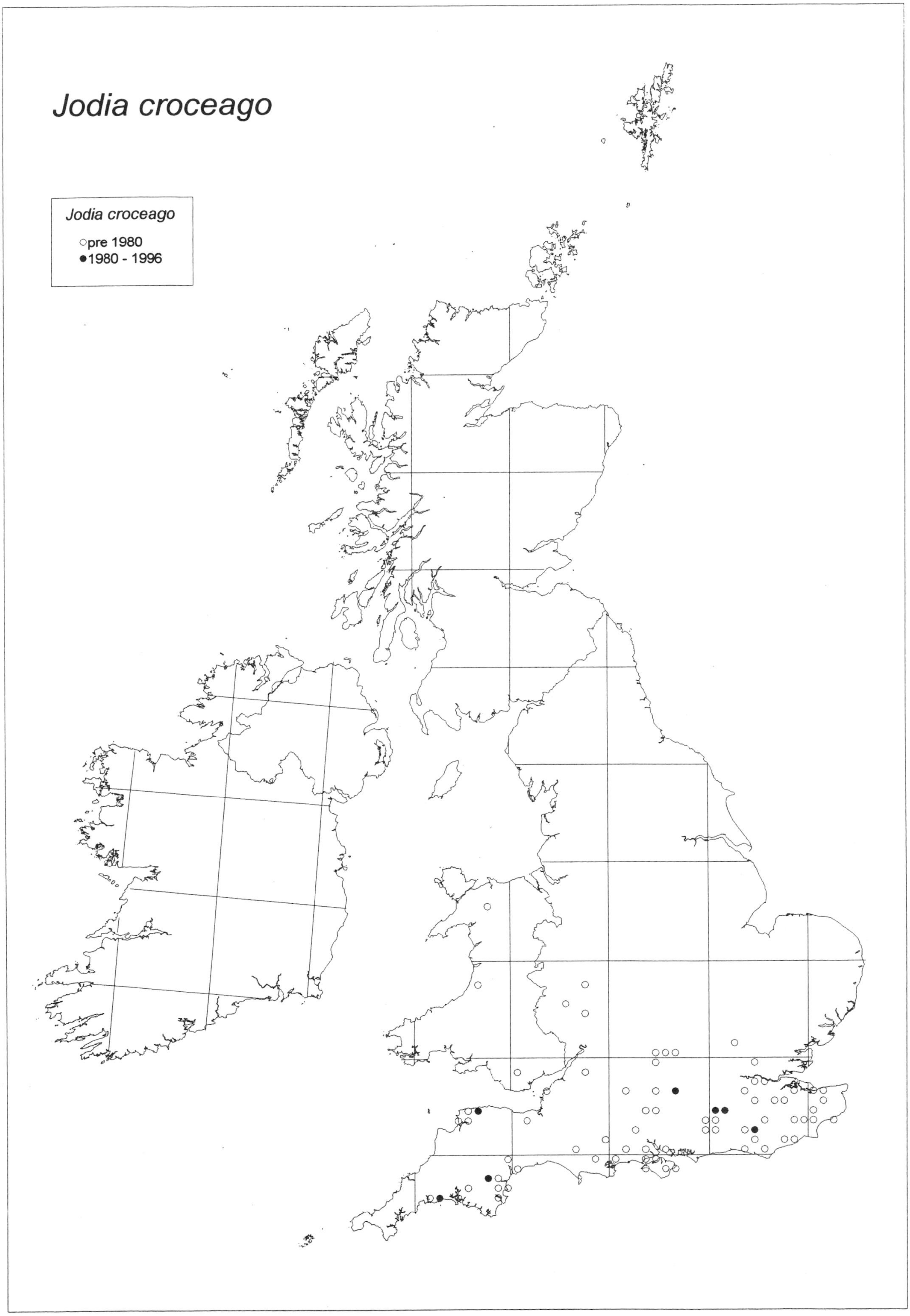

Distribution of Jodia croceago - orange upperwing in Britain, by 10km square.
Source: P. Waring - Joint Nature Conservation Committee/Butterfly Conservation Rare Moth Project.

Adonis blue (*Lysandra bellargus*)
Action Plan

1. Current status

1.1 The Adonis blue breeds in unimproved calcareous grassland, especially steep, south-facing chalk downland, where its larval food plant, horseshoe vetch *Hippocrepis comosa*, grows in a short, heavily grazed turf. It has two generations a year, with adults flying in May/early June and again, usually in larger numbers, in August and September.

1.2 The Adonis blue is a highly restricted species which occurs chiefly in Dorset, Wiltshire and the Isle of Wight, with a few colonies in Sussex, Surrey, Buckinghamshire and Kent. The species underwent a rapid decline in range, estimated at 90%, in the 1950s following a decline in stock grazing on unimproved pasture and the loss of rabbits due to myxomatosis. The species became extinct in the 19th century in Cambridge, Essex, and Suffolk, while recent extinctions have occurred in Buckinghamshire (1980s), Bedfordshire (c1960), Hertfordshire (c1960), Hampshire (apart from one site on Dorset/Hampshire border, 1990s), Gloucestershire (1963) and Somerset (1963). Since the late 1970s there has been a partial recovery due to an increase in grazing, associated primarily with the recovery in rabbit numbers and increases in stock grazing, often for conservation. However, the Adonis blue is a highly sedentary species, and its recovery is hindered by the fragmentation and isolation of its calcareous grassland habitat. Recent records suggest that there are approximately 250 populations in 272 tetrads. The Adonis blue is widespread but declining in Europe and occurs across central Europe from Spain to the Ukraine.

1.3 In Great Britain this species is classified as *Nationally Scarce*. It is given protection under Schedule 5 of the Wildlife and Countryside Act 1981, with respect to sale only.

2. Current factors causing loss or decline

2.1 Inappropriate grazing intensity due to changes in stocking rates and fluctuations in rabbit populations.

2.2 Loss of unimproved calcareous grasslands and fragmentation of remaining habitat.

3. Current action

3.1 A species action plan, grant-aided by CCW, EN, SNH and WWF, was published by Butterfly Conservation in 1997.

3.2 Conservation management is being implemented on several nature reserves and SSSIs, and under agri-environment schemes within the South Downs and South Wessex Downs ESAs and through Countryside Stewardship Scheme agreements.

3.3 There have been recent surveys to assess the butterfly's status in some parts of its range.

4. Action plan objectives and targets

4.1 Maintain existing populations, concentrating on a network of sites that contain at least some large populations.

4.2 Restore populations to the 1970-82 distribution by 2010, using reintroductions if necessary.

5. Proposed action with lead agencies

The objectives of the plan will be achieved by: encouraging beneficial land management on existing sites, especially those that occur on nature reserves; surveying sites for the Adonis blue and reviewing its status in the UK; and restoring and maintaining networks of suitable habitats. Research will support these actions, particularly conservation management, the role of ants in the life cycle, metapopulation structure, and the ecology of the species.

5.1 Policy and legislation

5.1.1 Where appropriate, include the requirements of the Adonis blue when preparing or revising prescriptions for agri-environment schemes. (ACTION: EN, MAFF)

5.2 Site safeguard and management

5.2.1 Ensure that the habitat requirements of the Adonis blue are taken into account in relevant development policies, plans and proposals affecting any site supporting large populations of the species. (ACTION: EN, LAs)

5.2.2 Where possible, ensure that all occupied habitat is appropriately managed by 2008, for example through SSSI or agri-environment scheme management agreements. (ACTION: EN, MAFF)

5.2.3 Where possible, increase the available habitat at known sites and in adjacent areas, and attempt to link up existing fragments of habitat. (ACTION: EN, MAFF)

5.2.4 Ensure that the species is included in site management documents for all relevant SSSIs. (ACTION: EN)

5.2.5 Consider notifying as SSSIs sites holding key populations of the species where this is necessary to secure their long-term protection and appropriate management. (ACTION: EN)

5.3 Species management and protection

5.3.1 Consider reintroductions into suitably restored habitat, if beyond the limits of natural spread. (ACTION: EN)

5.4 Advisory

5.4.1 Advise landowners and managers of the presence of the species and the importance of beneficial management for its conservation. (ACTION: EN, MAFF)

5.4.2 As far as possible, ensure that all relevant agri-environment project officers, and members of regional agri-environment consultation groups, are advised of locations of this species, its importance, and the management needed for its conservation. (ACTION: EN, MAFF)

5.5 Future research and monitoring

5.5.1 Undertake further surveys to determine the status of the species. (ACTION: EN)

5.5.2 Collate population monitoring data and management data from all monitored sites annually, and calculate an annual index to compare trends on individual sites. Review and extend the network if necessary. (ACTION: EN, JNCC)

5.5.3 Conduct targeted autecology research, including the possible impact of RVHD (rabbit viral haemorrhagic disease) and other new rabbit viruses, the relationship with ants and the structure of metapopulations, in order to inform habitat management. (ACTION: EN, DETR)

5.5.4 Pass information gathered during survey and monitoring of this species to a central database for incorporation in national and international databases.(ACTION: EN)

5.6 Communications and publicity

5.6.1 Promote opportunities for the appreciation of this butterfly and its habitat, and the measures being taken to conserve them, possibly through the production of a booklet. (ACTION: EN)

5.7 Links with other action plans

5.7.1 This action plan should be considered in conjunction with that for lowland calcareous grassland.

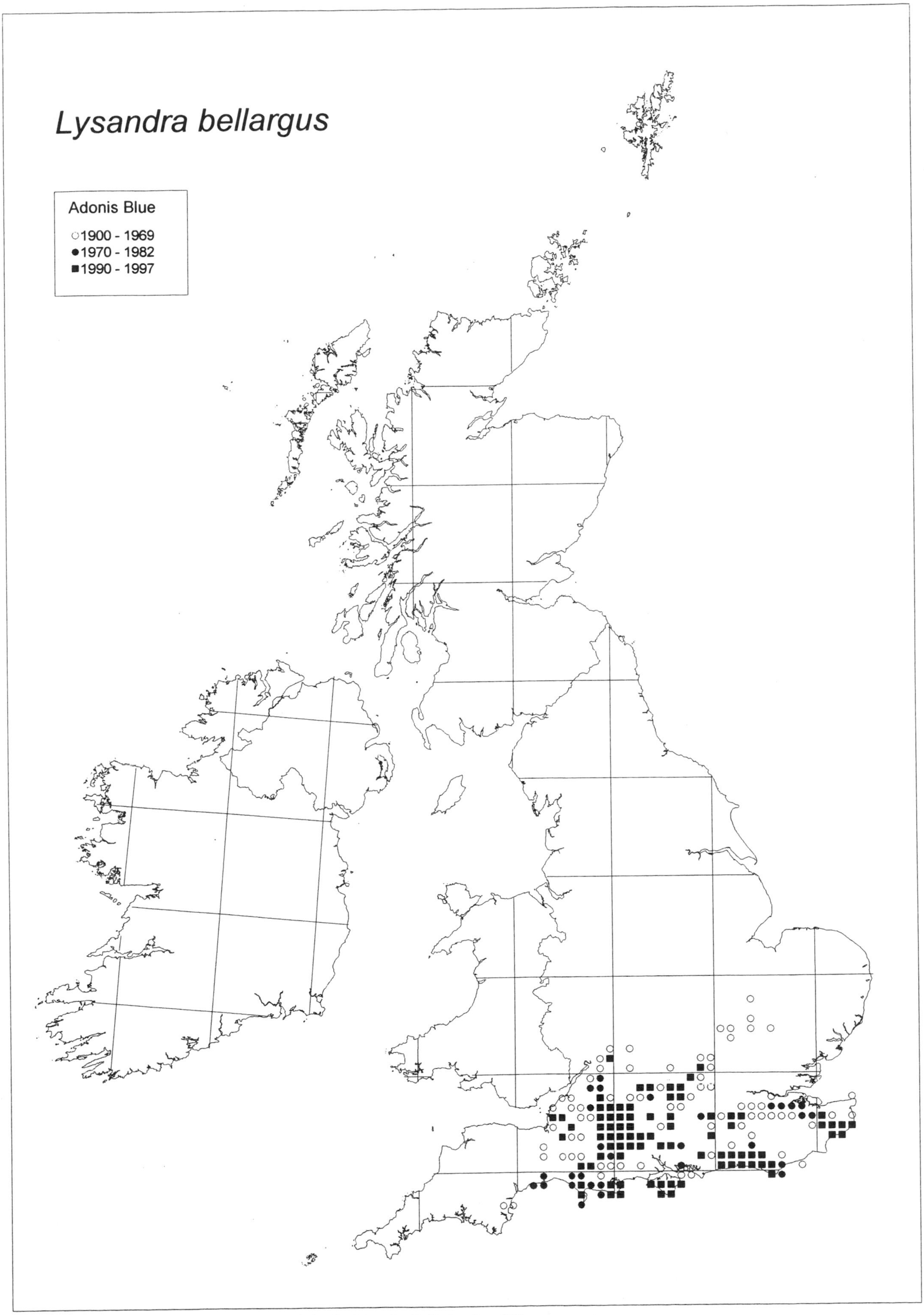

Distribution of Lysandra bellargus - Adonis blue in Britain, by 10km square.

Source: Buttefly Conservation and Biological Records Centre (ITE). The 1990 - 1997 records are provisional data from the ongoing Butterflies for the New Millennium project.

Double line (*Mythimna turca*)
Action Plan

1. Current status

1.1 The double line occurs in wet grasslands, and woodland clearings and rides. In the south west of England, the moth is able to survive in exposed situations such as open moorland and coastal grassland. Little is known about its ecology, although the larvae feed at night on grasses such as common bent-grass, creeping soft-grass and cock's-foot.

1.2 In Europe, this moth is widely distributed but local from Spain to Sweden, and is also found through Asia to Japan. In the UK, the double line is now virtually confined to western Wales and south-west England (Somerset, Devon and Cornwall), where it is chiefly associated with wet grassland. It has been recorded from south-east England in open woodland, but has now apparently largely disappeared from this habitat, perhaps due to changes in woodland management such as the shading out of woodland rides. Previously recorded from the New Forest, Savernake Forest, Epping Forest and sites in Cheshire, Buckinghamshire, Hertfordshire and West Sussex, it appears to have disappeared from all of these areas. It is still known from Richmond Park with occasional records from Wimbledon Common and Berkshire.

1.3 In Great Britain this species is classified as *Nationally Scarce*.

2. Current factors causing loss or decline

2.1 Changes in woodland management resulting in the shading out of woodland rides and glades.

2.2 Agricultural improvement of wet grassland.

2.3 Over-grazing.

3. Current action

3.1 This species is present on at least three NNRs, whilst many other populations occur on SSSIs and other nature reserves. Cors Caron and part of the Culm Measures in Devon are candidate SACs.

4. Action plan objectives and targets

4.1 Maintain populations at all known sites.

4.2 Restore populations to five former woodland sites by 2010.

5. Proposed action with lead agencies

The objectives of this plan will be achieved by securing sympathetic management of sites known to support populations, and by undertaking reintroductions to woodland sites within the former range. Research should focus on the ecological requirements of the species, whilst monitoring the effects of habitat management designed to meet these needs.

5.1 Policy and legislation

5.1.1 Where appropriate, include the requirements of the species when preparing or revising prescriptions for agri-environment schemes (eg ESAs, Woodland Grant Schemes). (ACTION: CCW, EN, FC, MAFF, WOAD)

5.2 Site safeguard and management

5.2.1 Where possible, ensure that all occupied habitat is appropriately managed by 2008, for example through SSSI or agri-environment scheme management agreements. (ACTION: CCW, EN, FC, LAs, MAFF, WOAD)

5.2.2 Ensure that the habitat requirements of this species are taken account of in relevant development policies, plans and proposals. (ACTION: CCW, EN, LAs)

5.2.3 Ensure that the double line moth is included in site management documents for all relevant SSSIs. (ACTION: CCW, EN)

5.3 Species management and protection

5.3.1 Restore populations to five former woodland sites by 2010. (ACTION: EN, FC)

5.4 Advisory

5.4.1 Advise landowners and managers of the presence of the double line and the importance of beneficial management for its conservation. (ACTION: CCW, EN, MAFF, WOAD)

5.4.2 As far as possible, ensure that all relevant agri-environment project officers, and members of regional agri-environment consultation groups, are advised of locations of this species, its importance, and the management needed for its conservation. (ACTION: CCW, EN, MAFF, WOAD)

5.5 Future research and monitoring

5.5.1 Undertake surveys to determine the current status of the double line moth. (ACTION: EN)

5.5.2 Conduct targeted autecological research to inform habitat management. (ACTION: CCW, EN).

5.5.3 Establish a regular monitoring programme for this species on key sites. (ACTION: CCW, EN)

5.5.4 Pass information gathered during the survey and monitoring of this species to a central database so that it can be incorporated into national and international databases. (ACTION: CCW, EN)

5.6 Communications and publicity

5.6.1 Promote opportunities for the appreciation of this species and the conservation issues associated with its habitats. This should be achieved through articles within appropriate journals, as well as by a publicity leaflet. (ACTION: CCW, EN)

5.7 Links with other action plans

5.7.1 Implementation of this action plan could benefit other species of wet grasslands, including the marsh fritillary *Eurodryas aurinia,* and the narrow-bordered bee hawk-moth *Hemaris tityus.*

5.7.2 This plan should be considered in conjunction with those for purple moor-grass and rush pastures, and coastal and floodplain grazing marsh.

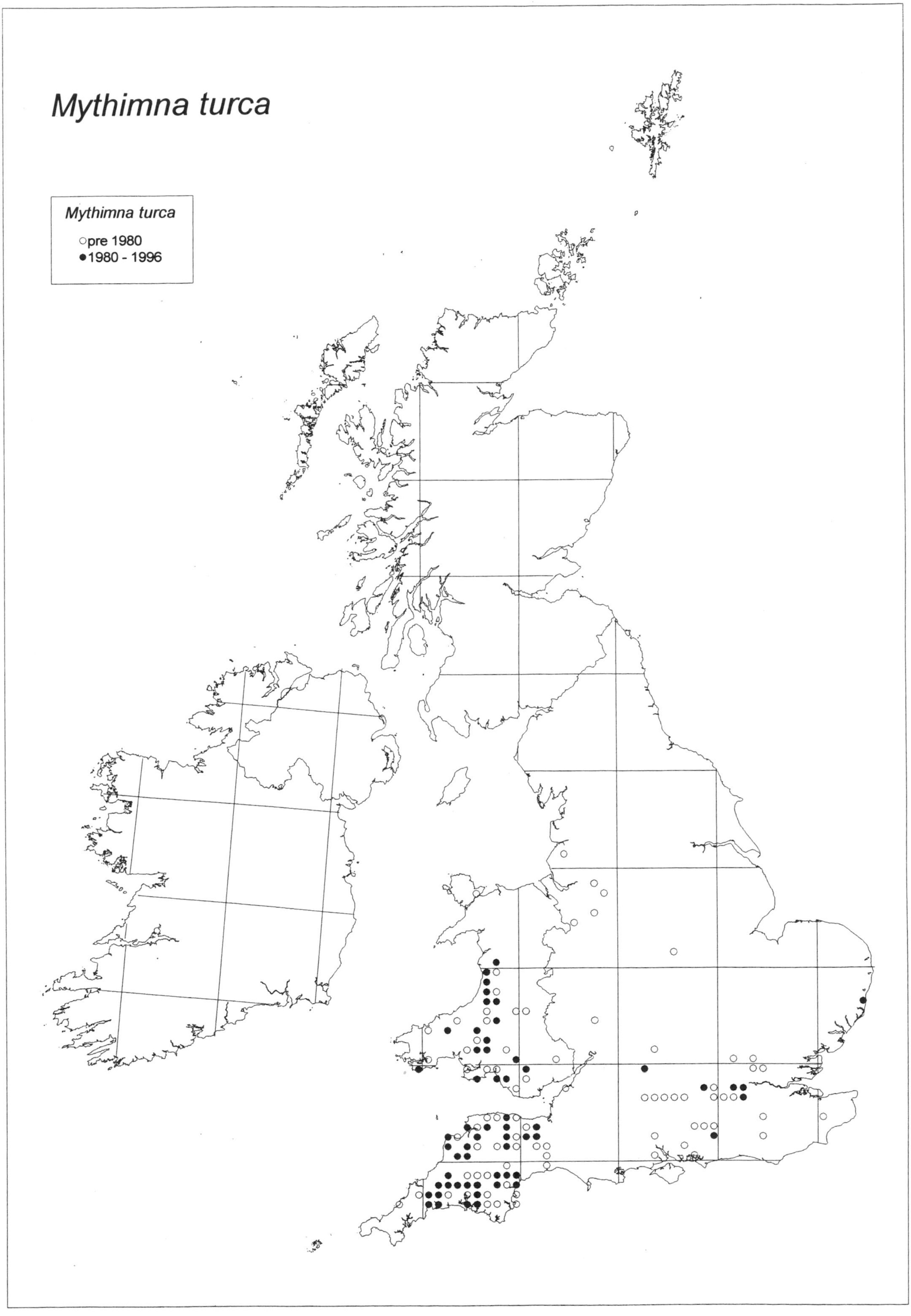

Distribution of Mythimna turca - double line in Britain, by 10km square.
Source: P. Waring - Joint Nature Conservation Committee/Butterfly Conservation Rare Moth Project.

Brighton wainscot (*Oria musculosa*)
Action Plan

1. Current status

1.1 The Brighton wainscot is now primarily associated with cereal field margins. Its eggs, which overwinter, are laid on or near various grasses and cereals. The larvae feed between April and June on winter wheat, summer rye, oats or barley.

1.2 In the UK, the Brighton wainscot has always been confined to central-southern England, with the most recent records being from south Wiltshire and north Hampshire. Since 1980 it has been reported from less than 25% of the ten km squares with previous records. The species occurs throughout central and southern Europe eastwards to Iran. It is considered to be an agricultural pest in some southern parts of its range.

1.3 In Great Britain this species is classified as *Nationally Scarce*.

2. Current factors causing loss or decline

2.1 Changes in farming practice, including choice of crops and time of sowing.

2.2 Use of insecticides.

3. Current action

3.1 None known.

4. Action plan objectives and targets

4.1 Maintain populations at all known sites.

4.2 Maintain 20 viable populations within the known range.

5. Proposed action with lead agencies

The objectives of the plan will be achieved by encouraging beneficial land management on existing sites, surveying available habitat for undiscovered populations, and restoring a network of habitat to combat potential isolation effects. Research should focus on the ecological requirements of the species, monitoring the effects of habitat management designed to meet these needs, and detection of any changes in the population which may be due to isolation.

5.1 Policy and legislation

5.1.1 Where appropriate, include the requirements of the species when preparing or revising prescriptions for agri-environment schemes. (ACTION: EN, MAFF)

5.2 Site safeguard and management

5.2.1 Encourage an increase in suitable habitat by appropriate management of cereal crops and field margins. (ACTION: EN, MAFF)

5.2.2 Where relevant, require that by 2005 management plans, which are agreed for agri-environment scheme funding, take account of the moth's requirements. (ACTION: EN, MAFF)

5.3 Species management and protection

5.3.1 None proposed.

5.4 Advisory

5.4.1 Advise landowners and managers of the presence of the species and the importance of beneficial management for its conservation. (ACTION: EN, MAFF)

5.4.2 As far as possible, ensure that all relevant agri-environment project officers, and members of regional agri-environment consultation groups, are advised of locations of this species, its importance, and the management needed for its conservation. (ACTION: EN, MAFF)

5.5 Future research and monitoring

5.5.1 Undertake surveys to determine the status of the species. (ACTION: EN)

5.5.2 Conduct targeted autecological research to inform habitat management. (ACTION: EN)

5.5.3 Pass information gathered during survey and monitoring of this species to a central database for incorporation in national and international databases. (ACTION: EN)

5.5.4 Encourage research on the ecology and conservation of this species on an international level, and use the experience gained towards its conservation in the UK. (ACTION: EN, JNCC)

5.6 Communications and publicity

5.6.1 Promote opportunities for the appreciation of this species and the conservation issues associated with its habitat. This should be achieved through articles within appropriate journals, as well as by a publicity leaflet. (ACTION: EN, MAFF)

5.7 Links with other action plans

5.7.1 This action plan should be considered in conjunction with that for cereal field margins.

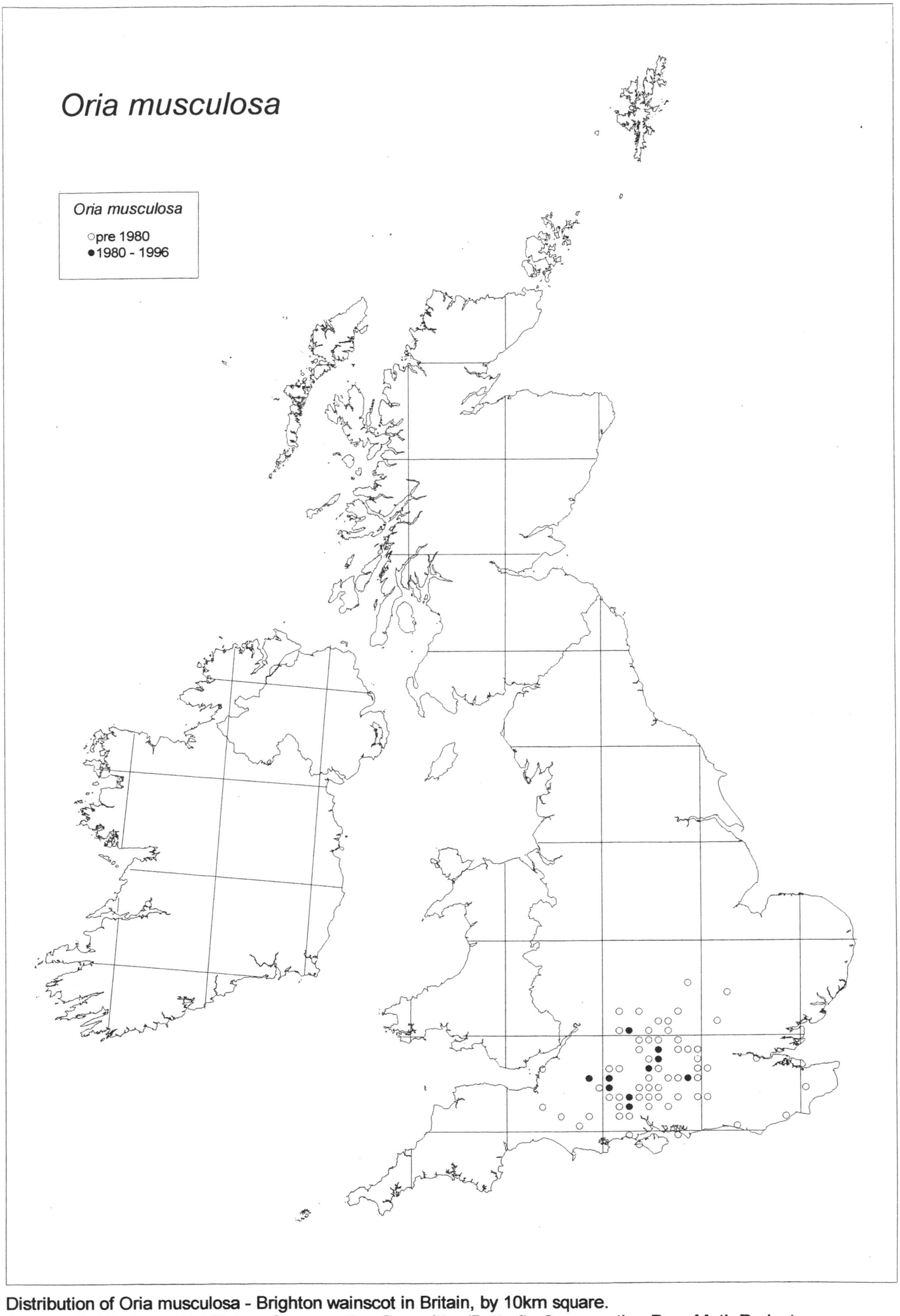

Distribution of Oria musculosa - Brighton wainscot in Britain, by 10km square.
Source: P. Waring - Joint Nature Conservation Committee/Butterfly Conservation Rare Moth Project.

Barberry carpet (*Pareulype berberata*) Action Plan

1. Current status

1.1 The barberry carpet is named after the foodplant of its larvae, barberry *Berberis vulgaris,* which occurs in hedgerows and woodland edges in sunny situations.

1.2 In the UK five colonies are known to remain in the wild: one in each of Suffolk, Gloucestershire, Wiltshire, Hampshire and Dorset. Formerly the moth occurred in other counties from Devon and Sussex north to Yorkshire. The species has been recorded from most European countries eastwards to Asia Minor and the Caucasus and reaches its northernmost limit in south-east Sweden.

1.3 In Great Britain this species is classified as *Endangered*. It is given full protection under Schedule 5 of the Wildlife and Countryside Act 1981.

2. Current factors causing loss or decline

2.1 Widespread eradication of the foodplant since the 19th century because it is a host of the wheat-rust fungus *Puccinia graminis* (to which most strains of wheat are now resistant).

2.2 Damage to the foodplant by burning, mechanised hedge trimming and hedgerow removal.

3. Current action

3.1 The species has been the subject of an EN Species Recovery Programme since 1995.

3.2 One site has been notified as an SSSI.

4. Action plan objectives and targets

4.1 Maintain populations at all known sites.

4.2 Enhance the population size at all known sites by 2010.

4.2 Restore the species to an additional series of 10 viable populations within its former range by 2010.

5. Proposed action with lead agencies

The objectives of the plan will be achieved by encouraging beneficial land management on existing sites, surveying all available habitat for undiscovered populations, and restoring a network of habitat, if necessary with introductions of the species, to combat potential isolation effects. Research should focus on the ecological requirements of the species, monitoring the effects of habitat management designed to meet these needs, and detection of any changes in the population which may be due to isolation.

5.1 Policy and legislation

5.1.1 Where appropriate, encourage the planting of native barberry through agri-environment, hedgerow and woodland grant schemes. (ACTION: EN, FC, MAFF)

5.2 Site safeguard and management

5.2.1 Where possible, ensure that all occupied habitat is appropriately managed by 2008, for example through SSSI or agri-environment scheme management agreements. Emphasis should be given to the appropriate management of hedgerows. (ACTION: EN)

5.2.2 Ensure that the habitat requirements of the barberry carpet are taken into account in relevant development policies, plans and proposals. (ACTION: LAs)

5.2.3 Ensure that the barberry carpet is included in site management documents for all relevant SSSIs. (ACTION: EN)

5.2.4 Consider sites supporting the barberry carpet for notification as SSSIs where this is necessary to secure their long-term protection and appropriate management. (ACTION: EN)

5.3 Species management and protection

5.3.1 Initiate a programme of captive breeding to provide material for experimental study and establishment trials. (ACTION: EN)

5.3.2 Reintroduce the barberry carpet to a series of former sites, if necessary to establish an additional 10 self-sustaining populations. (ACTION: EN)

5.3.3 Enforce current legislation in cases of collecting. (ACTION: EN, Police authorities)

5.4 Advisory

5.4.1 Advise landowners and managers of the presence of the species and the importance of beneficial management for its conservation. (ACTION: EN, MAFF)

5.4.2 As far as possible, ensure that all relevant agri-environment project officers, and members of regional agri-environment consultation groups, are advised of locations of this species, its importance, and the management needed for its conservation. (ACTION: EN, MAFF)

5.5 **Future research and monitoring**

5.5.1 Undertake surveys to determine the status of the species. (ACTION: EN)

5.5.2 Conduct targeted autecological research to inform habitat management. (ACTION: EN)

5.5.3 Establish a regular monitoring programme for the species, including an assessment of occupied and potential sites, to monitor the effectiveness of management agreements. (ACTION: EN)

5.5.4 Pass information gathered during survey and monitoring of this species to a central database for incorporation in national and international databases. (ACTION: EN)

5.5.5 Encourage research on the ecology and conservation of this species on an international level, and use the experience gained towards its conservation in the UK. (ACTION: EN, JNCC)

5.6 **Communications and publicity**

5.6.1 Promote opportunities for the appreciation of this species and the conservation issues associated with its habitat. This should be achieved through articles within appropriate journals, as well as by a publicity leaflet. (ACTION: EN)

5.7 **Links with other action plans**

5.7.1 This action plan should be considered in conjunction with those for cereal field margins, and ancient and species-rich hedgerows.

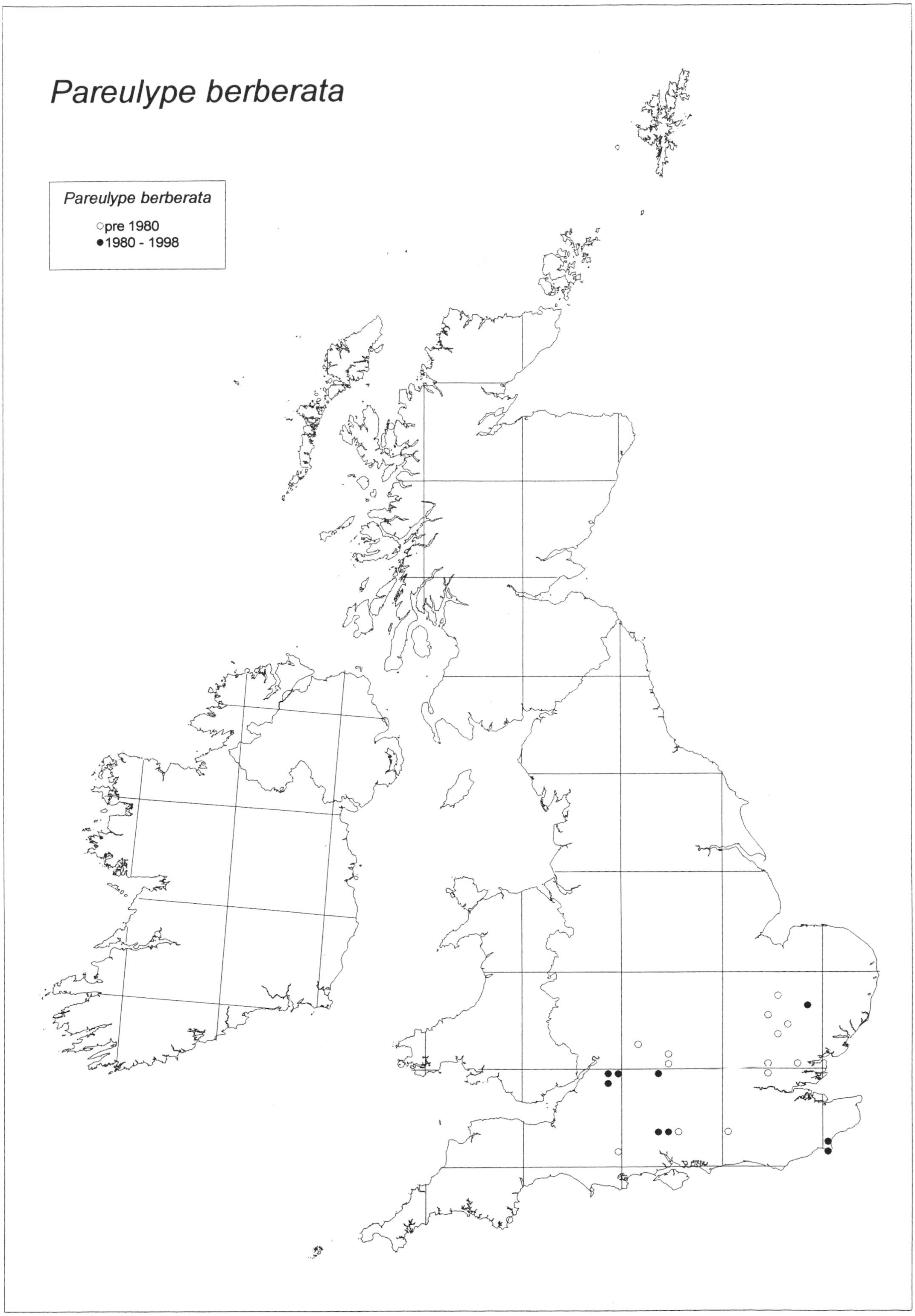

Distribution of Pareulype berberata - Barberry carpet in Britain, by 10km square.
Source: P. Waring - Joint Nature Conservation Committee/Butterfly Conservation Rare Moth Project.

Common fan-foot (*Pechipogo strigilata*)
Action Plan

1. Current status

1.1 The common fan-foot is a moth of broadleaved woodland where the larvae begin development on fresh or wilting foliage of oak, *Quercus* spp, and probably other trees and shrubs. They later prefer withered and decaying leaves on the tree or on the ground.

1.2 The moth formerly occurred throughout most of southern England and Wales, but it has declined greatly in recent decades and now survives in only a small number of oakwoods on heavy clay soils in the Midlands and south-central England. The species has been reported from almost every country in Europe except Albania, Greece, Crete and Turkey, but its current status is unclear. The range extends eastwards through Russia to Japan.

1.3 In Great Britain this species is classified as *Nationally Scarce*.

2. Current factors causing loss or decline

2.1 Not known.

3. Current action

3.1 Some of the surviving populations are on SSSIs.

4. Action plan objectives and targets

4.1 Maintain populations at all known sites.

4.2 Enhance the population size at all known sites by 2010.

4.3 Restore viable populations to five additional sites within the historic range by 2010.

5. Proposed action with lead agencies

The objectives of the plan will be achieved by encouraging beneficial land management on existing sites, surveying all available habitat for undiscovered populations, and restoring a network of habitat, if necessary with strategic introductions of the species, to combat potential isolation effects. Research should focus on the ecological requirements of the species, monitoring the effects of habitat management designed to meet these needs, and detection of any changes in the population which may be due to isolation.

5.1 Policy and legislation

5.1.1 Where appropriate, include the requirements of the species when preparing or revising prescriptions for agri-environment (farm woodland) or woodland management schemes. (ACTION: EN, FC, MAFF)

5.2 Site safeguard and management

5.2.1 Where possible, ensure that all occupied and nearby potential habitat is appropriately managed by 2005, for example through SSSI or woodland grant scheme management agreements. (ACTION: EN, FC, MAFF)

5.2.2 Increase the available habitat on the known sites and in adjacent sites, and attempt to link up existing fragments of habitat. (ACTION: EN, FC)

5.2.3 Ensure that the habitat requirements of the common fan-foot are taken into account in relevant development policies, plans and proposals, and forest (re)planting proposals. (ACTION: FC, LAs)

5.2.4 Ensure that the common fan-foot is included in site management documents for all relevant SSSIs. (ACTION: EN)

5.3 Species management and protection

5.3.1 Reintroduce the common fan-foot to a series of former sites, if necessary to establish five new viable populations. (ACTION: EN)

5.4 Advisory

5.4.1 Advise landowners and managers of the presence of the species and the importance of beneficial management for its conservation. (ACTION: EN)

5.5 Future research and monitoring

5.5.1 Undertake surveys by 2004 to determine the status of the species. (ACTION: EN)

5.5.2 Conduct targeted autecological research to inform habitat management. (ACTION: EN)

5.5.3 Establish a regular monitoring programme for the species in all core areas, including an assessment of potential sites, to monitor the effectiveness of management agreements. (ACTION: EN)

5.5.4 Pass information gathered during survey and monitoring of this species to a central database

for incorporation in national and international databases. (ACTION: EN)

5.6 Communications and publicity

5.6.1 Promote opportunities for the appreciation of this species and the conservation issues associated with its habitat. This should be achieved through articles within appropriate journals, as well as by a publicity leaflet. (ACTION: EN)

5.7 Links with other action plans

5.7.1 Implementation of this action plan could benefit other species of lowland coppiced woodland, including the drab looper *Minoa murinata*; and of mature oak woodland, including the light crimson underwing *Catocala promissa*, and the dark crimson underwing *Catocala sponsa*.

5.7.2 This plan should be considered in conjunction with that for lowland wood pastures and parklands.

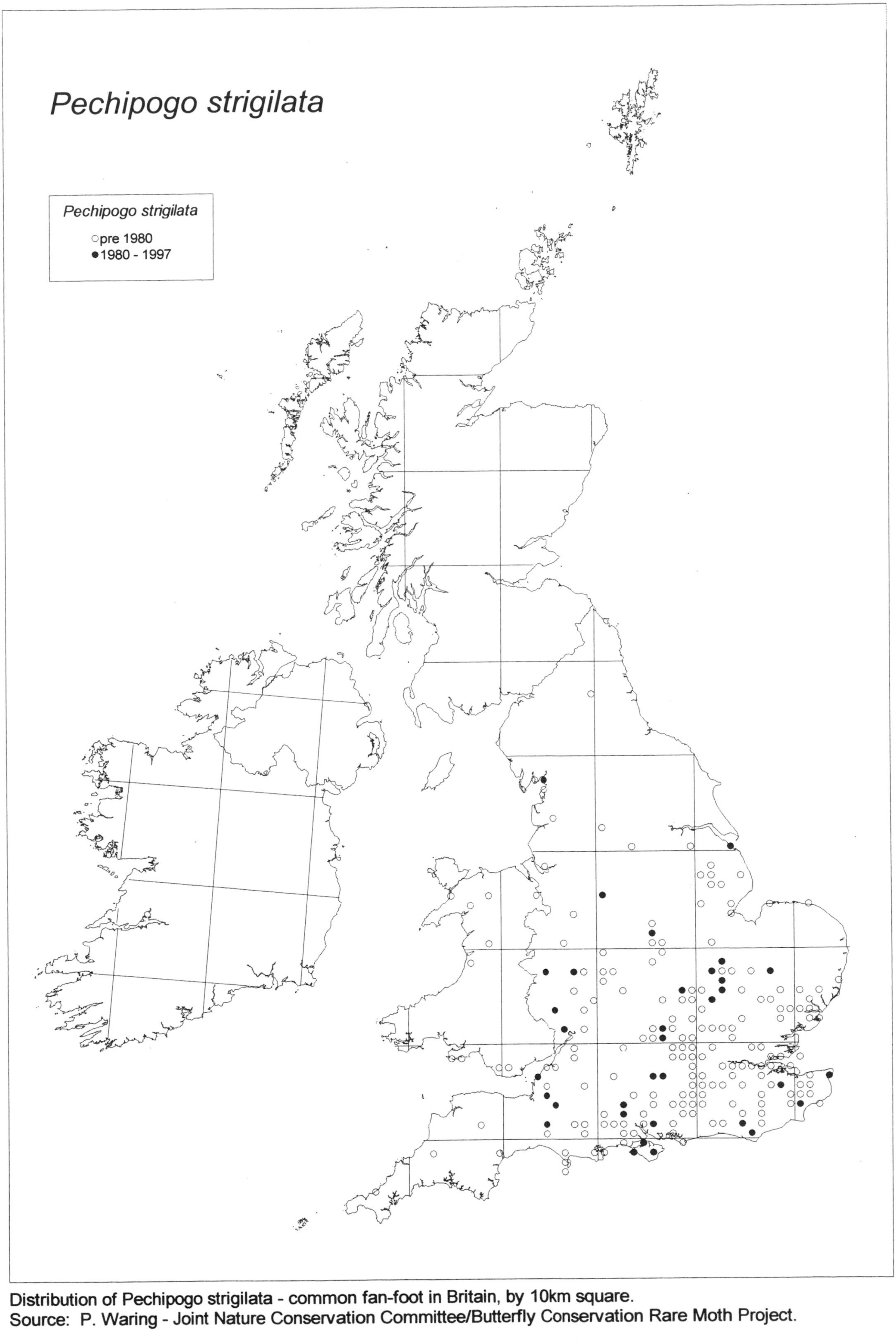

Distribution of Pechipogo strigilata - common fan-foot in Britain, by 10km square.
Source: P. Waring - Joint Nature Conservation Committee/Butterfly Conservation Rare Moth Project.

Silver-studded blue (*Plebejus argus*)
Action Plan

1. Current status

1.1 The silver-studded blue occurs on lowland heathland, calcareous grassland and at a single peatland site in Wales. In all habitats, the species requires the presence of ant species of the genus *Lasius*, open ground for breeding, and either bare soil or short vegetation. The preferred conditions produce warm microclimates at ground level for the larvae, a factor that is especially important towards the north of the species' range. Early successional stages are preferred, particularly where succession is held in check by grazing. Most heathland colonies exist on sites that have been either recently disturbed, such as sand pits, quarries and firebreaks, or burnt. Conditions usually become suitable after 2-5 years of re-growth. In the absence of traditional management (such as the cutting of heather and invasive scrub, grazing of domestic animals, or burning to encourage young growth for livestock), suitable conditions on heathlands are short-lived, perhaps lasting 5-10 years. In most situations, the silver-studded blue appears to exist in metapopulations, with patches of suitable habitat linked by the occasional dispersal of adults.

1.2 The silver-studded blue has undergone a severe decline in range this century, estimated at 80%. It has become extinct in Scotland and northern England, and throughout most of central, eastern and south-eastern England. It remains widespread only on the heaths of Dorset and Hampshire, although strong populations also occur in North Wales. It occurs throughout Europe except Scandinavia, occurring in a wide range of habitat, including alpine grassland, meadows, forest clearings and xerophytic scrubland, but it is declining in the west of Europe (eg Belgium, the Netherlands and Denmark).

1.3 In Great Britain the silver-studded blue is classified as *Nationally Scarce*. It is protected under Schedule 5 of the Wildlife and Countryside Act 1981, with respect to sale only.

2. Current factors causing loss or decline

2.1 Loss of heathland to development and agriculture

2.2 Fragmentation and isolation of habitat.

2.3 Inappropriate heathland and grassland management.

2.4 Increased quarrying activities, particularly on the Isle of Portland, Dorset.

3. Current action

3.1 A species action plan, grant-aided by CCW, EN, SNH and WWF, was published by Butterfly Conservation in 1996.

3.2 The silver-studded blue is well represented on nature reserves, SSSIs and other protected areas. Several populations are present on candidate SACs.

3.3 In 1995 EN published a booklet on the conservation of the silver-studded blue in lowland heathlands.

3.4 A number of introductions and reintroductions of the silver-studded blue have been attempted by conservationists including well-documented introductions in North Wales and Suffolk.

3.5 Three silver-studded blue populations are covered by transects operated under the Butterfly Monitoring Scheme and many more are covered by independent transects undertaken by site managers or volunteers.

4. Action plan objectives and targets

4.1 Maintain populations at all known sites.

4.2 Restore populations to former sites occupied post-1970 by 2010, using reintroductions if necessary.

5. Proposed action with lead agencies

The objectives of this plan will be achieved by: encouraging beneficial land management on existing sites; restoring and maintaining a network of habitat between existing sites and within its former range; and conducting re-introductions. Further research and survey will be supported, particularly into the status and ecology of the species in relatively poorly-described parts of its range.

5.1 Policy and legislation

5.1.1 Where appropriate, include the requirements of the silver-studded blue when preparing or revising prescriptions for agri-environment schemes. (ACTION: CCW, EN, FC, MAFF, WOAD)

5.2 Site safeguard and management

5.2.1 Where possible, ensure that all occupied habitat is appropriately managed by 2008, for example through SSSI or agri-environment scheme management agreements. (ACTION: CCW, EN, FC, MAFF, WOAD)

5.2.2 Where possible, ensure that existing populations do not become fragmented by management practices or development. (ACTION: CCW, EN, FC, LAs, MAFF, WOAD)

5.2.3 Where possible, increase the available habitat at known sites and adjacent areas, and attempt to link up existing fragments of habitat. (ACTION: CCW, EN, FC, MAFF, WOAD)

5.2.4 Restore suitable habitats in the English part of former range, initially concentrating on areas close to existing populations (south-east, south-west, eastern and midland England). (ACTION: EN)

5.2.5 Ensure that the habitat requirements of this species are taken account of in relevant development policies, plans and proposals. (ACTION: CCW, EN, LAs)

5.2.6 Ensure that the species is included in site management documents for all relevant SSSIs. (ACTION: CCW, EN)

5.3 Species management and protection

5.3.1 Consider reintroducing the silver-studded blue to a series of sites within its former range. (ACTION: CCW, EN)

5.4 Advisory

5.4.1 Advise landowners and managers of the presence of the silver-studded blue and the importance of beneficial management for its conservation. (ACTION: CCW, EN, MAFF, WOAD)

5.4.2 As far as possible, ensure that all relevant agri-environment project officers, and members of regional agri-environment consultation groups, are advised of locations of this species, its importance, and the management needed for its conservation. (ACTION: CCW, EN, MAFF, WOAD)

5.5 Future research and monitoring

5.5.1 Undertake surveys to determine the current status of the silver-studded blue. (ACTION: CCW, EN)

5.5.2 Conduct targeted autecological research to inform habitat management. (ACTION: CCW, EN)

5.5.3 Collate transect and management data from all monitored sites (in addition to Butterfly Monitoring Scheme sites) annually, and calculate an annual index to compare trends on individual sites. Review and extend series of monitored sites if necessary. (ACTION: CCW, EN)

5.5.4 Pass information gathered during survey and monitoring of this species to a central database for incorporation in national and international databases. (ACTION: CCW, EN)

5.6 Communications and publicity

5.6.1 Promote opportunities for the appreciation of the silver-studded blue and the conservation issues associated with lowland heathland and lowland calcareous grassland. (ACTION: CCW, EN)

5.7 Links with other action plans

5.7.1 Implementation of this action plan could benefit other species of lowland heathland and grasslands, including the silky wave moth *Idaea dilutaria*.

5.7.2 This plan should be considered in conjunction with those for lowland calcareous grassland, and lowland heathland.

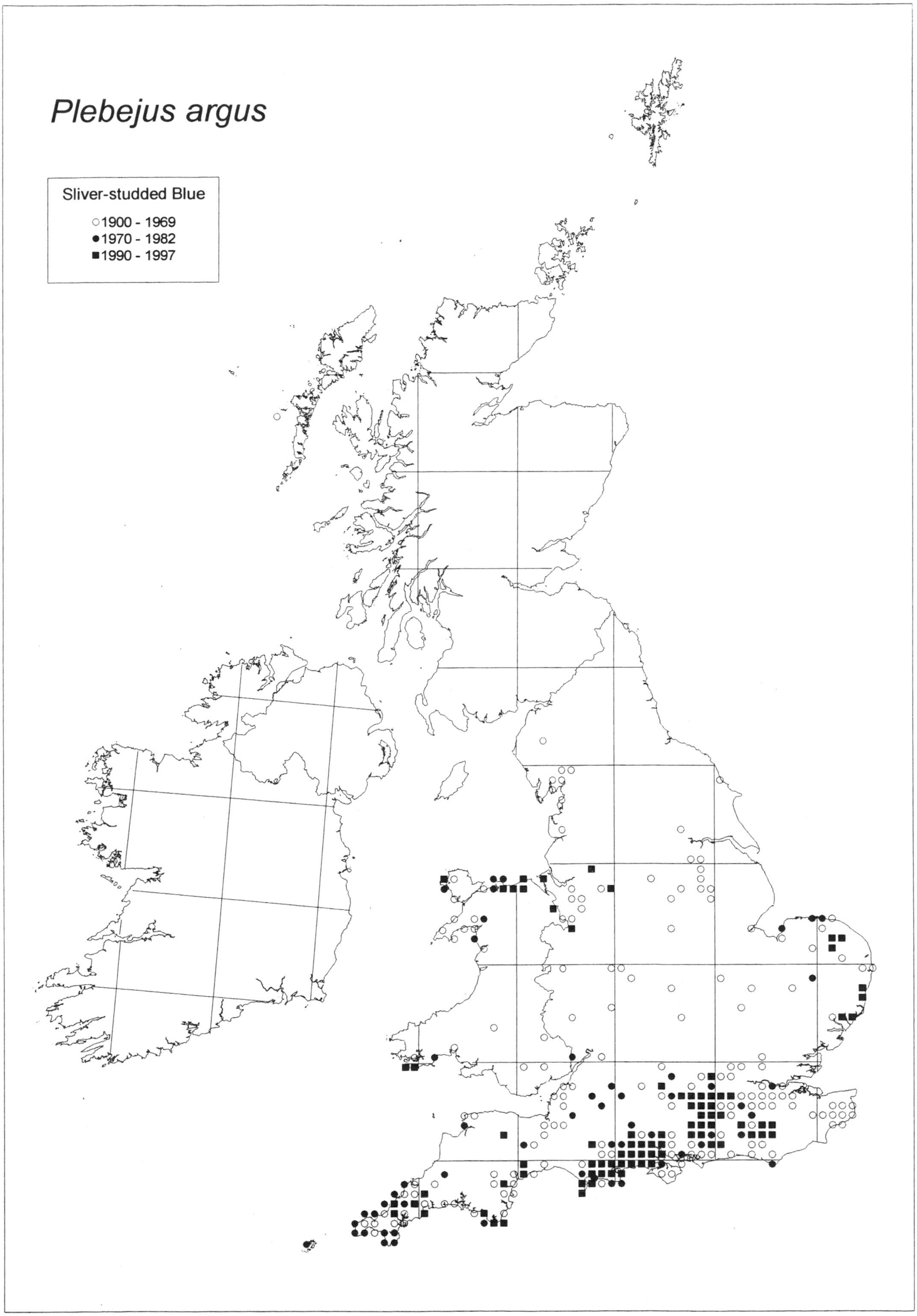

Distribution of Plebejus argus - Silver-studded Blue in Britain, by 10km square.
Source: Butterfly Conservation and Biological Records Centre (ITE). The 1990 - 1997 records are provisional data from the ongoing Buterflies for the New Millennium project.

Pale shining brown (*Polia bombycina*) Action Plan

1. Current status

1.1 The main habitat of the pale shining brown is scrubby grassland on light calcareous soils. The larval foodplant in the wild is unknown, but it has been reared in captivity on various herbaceous plants and may eat buds of low woody growth in the spring.

1.2 In the UK it formerly occurred widely in England, mainly south of a line between the Severn and the Humber, but it has declined substantially with records from about 20 scattered sites since 1980, only a few of which have strong colonies. It was formerly, and may still be, present on the coast of North Wales. This moth has been recorded from almost every country in Europe.

1.3 In Great Britain this species is classified as *Local*.

2. Current factors causing loss or decline

2.1 Not known.

3. Current action

3.1 A number of the current and former sites are SSSIs.

4. Action plan objectives and targets

4.1 Maintain populations at all known sites.

4.2 Enhance the population size at all known sites by 2010.

5. Proposed action with lead agencies

The objectives of the plan will be achieved by encouraging beneficial land management on existing sites, undertaking surveys for undiscovered colonies, and restoring a network of populations to combat the potential effects of habitat fragmentation. Research should focus on the ecological requirements of the species, monitoring the effects of habitat management designed to meet these needs, and detection of any changes in the population which may be due to isolation of colonies.

5.1 Policy and legislation

5.1.1 Where appropriate, include the requirements of the species when preparing or revising prescriptions for agri-environment and woodland grant schemes. (ACTION: CCW, EN, FC, MAFF, WOAD)

5.2 Site safeguard and management

5.2.1 Where possible, ensure that all occupied habitat is appropriately managed by 2005, for example, through SSSI or agri-environment scheme management agreements. (ACTION: CCW, EN, MAFF, WOAD)

5.2.2 Increase the available habitat on the known sites and in adjacent sites, and attempt to link up existing fragments of habitat. (ACTION: CCW, EN, MAFF, WOAD)

5.2.3 Ensure that the habitat requirements of this species are taken account of in relevant development policies, plans and proposals. (ACTION: EN, LAs)

5.2.4 Ensure that the pale shining brown is included in site management documents for all relevant SSSIs. (ACTION: CCW, EN)

5.3 Species management and protection

5.3.1 None proposed.

5.4 Advisory

5.4.1 Advise landowners and managers of the presence of this species and the importance of beneficial management for its conservation. (ACTION: CCW, EN)

5.4.2 As far as possible, ensure that all relevant agri-environment project officers, and members of regional agri-environment consultation groups, are advised of locations of this species, its importance, and the management needed for its conservation. (ACTION: CCW, EN, MAFF, WOAD)

5.5 Future research and monitoring

5.5.1 Undertake surveys to determine current distribution. (ACTION: CCW, EN)

5.5.2 Conduct targeted autecological research to elucidate the causes of decline and inform habitat management. (ACTION: CCW, EN)

5.5.3 Establish a regular monitoring programme for this species. (ACTION: CCW, EN)

5.5.4 Pass the information gathered during survey and monitoring of this species to a central database for incorporation in national and international databases. (ACTION: CCW, EN)

5.5.5 Encourage research on the ecology and conservation of this species on an international level, and use the experience gained towards its conservation in the UK. (ACTION: CCW, EN, JNCC)

5.6 Communications and publicity

5.6.1 Promote understanding and appreciation of this moth and the conservation issues associated with its habitat. This should be achieved through articles within appropriate journals, as well as by a publicity leaflet. (ACTION: CCW, EN)

5.7 Links with other action plans

5.7.1 This action plan should be considered in conjunction with that for lowland calcareous grassland.

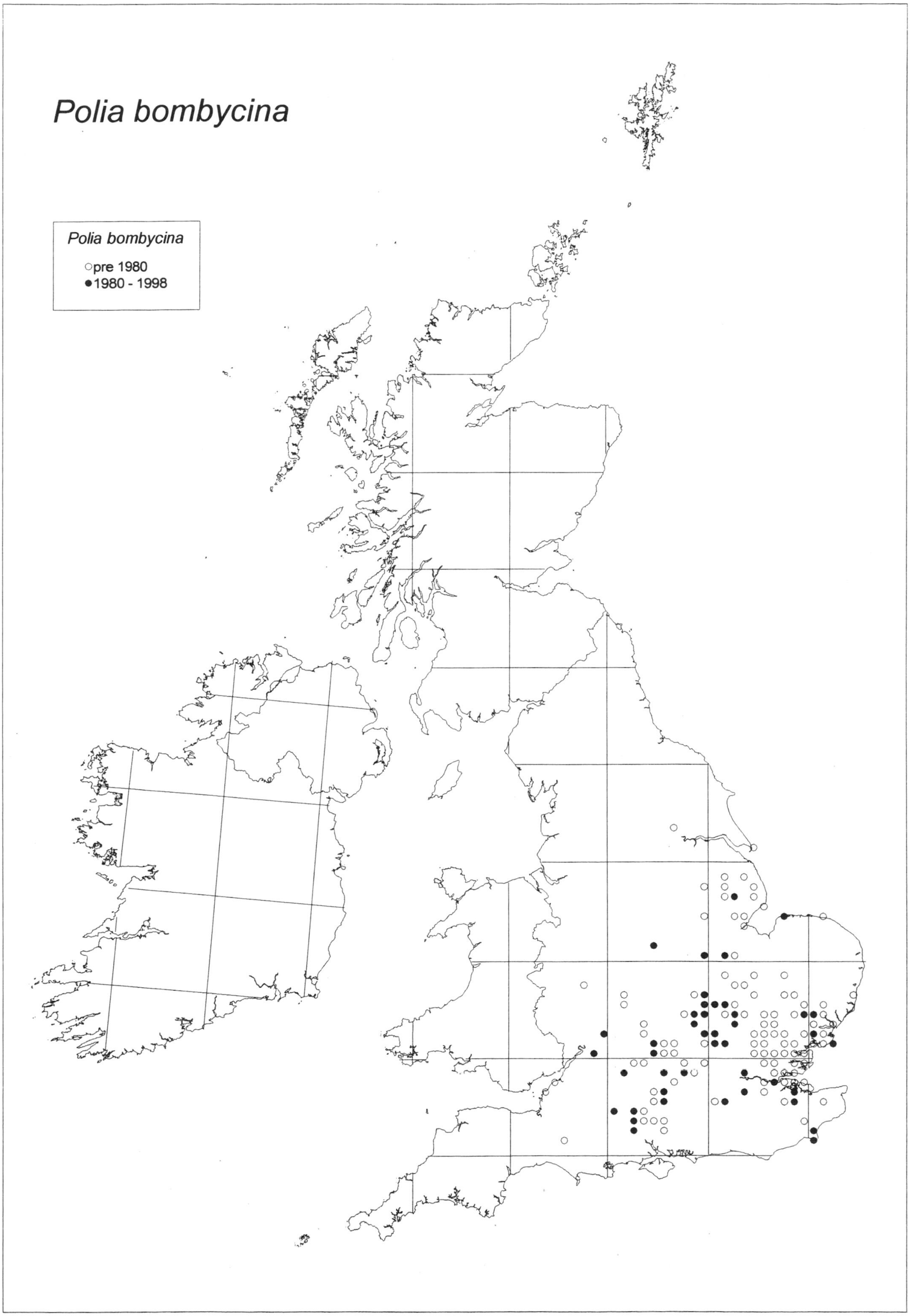

Distribution of Polia bombycina - pale shining brown in Britain, by 10km square.
Source: P. Waring - Joint Nature Conservation Committee/Butterfly Conservation Rare Moth Project.

Netted mountain moth (*Semiothisa carbonaria*) Action Plan

1. Current status

1.1 The netted mountain moth inhabits open moorland and mountainsides. The larva feeds by night on the foliage of bearberry, resting by day on the underside of a leaf. The larval period coincides with the time when young shoots are available, and the adults fly between April and early June when these shoots are forming. Larvae have been reared in captivity on birch, sallow, and bilberry, but there is no evidence that these are used in the wild. They overwinter as pupae.

1.2 This is a moth of northern Europe; it is quite common in northern parts of Norway, Sweden and Finland. It also occurs in the mountains of central Europe, south to the Alps and eastwards through Russia to north-east Siberia. It is not recorded from Ireland. In the UK it has a scattered distribution in the central Scottish Highlands, where it is known from fewer than 15 ten km squares, though it may be under-recorded owing to the remoteness of the moorland and mountainside habitats it occupies. The habitat of this moth, *Arctostaphylos* heath, is threatened by a range of factors including over-grazing, afforestation and neglect.

1.3 In Great Britain this species is classified as *Rare*.

2. Current factors causing loss or decline

2.1 Inappropriate moorland management, including neglect.

2.2 Uncontrolled burning

2.3 Over-grazing.

3. Current action

3.1 Some of the occupied sites are SSSIs and/or nature reserves, including NNRs.

3.2 Some colonies of the moth were surveyed for SNH in 1996.

4. Action plan objectives and targets

4.1 Maintain populations at all known sites.

4.2 Enhance the population size at known sites by 2010.

5. Proposed action with lead agencies

The main priorities for the netted mountain moth are to ensure that suitable management is implemented on known sites, and to prevent fragmentation of occupied patches. Surveys will be required to clarify the status of this species, and research will be necessary to elucidate its habitat requirements.

5.1 Policy and legislation

5.1.1 Where appropriate, include the requirements of the species when preparing or revising prescriptions for agri-environment schemes and grants, especially woodland grant schemes for areas on or near to colonies. (ACTION: FC, SNH, SOAEFD)

5.2 Site safeguard and management

5.2.1 Where possible, ensure that occupied and nearby potential habitat is appropriately managed by 2005, considering management agreements where this will improve long-term results. (ACTION: SNH)

5.2.2 Ensure that existing populations do not become fragmented by management practices or development. (ACTION: FC, LAs, SNH)

5.2.3 Ensure that this species is included in site management documents for relevant SSSIs. (ACTION: SNH)

5.3 Species management and protection

5.3.1 None proposed

5.4 Advisory

5.4.1 Advise landowners and managers of the presence of this species and the importance of beneficial management for its conservation. (ACTION: SNH)

5.5 Future research and monitoring

5.5.1 Undertake further surveys to determine the range and status of the netted mountain moth. (ACTION: SNH)

5.5.2 Conduct targeted autecological research to inform habitat management. (ACTION: SNH)

5.5.3 Establish a regular monitoring programme for this moth. (ACTION: SNH)

5.5.4 Encourage research on the ecology and conservation of this species at an international level, and use the experience gained to inform its conservation in the UK. (ACTION: JNCC, SNH)

5.5.5 Pass information gathered during survey and monitoring of this moth to a central database for incorporation into national and international databases. (ACTION: SNH)

5.6 Communications and publicity

5.6.1 Promote opportunities for the appreciation of this moth and the conservation issues associated with its habitat. This should be achieved through articles within appropriate journals, as well as by publicity leaflets. (ACTION: SNH)

5.7 Links with other action plans

5.7.1 This action plan should be considered in conjunction with that for upland heathland.

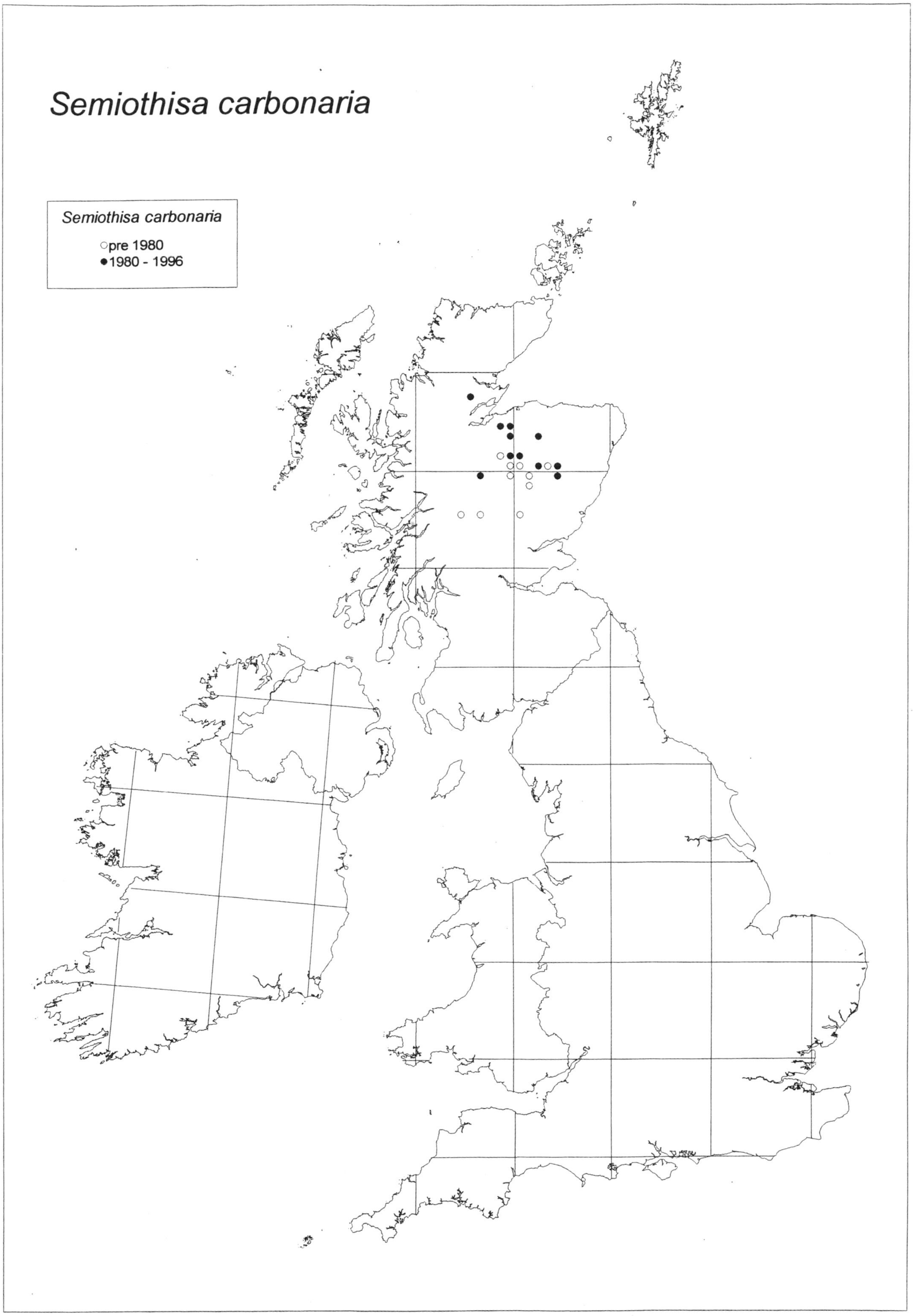

Distribution of Semiothisa carbonaria - netted mountain moth in Britain, by 10km square.
Source: P. Waring - Joint Nature Conservation Committee/Butterfly Conservation Rare Moth Project.

Black-veined moth (*Siona lineata*)
Action Plan

1. Current status

1.1 The black-veined moth is a species of lowland calcareous grasslands. The main larval foodplant in the UK is marjoram *Origanum vulgare*, and the larvae probably also feed on the leaves of other herbs. All of the surviving sites are dominated by tor-grass *Brachypodium pinnatum* and moderate sward heights of 10-25 cm are preferred.

1.2 This moth is now apparently restricted to four fields on chalk in Kent. Formerly the moth was more widespread, with populations in other parts of Kent, in Somerset, Dorset, Sussex, and Essex, with single records from Gloucestershire and Hertfordshire. This species has been recorded from most countries in Europe eastwards to Siberia.

1.3 In Great Britain this species is classified as *Endangered*. It is given full protection under Schedule 5 of the Wildlife and Countryside Act 1981.

2. Current factors causing loss or decline

2.1 Inappropriate grassland management leading to scrub encroachment.

2.2 Accidental or deliberate burning.

3. Current action

3.1 The species has been the subject of an EN Species Recovery Programme project since 1995.

3.2 Two of the occupied sites are SSSIs.

4. Action plan objectives and targets

4.1 Maintain populations at all known sites.

4.2 Restore at least 10 viable populations, each on at least 5 ha of suitable habitat, within the former range by 2005.

5. Proposed action with lead agencies

The objectives of the plan will be achieved by encouraging beneficial land management on existing sites, surveying all available habitat for undiscovered populations, and restoring a network of habitat, if necessary with introductions of the species, to combat potential isolation effects. Research should focus on the ecological requirements of the species, monitoring the effects of habitat management designed to meet these needs, and detection of any changes in the population which may be due to isolation.

5.1 Policy and legislation

5.1.1 Where appropriate, incorporate the requirements of the black-veined moth when preparing or revising prescriptions for agri-environment schemes. (ACTION: EN, MAFF)

5.2 Site safeguard and management

5.2.1 Where possible, ensure that all occupied and nearby potential habitat in the former range is appropriately managed by 2005. (ACTION: EN)

5.2.2 Increase the available habitat on the known sites and in adjacent sites, and attempt to link up existing fragments of habitat. (ACTION: EN)

5.2.3 Ensure that the habitat requirements of the black-veined moth are taken into account in relevant development policies, plans and proposals. (ACTION: LAs)

5.2.4 Ensure that black-veined moth is included in site management documents for all relevant SSSIs. (ACTION: EN)

5.2.5 Consider notifying as SSSIs sites supporting populations of this species if necessary to secure their long-term protection and appropriate management. (ACTION: EN)

5.3 Species management and protection

5.3.1 Initiate a programme of captive breeding to provide material for experimental study and reintroduction. (ACTION: EN)

5.3.2 Reintroduce the black-veined moth to a series of sites within the former range if necessary to establish 10 new viable populations by 2005. (ACTION: EN)

5.3.3 Enforce current legislation in cases of collecting. (ACTION: EN, Police authorities)

5.4 Advisory

5.4.1 Advise landowners and managers of the presence of the species and the importance of beneficial management for its conservation. (ACTION: EN)

5.5 Future research and monitoring

5.5.1 Undertake surveys to determine the status of the species. (ACTION: EN)

5.5.2 Conduct targeted autecological research to inform habitat management. (ACTION: EN)

5.5.3 Establish a regular monitoring programme for the species, including an assessment of occupied and potential sites, to monitor the effectiveness of management agreements. (ACTION: EN)

5.5.4 Pass information annually from survey and monitoring of this species to a central database for incorporation in national and international databases. (ACTION: EN)

5.5.5 Encourage research on the ecology and conservation of this species on an international level, and use the experience gained towards its conservation in the UK. (ACTION: EN, JNCC)

5.6 Communications and publicity

5.6.1 Promote opportunities for the appreciation of the black-veined moth and the conservation issues associated with its habitat. This should be achieved through articles within appropriate journals, as well as by a publicity leaflet. (ACTION: EN)

5.7 Links with other action plans

5.7.1 This action plan should be considered in conjunction with that for lowland calcareous grassland.

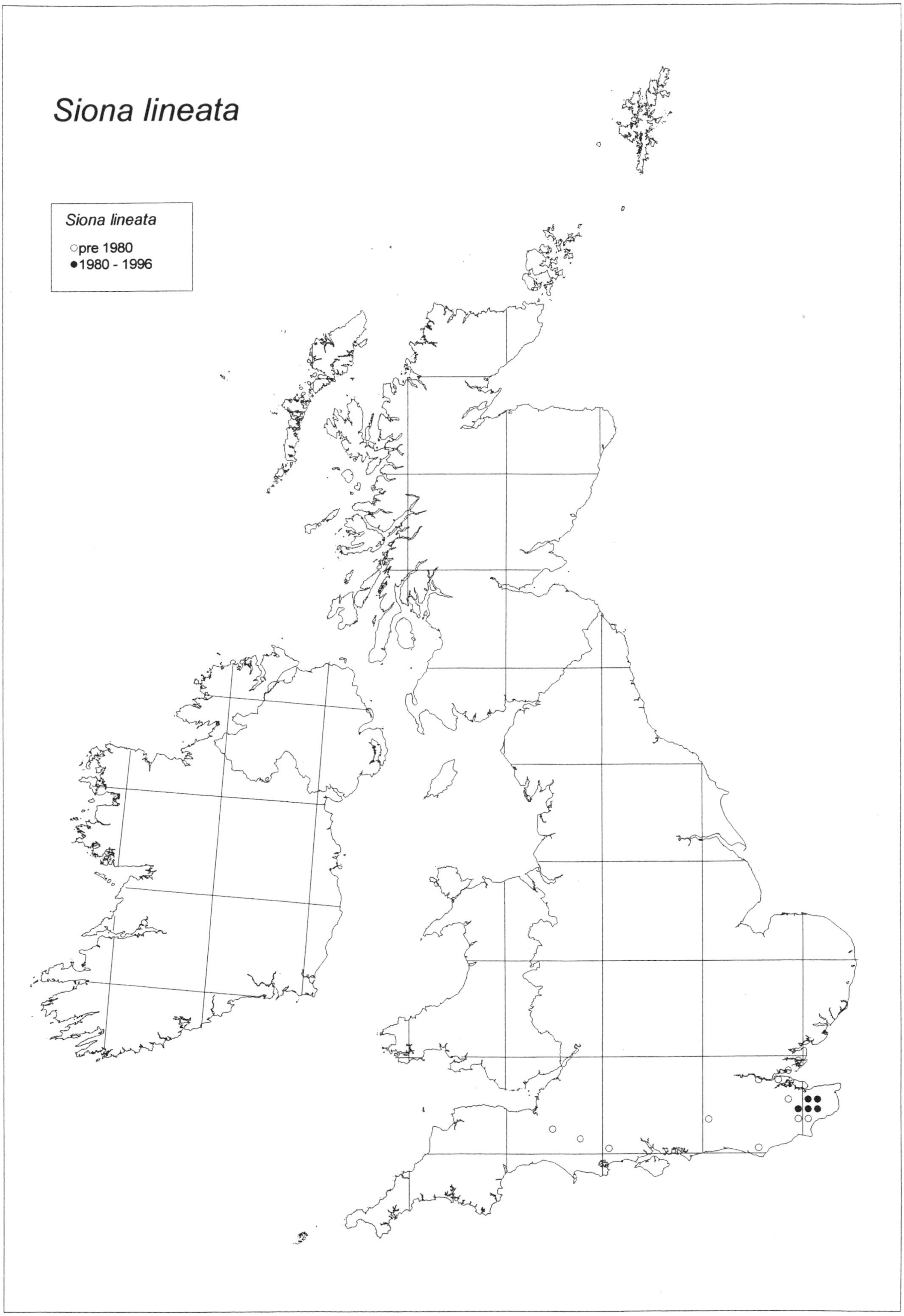

Distribution of Siona lineata - black-veined moth in Britain, by 10km square.
Source: P. Waring - Joint Nature Conservation Committee/Butterfly Conservation Rare Moth Project.

Four-spotted moth (*Tyta luctuosa*)
Action Plan

1. Current status

1.1 The four-spotted moth is a grassland species which is typically found on south-facing banks on well-drained soils with sparse vegetation and bare earth. The larva feeds on field bindweed *Convolvulus arvensis*, preferring the flowers and seeds initially.

1.2 This moth was formerly widespread and fairly common in England south of a line from Norfolk to Somerset. There has been a massive decline since the 1930s, and recently it has been reported from only 11 counties in southern England, chiefly on limestone grassland or in the Breckland. The moth has been recorded from every country in Europe except Ireland and Norway. The range extends eastwards to western Siberia and includes Morocco.

1.3 In Great Britain this moth is classified as *Vulnerable*.

2. Current factors causing loss or decline

2.1 Loss of habitat due to agricultural intensification and development.

2.2 Inappropriate grassland management.

3. Current action

3.1 Several occupied sites are SSSIs. Breckland is a proposed SAC.

4. Action plan objectives and targets

4.1 Maintain populations at all known sites.

4.2 Enhance the population size at all known sites by 2010.

4.3 Restore viable populations to 10 new sites throughout the former range of the moth by 2010.

5. Proposed action with lead agencies

The objectives of the plan will be achieved by encouraging beneficial land management on existing sites, surveying all available habitat for undiscovered populations, and restoring a network of habitat, if necessary with introductions of the species, to combat potential isolation effects. Research will focus on the ecological requirements of the species, monitoring the effects of habitat management designed to meet these needs, and detection of any changes in the population which may be due to isolation.

5.1 Policy and legislation

5.1.1 Where appropriate, include the requirements of the species when preparing or revising prescriptions for agri-environment schemes. (ACTION: EN, MAFF)

5.2 Site safeguard and management

5.2.1 Where possible, ensure that occupied and nearby potential habitat are appropriately managed by 2005. (ACTION: EN, MAFF)

5.2.2 Where possible, increase the available habitat on the known sites and in adjacent sites, and attempt to link up existing fragments of habitat. (ACTION: EN, MAFF)

5.2.3 Ensure that the habitat requirements of four-spotted moth are taken into account in relevant development policies, plans and proposals. (ACTION: LAs)

5.2.4 Ensure that the four-spotted moth is included in site management documents for all relevant SSSIs. (ACTION: EN)

5.3 Species management and protection

5.3.1 Reintroduce the four-spotted moth to a series of sites within the former range if necessary to restore 10 new viable populations by 2010. (ACTION: EN)

5.4 Advisory

5.4.1 Advise landowners and managers of the presence of the species and the importance of beneficial management for its conservation. (ACTION: EN, MAFF)

5.4.2 As far as possible, ensure that all relevant agri-environment project officers, and members of regional agri-environment consultation groups, are advised of locations of this species, its importance, and the management needed for its conservation. (ACTION: EN, MAFF)

5.5 Future research and monitoring

5.5.1 Undertake surveys to determine the status of the species. (ACTION: EN)

5.5.2 Conduct targeted autecological research to identify the precise habitat requirements of the species by 2000. (ACTION: EN)

5.5.3 Establish a regular monitoring programme for the species, including an assessment of potential sites to monitor the effectiveness of management agreements. (ACTION: EN)

5.5.4 Pass information gathered during survey and monitoring of this species to a central database for incorporation in national and international databases. (ACTION: EN)

5.6 Communications and publicity

5.6.1 Promote opportunities for the appreciation of the four-spotted moth and the conservation issues associated with its habitat. This should be achieved through articles within appropriate journals, as well as by a publicity leaflet. (ACTION: EN)

5.7 Links with other action plans

5.7.1 This action plan should be considered in conjunction with that for lowland calcareous grassland.

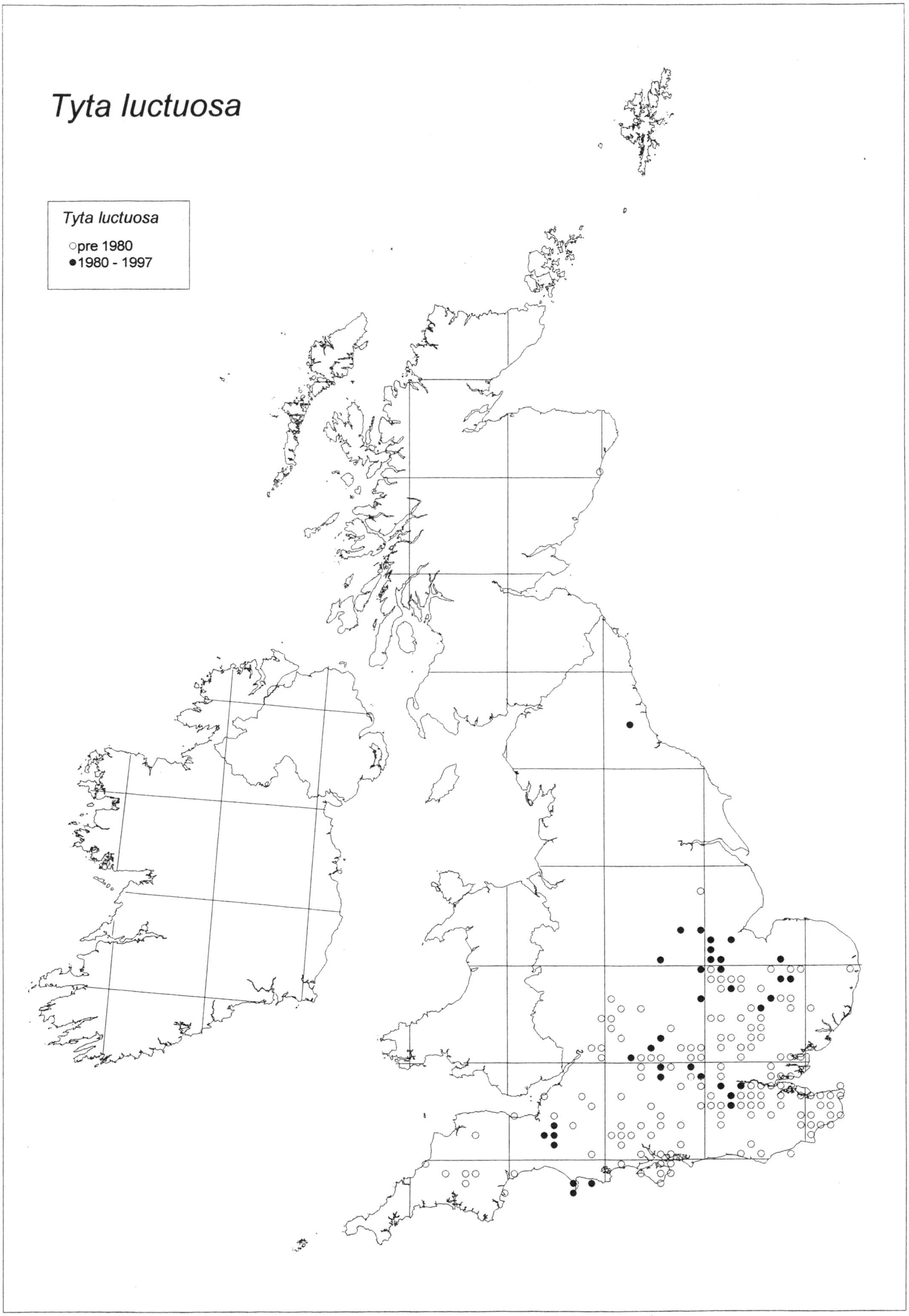

Distribution of Tyta luctuosa - four-spotted moth in Britain, by 10km square.
Source: P. Waring - Joint Nature Conservation Committee/Butterfly Conservation Rare Moth Project.

Sword-grass (*Xylena exsoleta*) Action Plan

1. Current status

1.1 The sword-grass has been recorded in a wide range of habitats, mostly in uplands and moorlands. The larval ecology in the wild is almost unknown. In captivity the larvae will eat the foliage of various herbaceous plants, including broadleaved dock and the leaves of some woody plants, including hawthorn, blackthorn and bird cherry, but they are selective and by no means widely polyphagous.

1.2 The sword-grass has been recorded from every country in Europe except Luxembourg and Albania. It reaches Iceland and its range extends to Japan. In the UK this moth was formerly widespread but has undergone a substantial decline since the 1960s. Since 1980 it has been recorded only occasionally in England, usually as singletons. In Wales and Northern Ireland the species is sparsely recorded but is still resident. Only in Scotland, including Shetland and Fair Isle, is the moth still being recorded regularly in numbers at various upland sites, and it is probably breeding over large areas here.

1.3 In Great Britain this species is classified as *Nationally Scarce*.

2. Current factors causing loss or decline

2.1 Not known.

3. Current action

3.1 Some of the occupied sites are SSSIs.

4. Action plan objectives and targets

4.1 Maintain populations at all known sites.

4.2 Enhance the population size at all known sites by 2010.

5. Proposed action with lead agencies

The recovery of sword-grass will be dependent on encouraging beneficial land management on existing sites and suitable habitat nearby, and undertaking surveys for undiscovered colonies. Research should focus on the ecological requirements of the moth, monitoring the effects of habitat management designed to meet these needs, and detection of any changes in the populations which may be due to isolation of colonies.

5.1 Policy and legislation

5.1.1 Where appropriate, include the requirements of the species when preparing or revising prescriptions for agri-environment schemes. (ACTION: CCW, DANI, EHS, EN, MAFF, SNH, SOAEFD, WOAD)

5.2 Site safeguard and management

5.2.1 Where possible, ensure that all occupied and nearby potential habitat is appropriately managed, for example through SSSI or agri-environment scheme management agreements. (ACTION: CCW, DANI, EHS, EN, MAFF, SNH, SOAEFD, WOAD)

5.2.2 Where possible, increase the available habitat on the known sites and adjacent areas, and attempt to link up existing fragments of habitat. (ACTION: CCW, DANI, EHS, EN, MAFF, SNH, SOAEFD, WOAD)

5.2.3 Ensure that the existing populations do not become fragmented by management practices or development. (ACTION: CCW, EHS EN, LAs, SNH)

5.2.4 Ensure that the habitat requirements of this species are taken account of in relevant development policies, plans and proposals. (ACTION: CCW, EHS, EN, LAs, SNH)

5.2.5 Ensure that the sword-grass is included in site management documents for all relevant SSSIs/ASSIs. (ACTION: CCW, EHS, EN, SNH)

5.3 Species management and protection

5.3.1 None proposed.

5.4 Advisory

5.4.1 Advise landowners and managers of the presence of the species and the importance of beneficial management for its conservation. (ACTION: CCW, DANI, EHS, EN, MAFF, SNH, SOAEFD, WOAD)

5.4.2 As far as possible, ensure that all relevant agri-environment project officers, and members of regional agri-environment consultation groups, are advised of locations of this species, its importance, and the management needed for its conservation. (ACTION: CCW, DANI, EHS, EN, MAFF, SNH, SOAEFD, WOAD)

5.5 **Future research and monitoring**

5.5.1 Undertake surveys to determine current status of this species. (ACTION: CCW, EHS, EN, SNH)

5.5.2 Conduct targeted autecological research to elucidate the causes of decline and inform habitat management. (ACTION: CCW, EHS, EN, SNH)

5.5.3 Establish a regular monitoring programme for the species. (ACTION: CCW, EHS, EN, SNH)

5.5.4 Pass the information gathered during survey and monitoring of this species to a central database for incorporation in national and international databases. (ACTION: CCW, EHS, EN, SNH)

5.5.5 Encourage research on the ecology and conservation of this species on an international level, and use the experience gained towards its conservation in the UK. (ACTION: CCW, EHS, EN, JNCC, SNH)

5.6 **Communications and publicity**

5.6.1 Promote opportunities for the appreciation of the sword-grass and the conservation issues associated with its habitat. This should be achieved through articles within appropriate journals, as well as by publicity leaflets. (ACTION: CCW, EHS, EN, SNH)

5.7 **Links with other action plans**

5.7.1 This action plan should be considered in conjunction with that for upland heathland.

Xylena exsoleta

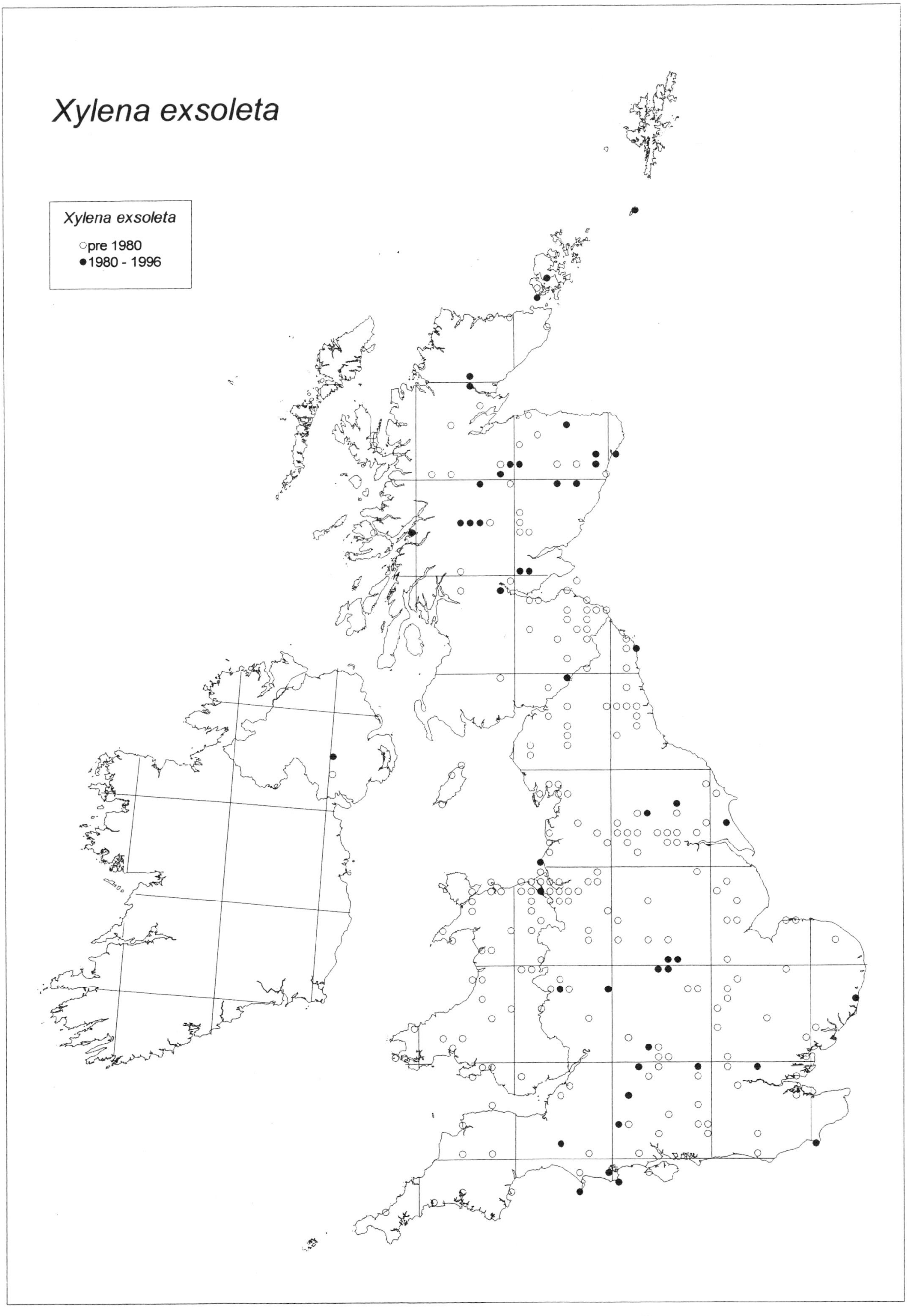

Distribution of Xylena exsoleta - sword-grass in Britain and Northern Ireland, by 10km square.
Source: P. Waring - Joint Nature Conservation Committee/Butterfly Conservation Rare Moth Project.

Slender Scotch burnet (*Zygaena loti scotica*)
Action Plan

1. Current status

1.1 The colonies of the slender Scotch burnet are on steep south - or south-west - facing slopes, usually below coastal cliffs. The slopes have thin base-rich soils and short, early successional vegetation that is maintained by erosion and grazing. The larvae bask near the foodplant, common bird's-foot trefoil, in areas open to the sun, for example on stones, bare soil or moss cushions. Larvae of the moth are absent from tall grass swards even though the foodplant may be present. Where grazing has been relaxed, bracken invasion has reduced the area available to some colonies. A proportion of the slender Scotch burnet larvae may re-enter diapause after emerging from hibernation. The number of successive years they can do this is not known. This diapause may explain some of the large annual fluctuations in the size of the adult population. The main colonies on Mull may function as one or two metapopulations, depending on the periodic re-creation of small patches of suitable habitat by grazing and natural erosion. Two of the known colonies are highly isolated, and suitable habitats elsewhere in the range are unlikely to be colonised. Potential colonisation is limited because the adults are largely sedentary; few stray beyond the immediate boundaries of colonies.

1.2 *Z. loti* is widespread in central Europe, occurring north to the Baltic, south to the Mediterranean and east to the Caucasus and northern Iran. However, the subspecies *scotica* is presumed to be endemic to Scotland. The slender Scotch burnet has a very limited distribution within the UK; it is now confined to the islands of Mull and Ulva. Colonies are known to have become extinct on Morvern and at two sites in northern Mull. Further areas near existing populations on Mull were once occupied, and the existing colonies have contracted in size and extent. Previous decline and the status of the individual colonies suggest that, unless action is taken, further decline is probable. Any such decline will lead to the further isolation of the existing colonies, and increasing risk of eventual extinction of this species in the UK.

1.3 In Great Britain the slender Scotch burnet is classified as *Rare*.

2. Current factors causing loss or decline

2.1 Inappropriate grazing levels.

2.2 Afforestation.

2.3 Isolation of colonies.

3. Current action

3.1 The slender Scotch burnet is included in the SNH Species Action Programme.

3.2 All known colonies were surveyed in 1997.

3.3 Habitat management for this species is being undertaken on some sites.

3.4 All but five of the existing populations are within an SSSI and a National Trust For Scotland property. The requirements of the species are included in the relevant SSSI management plans.

3.5 Monitoring transects were established on six sites in 1995.

4. Action Plan Objectives and Targets

4.1 Maintain populations at all known sites.

4.2 Enhance population size at known sites by 2010.

4.3 Maintain and seek to enhance current metapopulation links between colonies by 2010.

5. Proposed Actions with Lead Agencies

The main priorities under this plan are to ensure correct management of the areas occupied by the colonies, and to enhance the number and strength of populations, by improving habitat quality and by reducing habitat fragmentation. Further autecological studies may need to be undertaken to investigate the factors affecting populations.

5.1 Policy and legislation

5.1.1 Where appropriate, include the requirements of this species when preparing or revising prescriptions for agri-environment schemes, including the Argyll Islands ESA. (ACTION: SNH, SOAEFD)

5.1.2 When considering land management grant applications, such as the Woodland Grant Scheme, in the vicinity of colonies, take the distribution and requirements of the moth into account. (ACTION: FC, SNH)

5.2 Site safeguard and management

5.2.1 Where possible, ensure that all occupied and potential habitat is appropriately managed by 2008, for example through SSSI or agri-environment scheme management agreements. (ACTION: SNH, SOAEFD)

5.2.2 Where possible, increase the available habitat at known sites and adjacent areas, and attempt to link up existing fragments of habitat. (ACTION: SNH)

5.3 Species management and protection

5.3.1 None proposed.

5.4 Advisory

5.4.1 Advise landowners and managers of the presence of the species and the importance of beneficial management for its conservation. (ACTION: SNH)

5.5 Future research and monitoring

5.5.1 Every three years, confirm current status by surveying the distribution, extent, size and management of all known colonies. (ACTION: SNH)

5.5.2 Continue annual monitoring of adult abundance and habitat condition at all sites with existing transects. (ACTION: SNH)

5.5.3 Consider experiments on the efficacy of different methods of creating additional habitat near existing colonies. (ACTION: SNH)

5.5.4 Survey other areas of potential habitat on south-facing basalt slopes in the Inner Hebrides. (ACTION: SNH)

5.5.5 Encourage the investigation of factors affecting the abundance, survival, development and diapause of the larvae, including interactions with the parasitoid complex of this moth. (ACTION: SNH)

5.6 Communications and publicity

5.6.1 Promote opportunities for the appreciation of the slender Scotch burnet and the conservation issues associated with its habitat. This should be achieved through articles within appropriate journals, as well as by publicity leaflets. (ACTION: SNH)

5.7 Links with other action plans

5.7.1 This plan should be considered in conjunction with those for upland calcareous grassland, and maritime cliffs and slopes.

(Map not provided, for site confidentiality.)

New Forest burnet (*Zygaena viciae argyllensis*) Action Plan

1. Current status

1.1 The New Forest burnet inhabits relatively long grassland where its larvae feed on meadow vetchling and bird's-foot trefoil. When discovered in 1963 the site in western Argyll was only lightly grazed and the moths were widespread. However, the area became heavily grazed, and no New Forest burnet moths were found at the site between 1986 and 1989. It was thought that the population could be extinct. However, the moth was rediscovered in 1990 on a single ledge where the vegetation had been inaccessible to sheep during the preceding period of heavy sheep grazing. Fences were erected in 1991, and since then the vegetation has begun to recover and the moth is beginning to recolonise the bulk of the site.

1.2 In Europe *Z. viciae* is found from the northern Iberian Peninsula to southern Scandinavia. Its range extends eastwards into the Balkans, northern Iran, the Caucasus, and into Russia as far as eastern Siberia. Scattered populations also occur in Mongolia and central Asia. It was first found in Britain in 1869 in the New Forest. The populations in the New Forest represented a distinct subspecies, *Z. viciae ytenensis*, but the last specimen was caught in 1927 and no more colonies have been found since. The New Forest burnet was thought to be extinct in the British Isles until it was discovered at a single site in western Argyll, in 1963. This isolated population represents a second distinct endemic subspecies: *Z. viciae argyllensis*. Since 1963 several other apparently suitable sites have been surveyed in western Argyll but the moth has not been found away from the original site.

1.3 In Great Britain this species is classified as *Endangered*. It is given full protection under Schedule 5 of the Wildlife and Countryside Act 1981.

2. Current factors causing loss or decline

2.1 Accidental sheep grazing.

2.2 Isolation of the single colony.

2.3 Collecting of adults or larvae.

3. Current action

3.1 The site is within an SSSI notified, in part, for its Lepidoptera. The requirements of the New Forest burnet are included in an SNH management agreement with the owner.

3.2 The site was fenced by NCC (Scotland) in 1991 to exclude sheep. Additional fencing and repairs have been carried out since then.

3.3 The New Forest burnet is included in the SNH Species Action Programme.

3.4 The known colony is monitored annually, and the extent of the larval foodplant on the site is also mapped annually.

4. Action plan objectives and targets

4.1 Maintain the population size at the known site.

4.2 Enhance the population size at the known site to a target population of over 250 adults by 2010.

5. Proposed action with lead agencies

The main focus for action is to continue to restore the extant site to a suitable condition for the New Forest burnet, thus aiding its recovery. Further isolated colonies of the moth may exist in the area and it is important to continue the search.

5.1 Policy and legislation

5.1.1 None proposed.

5.2 Site safeguard and management

5.2.1 Maintain the condition of the fence to permit exclusion or managed grazing by domestic herbivores under the management agreement. (ACTION: SNH)

5.2.2 Where possible, increase the available habitat at the known site. (ACTION: SNH)

5.3 Species management and protection

5.3.1 Continue to take account of the New Forest burnet in the SSSI management agreement. (ACTION: SNH)

5.3.2 Enforce current legislation in cases of collecting. (ACTION: Police authorities, SNH)

5.4 Advisory

5.4.1 Maintain liaison with the owners and managers of the estate. (ACTION: SNH)

5.5 Future research and monitoring

5.5.1 Re-sample the vegetation and analyse any changes every 3-5 years using the results to inform management of the site. (ACTION: SNH)

5.5.2 Continue to monitor the moth population annually using the results to inform management of the site. (ACTION: SNH)

5.5.3 Undertake surveys to clarify the distribution of this species. (ACTION: SNH)

5.5.4 Conduct targeted autecological research to inform habitat management. (ACTION: SNH)

5.5.5 Encourage research on the ecology and conservation of this species at an international level, and use the experience gained towards its conservation in the UK. (ACTION: SNH, JNCC)

5.6 Communications and publicity

5.6.1 Where it is consistent with maintaining site confidentiality, promote opportunites for the appreciation of the New Forest burnet moth, and the measures being taken to conserve it. (ACTION: SNH)

5.7 Links with other action plans

5.7.1 None proposed.

(Map not provided, for site confidentiality.)

Northern brown argus (*Aricia artaxerxes*)
Species Statement

1. Current status

1.1 The northern bown argus occurs on well-drained, and usually base-rich, sites on thin soils that are usually south facing and up to 350 m altitude. Its larvae feed on common rock rose. Primarily occuring on limestone grassland, it is also associated with coastal valleys and quarries, limestone pavement and outcrops. The lightly grazed or ungrazed grassland habitat often has a profusion of the larval foodplant, nectar sources such as thyme and bird's-foot trefoil, and patches of bare ground resulting from grazing, landslips, footpaths or rock outcrops. In Scotland, the northern brown argus is also found on sites with relatively low pH dominated by heathers, but these are always well-drained. The taxonomic status of the *Aricia* complex is unclear across Europe and is the subject of current research at the University of Birmingham.

1.2 The northern brown argus is represented in Britain by two subspecies, both of which may be endemic. Closely related species, which may prove to be conspecific, occur across the western Palearctic from Spain and northern Africa to central Asia. Populations are believed to be relatively stable in most areas, although in some countries, such as Poland, they have undergone a massive decline. In England the northern brown argus is locally distributed in the Derbyshire Peak District, Yorkshire, Cumbria and County Durham. In southern Scotland, it is found in the Borders, along the east coast and in Dumfries and Galloway in the west, but then has a primarily eastern distribution northwards through Fife and Grampian to south-east Sutherland, with strong populations in Perthshire and northern Tayside. Small populations may occur in Clwyd, North Wales, but their taxonomic status is unclear. There has been a decline in range, with extinctions in southern Scotland, Northumberland and Yorkshire. Recent surveys, however, have located several new colonies in northern Scotland where the species is under recorded.

1.3 In Great Britain the northern brown argus is classified as *Nationally Scarce*. It is protected under Schedule 5 of the Wildlife and Countryside Act 1981, with respect to sale only.

2. Current factors causing loss or decline

2.1 Inappropriate grazing management.

2.2 Afforestation in parts of Scotland.

3. Current action

3.1 A species action plan, grant-aided by CCW, EN, SNH and WWF, was published by Butterfly Conservation in 1996.

3.2 Some reduction in grazing on reserves has been carried out, for example at St Abb's Head NNR in the Borders.

3.3 Reintroductions of the species have been attempted in Durham.

3.4 SNH is preparing an information and advice note on habitat management for this butterfly.

4. Objective for the species

4.1 Maintain the range of the northern brown argus.

5. Proposed action

5.1 Monitoring only. The requirements of the species should be taken into account in the delivery of the action plan for lowland calcareous grassland.

Toadflax brocade (*Calophasia lunula*) Species Statement

1. Current status

1.1 The toadflax brocade occurs on shingle at Dungeness, and less commonly on roadside verges, waste ground and in gardens where the foodplant grows in open situations. Its larvae chiefly occur on yellow toadflax *Linaria vulgaris*, but also on other *Linaria* spp and on small toadflax *Chaenorhinum minus*.

1.2 Resident populations of toaflax brocade are confined to a few sites on the south coasts of Kent and Sussex. The moth has declined recently and is seldom reported away from Dungeness. It has been recorded from almost every country in Europe, from the Mediterranean to southern Norway. Its range extends through Asia Minor east to the Amur and Ussuri regions. It is an established introduction in North America.

1.3 In Great Britain this species is classified as *Rare*.

2. Current factors causing loss or decline

2.1 This species is at the northern limit of its range in Britain and is probably limited by climate rather than habitat, with retractions in range during unfavourable climatic periods.

2.2 Coastal development, sea defence work and road-widening projects threaten remaining habitat.

3. Current action

3.1 Nuclear Electric at Dungeness have been made aware of the importance of the site around their power station and associated holdings.

3.2 Some of the breeding areas are within SSSIs, including Dungeness (a proposed SAC) and Folkestone Warren.

4. Objective for the species

4.1 Maintain existing populations of the toadflax brocade.

5. Proposed action

5.1 Monitoring only. The requirements of the species should be considered in the implementation of the coastal vegetated shingles action plan.

White-spot (*Hadena albimacula*)
Species Statement

1. Current status

1.1 The white-spot is a moth of shingle or calcareous cliffs, the larvae feeding on the seed capsules of Nottingham catchfly *Silene nutans*.

1.2 Single populations are known at Dungeness (Kent), near Gosport (Hampshire), and at least one site on the south coast of Devon between Sidmouth and Seaton. Records suggest there may be other populations on the south coasts of Dorset, Kent and the Isle of Wight. All three known populations are very localised and vulnerable to existing threats. Records suggest that in Devon the population, and its area of occupancy, has declined substantially over the last 25 years. The moth has been reported from every country in Europe except Ireland, Luxembourg, Albania and the island of Malta, and the range extends to western Siberia, Iran and Morocco. It becomes rarer and more coastal in the north of its range.

I.3 In Great Britain this species is classified as *Vulnerable*.

2. Current factors causing loss or decline

2.1 Recreation, small-scale coastal developments, and coastal defence work.

2.2 Commercial extraction of shingle, gravel and sand.

3. Current action

3.1 Part of the Dungeness area is within the grounds of a Nuclear Electric power station and receives some protection. Dungeness is a candidate SAC.

3.2 Surveys of the adult moth at Dungeness took place in 1988 and 1989, jointly funded by Nuclear Electric and the Nature Conservancy Council.

4. Objective for the species

4.1 Maintain existing populations of the white-spot.

5. Proposed action

5.1 Monitoring only. The requirements of the species should be considered in conjunction with the action plans for coastal vegetated shingles, and maritime cliffs and slopes.

Marsh mallow moth (*Hydraecia osseola hucherardi*)
Species Statement

1. Current status

1.1 The marsh mallow moth is named after the sole larval foodplant of the species, marsh mallow *Althaea officinalis,* which is found in damp, low-lying places by water courses.

1.2 This moth formerly bred widely in the Romney Marsh to Rye area on the border of East Sussex and Kent, but it now appears to be restricted to a single site here. There is also a single population on the banks of the Medway between Maidstone and Rochester, Kent. The moth has an extremely restricted distribution in Europe, with a few scattered colonies in France, Spain, Italy, Sardinia, Romania and Greece. Its range extends to southern Russia.

1.3 In Great Britain this species is now classified as *Rare*.

2. Current factors causing loss or decline

2.1 Destruction of the foodplant due to agricultural practices including land drainage, frequent and extensive mechanised ditch clearance, use of herbicides and overgrazing by sheep.

3. Current action

3.1 Both extant populations are on SSSIs, one of which is a nature reserve of the Kent Trust for Nature Conservation.

3.2 Surveys of the known populations and potential habitat in the vicinity were undertaken between 1993 and 1996 by a partnership between JNCC, EN, Butterfly Conservation and the Sussex Moth Group.

4. Objective for the species

4.1 Maintain existing populations of the marsh mallow moth.

5. Proposed action

5.1 Monitoring only. The requirements of the species should be considered in the implementation of the coastal grazing marshes action plan.

Drab looper (*Minoa murinata*) Species Statement

1. Current status

1.1 The larva of the drab looper feeds on wood spurge *Euphorbia amygdaloides*, preferring the flowers and floral leaves of plants growing in full sun. Both the moth and the foodplant are associated with areas of recent felling and coppicing in woodland. Males fly in sunshine in the middle of the day.

1.2 In the UK this species has two centres of distribution, one extending from Gloucestershire and Monmouthshire northwards through Herefordshire and Worcestershire, and the other centred on Hampshire and including south Wiltshire, Berkshire and West Sussex. There are outlying colonies in Somerset, Kent and, possibly, South Wales. It has been lost from many woods in these areas. It formerly occurred in Oxfordshire and eastwards to Bedfordshire and Essex, where it has been lost since the 1940s. The moth has been reported from most countries in central and southern Europe, from the Mediterranean north to Poland, but does not reach Scandinavia or Ireland.

1.3 In Great Britain this species is classified as *Nationally Scarce*.

2. Current factors causing loss or decline

2.1 Cessation of woodland coppice management.

2.2 Replacement of small-scale rotational felling by management of large-scale plantations of even-aged tree crops, particularly conifers.

3. Current action

3.1 Many of the surviving colonies are on SSSIs.

4. Objective for the species

4.1 Maintain the range of the drab looper.

5. Proposed action

5.1 Monitoring only. The requirements of the drab looper should be considered in the implementation of the lowland beech woodland action plan.

Scarce merveille du jour (*Moma alpium*) Species Statement

1. Current status

1.1 The scarce merveille du jour is associated with large pedunculate and sessile oak trees (*Quercus robur* and *Q. petraea*). It is thought that the egg is laid and larvae feed in the tree canopy. Emergence from the pupa may be delayed for several years, giving rise to apparent large fluctuations in population size. The ecology of this species is poorly known and the link with large oak trees not fully understood.

1.2 This moth is found only in semi-natural ancient woodland with mature oaks within 80 km of the coast. Current strongholds are in Wiltshire, Hampshire and West Sussex, with colonies in East Sussex, Kent, Cornwall and Devon, but it has probably disappeared from Suffolk and Essex. Current population trends may be static, and there may be undiscovered populations in Devon and Cornwall. This moth is widely distributed in Europe as far north as Sweden.

1.3 In Great Britain this species is classified as *Rare*.

2. Current factors causing loss or decline

2.1 Clearance of oak woodlands.

2.2 Woodland management leading to the non-replacement of mature oak trees.

3. Current action

3.1 The New Forest is a candidate SAC. Ham Street is a NNR.

3.2 The Cornish site is monitored regularly in conjunction with FE and further surveys have been conducted in suitable woodlands.

4. Objective for the species

4.1 Maintain the range of the scarce merveille du jour.

5. Proposed action

5.1 Monitoring only. It is likely that the scarce merveille du jour may benefit from the action plans for other species of lowland oakwoods, including the light crimson underwing *Catocala promissa* and the dark crimson underwing *Catocala sponsa*. The requirements of the species should be considered in the implementation of the lowland wood pastures and parklands action plan.

Clay fan-foot (*Paracolax tristalis = derivalis*)
Species Statement

1. Current status

1.1 The clay fan-foot is usually associated with small sheltered clearings and coppiced areas in woodland. The larva has been beaten from the foliage of oak *Quercus* spp in the autumn. It probably feeds on fallen leaves of oak and other broadleaves initially, and possibly on herbaceous plants in the spring.

1.2 This moth occurs very locally in a few woodlands in Kent, Sussex and Surrey. It was formerly present in Essex, Hampshire and south Wiltshire. It has suffered a 70% decline in area of occupancy within its historic range in south-east England. Old records from North Wales and Cheshire are erroneous. The clay fan-foot is widespread in southern Europe, becoming increasingly local and coastal farther north, and extends to southern Russia, China and Iran.

1.3 In Great Britain this species is classified as *Nationally Scarce*.

2. Current factors causing loss or decline

2.1 Cessation of traditional coppice management.

2.2 Replacement of small-scale rotational felling by management of large-scale plantations of even-aged tree crops, particularly conifers.

3. Current action

3.1 Most of the known surviving populations are on SSSIs.

3.2 The FC Woodland Improvement Grants for coppice restoration particularly the Coppice for Butterflies Challenge will help improve some habitats for this species.

4. Objective for the species

4.1 Maintain existing populations of the clay fan-foot.

5. Proposed action

5.1 Monitoring only. The species could benefit from the action plans for other species of lowland coppiced woodlands, including common fan-foot *Pechipogo strigilata* and drab looper *Minoa murinata*. The requirements of the species should be considered in the implementation of the lowland wood pastures and parklands action plan.

Cousin German (*Paradiarsia sobrina*)
Species Statement

1. Current status

1.1 The larva of the cousin German feeds initially on the foliage of bilberry and ling but, after over-wintering, it will climb low scrubby birch to complete its development on the young leaves. It is associated with birch woods and old Caledonian pine forest with widely spaced trees.

1.2 In Europe the cousin German occurs widely in the Scandinavian countries, with more localised populations in the mountains of central Europe, the Alps, the Pyrenees and Romania. Its range extends eastwards through the taiga in Russia, across the Urals to north-east Siberia and Korea. In the UK it has a scattered distribution in the central Scottish Highlands, where it is known from fewer than 15 ten km squares, although it is almost certainly under-recorded. Most of the records of this moth are from Rannoch and Aviemore, but there are also records from other parts of Strathspey and from the Dee Valley. In 1994 it was discovered in Wester Ross, in some of the most northerly Caledonian pine forest in Britain.

1.3 In Great Britain this species is classified as *Rare*.

2. Current factors causing loss or decline

2.1 Inappropriate grazing management of birch and pinewood pasture.

2.2 Burning.

3. Current action

3.1 Some of the occupied sites are SSSIs and/or nature reserves, including NNRs.

4. Objective for the species

4.1 Maintain the range of the cousin German.

5. Proposed action

5.1 Monitoring only. It is likely that this species will benefit from the action plans for other species of Scottish pinewoods, including the Scottish wood ant *Formica aquilonia* and twinflower *Linnaea borealis*. The requirements of the species should be considered in the implementation of the native pine woodland action plan.

Small lappet (*Phyllodesma ilicifolia*)
Species Statement

1. Current status

1.1 The small lappet is a moorland species whose larval foodplant in Britain is bilberry *Vaccinium myrtillus,* although on the dunes of western Jutland the larvae are fairly common on creeping willow *Salix repens* and bog whortleberry *Vaccinium uliginosum*.

1.2 This species was recorded historically from a few moorland sites from Yorkshire to Devon, but its continued presence is uncertain. The last confirmed record was of an adult in Somerset in 1965. A published report of several larvae from a site in Somerset in 1985 and 1986 is without foundation. In view of the sporadic nature of past records, and the extent of moorland habitat, there is a reluctance to presume the species extinct. The species has been reported from most countries in Europe including southern Norway and Sweden. The range extends to Siberia and Japan.

1.3 In Great Britain this species is now classified as *Rare*.

2. Current factors causing loss or decline

2.1 Not known.

3. Current action

3.1 Some of the former sites are SSSIs.

4. Objective for the species

4.1 Maintain any discovered populations of the small lappet.

5. Proposed action

5.1 Search only.

Black-banded (*Polymixis xanthomista*)
Species Statement

1. Current status

1.1 In Britain the black-banded is entirely coastal and occurs mainly on cliffs. The larvae feed chiefly on thrift (preferring plants growing close to the sea), whereas in Europe this species is largely restricted to mountains where the larvae feed on a variety of low-growing plants.

1.2 The black-banded is widely distributed in central and southern Europe. In the UK, it has been found on the Isles of Scilly, along the coasts of Devon, Cornwall, Pembrokeshire and Cardiganshire, and on the Isle of Man. The moth is under-recorded and its current distribution is poorly known. It is possible that the moth occurs in other suitable habitats around the south-west coasts of England and Wales. Some of the populations may form extensive colonies. There is no evidence of recent decline.

1.3 In Great Britain this species is classified as *Nationally Scarce*.

2. Current factors causing loss or decline

2.1 None known.

3. Current action

3.1 Many of the known sites are SSSIs and/or are owned by the National Trust. Some populations are contained within candidate SACs.

4. Objective for the species

4.1 Maintain the range of the black-banded.

5. Proposed action

5.1 Monitoring only. The requirements of the species should be considered in the delivery of the maritime cliffs and slopes action plan.

Olive crescent (*Trisateles emortualis*)
Species Statement

1. Current status

1.1 The larvae of the olive crescent feed initially in bunches of withering leaves of oak *Quercus* spp and beech *Fagus sylvatica* still attached to boughs, and later on recently fallen leaves on the ground.

1.2 The moth has been known as a resident in the UK from only a small wooded area of the Chilterns in Buckinghamshire, where it has declined in recent years, and in two woods near the coast in north Essex. This moth has been reported from most European countries from Norway to Albania. It is widespread and not uncommon in parts of central Europe and southern Scandinavia. The range extends to eastern Siberia, China and northern Iran.

1.3 In Great Britain this species is classified as *Rare*.

2. Current factors causing loss or decline

2.1 Changes in woodland structure and management.

3. Current action

3.1 At least part of both populations are within SSSIs.

4. Objective for the species

4.1 Maintain the existing populations of the olive crescent.

5. Proposed action

5.1 Monitoring only. The requirements of the species should be considered in the implementation of the lowland beech action plan.

Northern dart (*Xestia alpicola alpina*)
Species Statement

1. Current status

1.1 The northern dart is usually restricted to the tops of higher mountains, generally above 450 m, although it occurs at lower altitudes in the extreme north and west of its range. The main larval foodplant is crowberry, but it may also feed on ling, and possibly on bilberry and bearberry. Larval development takes two years.

1.2 This moth occurs in the Alps and the mountains of central Europe, and also extends north to the Arctic zones of Scandinavia and Russia. The form in the British Isles, which occurs in Scotland, northern England and north-west Ireland, is considered a distinct subspecies, *alpina*. The northern dart is under-recorded and its best known breeding areas are in the Cairngorms, the mountains south of Loch Rannoch, and in Cumbria. The moth also occurs on Harris, Lewis, the Orkney Islands and possibly on Shetland, and in the Cheviots.

1.3 In Great Britain this species is classified as *Nationally Scarce*.

2. Current factors causing loss or decline

2.1 Not known.

3. Current action

3.1 Some of the occupied sites are SSSIs/ASSIs, NNRs or nature reserves.

4. Objective for the species

4.1 Maintain the range of the northern dart.

5. Proposed action

5.1 Monitoring only. The requirements of the species should be considered in the delivery of the upland heathland action plan.

Other invertebrates

Clubiona rosserae (a spider)
(Order: Araneae)
Action Plan

1. Current status

1.1 *Clubiona rosserae* favours wet fen habitats and it has been recorded on several occasions in piles of cut sedge. Adults have been found in February, May, June, September and October. It was first described as recently as 1953, and it is possible that this species has been under recorded due to confusion with *C. stagnatilis*, a closely related and common species.

1.2 *Clubiona rosserae* has been found at only two sites in Britain: Chippenham Fen NNR (Cambridgeshire), and Tuddenham Fen (West Suffolk), which is part of the Cavenham Heath NNR. The population size at these two sites is not known. *C. rosserae* has also been found in Czechoslovakia, Poland and, possibly, Siberia.

1.3 In Great Britain this species is classified as *Endangered*.

2. Current factors causing loss or decline

2.1 Not known.

3 Current action

3.1 Both of the localities where this species has been recorded in Britain are NNRs.

4. Action plan objectives and targets

4.1 Maintain populations at all known sites.

5. Proposed action with lead agencies

This species is potentially threatened by changes in habitat quality at its known sites. To achieve the objectives of this plan it will be necessary to survey the two known sites to establish the status of the populations. If appropriate, potentially damaging changes caused by the lowering of the water table should be assessed, and action taken to halt or reverse the changes. Other sites in the same area with the potential to hold populations of the species should also be surveyed.

5.1 Policy and legislation

5.1.1 Address the requirements of this species in the LEAP process and in relevant WLMPs. (ACTION: EA, EN, IDBs, LAs, MAFF)

5.1.2 Take account of the species' requirements in response to applications for water abstraction licences. (ACTION: EA)

5.2 Site safeguard and management

5.2.1 Ensure that activities external to the extant sites do not further threaten the level of the water table. (ACTION: EA, EN)

5.2.2 Where possible, ensure that all occupied habitat is appropriately managed, including management of encroaching scrub, by 2008. (ACTION: EN)

5.2.3 Ensure that the species is included in site management documents for all relevant SSSIs. (ACTION: EN)

5.2.4 Consider notifying as SSSIs any newly-discovered sites holding key populations of *Clubiona rosserae* where this is necessary to secure their long-term protection and appropriate management. (ACTION: EN)

5.3 Species management and protection

5.3.1 None proposed.

5.4 Advisory

5.4.1 In the event of discovering populations at new sites, advise landowners and managers of the presence of the species and the importance of beneficial management for its conservation. (ACTION: EN)

5.5 Future research and monitoring

5.5.1 Undertake surveys to determine the status of this species, including potentially suitable sites within a radius of 25 km of the extant sites. (ACTION: EN)

5.5.2 Conduct targeted autecological research to inform habitat management. (ACTION: EN).

5.5.3 Establish an appropriate monitoring programme for the species. (ACTION: EN)

5.5.4 Pass the information gathered during survey and monitoring of this species to a central database for incorporation into national and international databases. (ACTION: EN)

5.6 Communication and publicity

5.6.1 Promote opportunities for the appreciation of the species and the conservation issues associated with its habitat. This should be achieved through articles within appropriate journals, as well as by a publicity leaflet. (ACTION: EN)

5.7 Links with other action plans

5.7.1 This action plan should be considered in conjunction with that for fens.

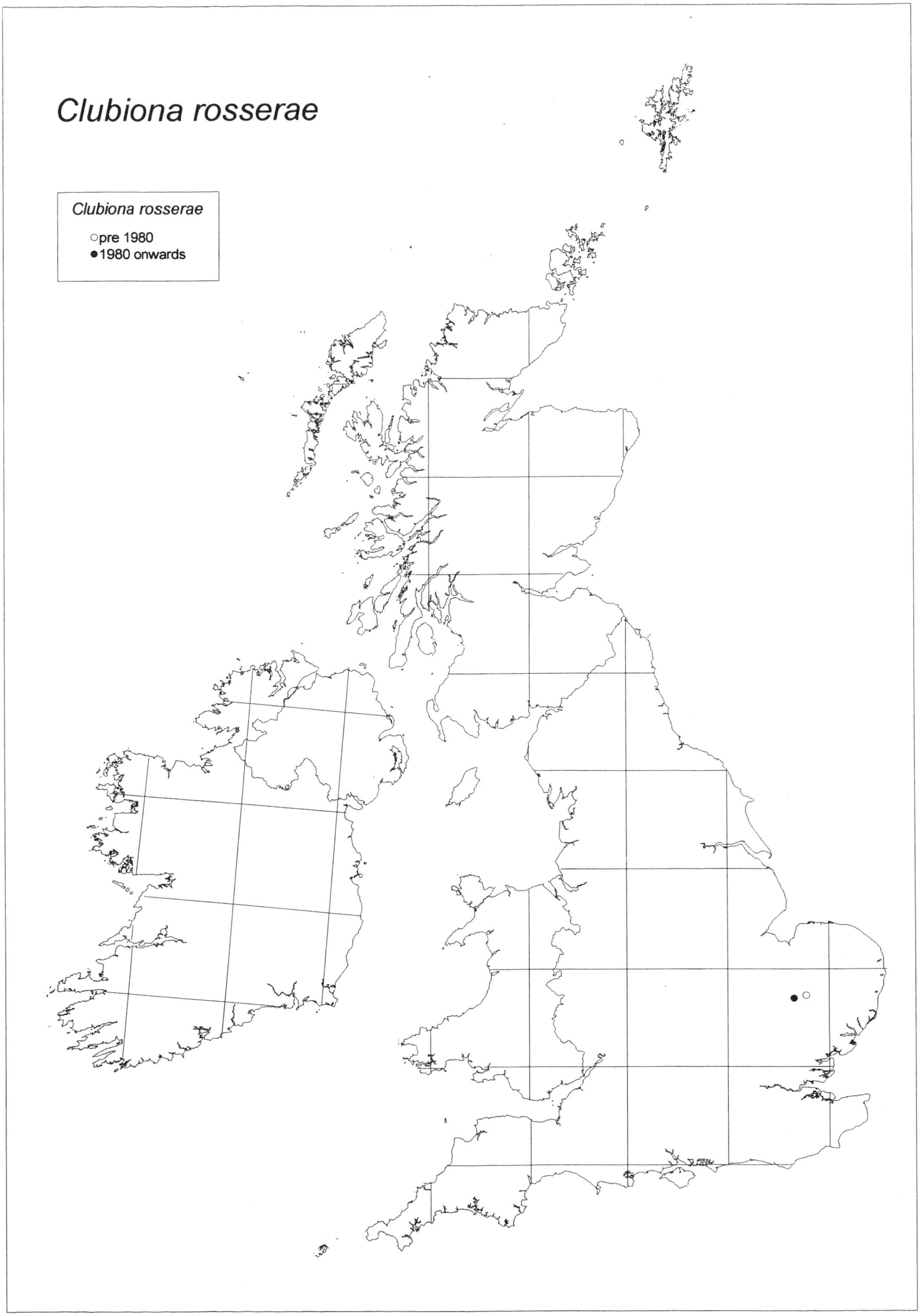

Distribution of Clubiona rosserae - a spider in Britain, by 10km square.
Source: The British Arachnological Society and English Nature - Invertebrate Site Register.

Fen raft spider (*Dolomedes plantarius*)
(Order: Araneae)
Action Plan

1. Current status

1.1 The fen raft spider is a wetland spider dependent on permanent, standing or slow moving water. It is associated with nutrient-poor water of near neutral or alkaline pH. It lives on the surface of pools and ditches, and amongst emergent vegetation; typically it hunts from 'perches' on stems emerging from the water, taking a wide range of invertebrate prey on or below the surface. Emergent, stiff-leaved vegetation in open, sunny conditions is also required for the construction of nursery webs in which the young are reared.

1.2 There are no reliable records of this species in the UK before its discovery in 1956, at Redgrave and Lopham Fen, on the Norfolk/Suffolk border. In 1988 it was discovered at a second site, the Pevensey Levels, Sussex, *c*160 km away. The Redgrave and Lopham Fen population has contracted progressively in range over the last 30 years and is now restricted to two, small, isolated centres. Since systematic monitoring began in 1991, numbers in these areas have fluctuated around very low levels, with no detectable temporal trends. The total population, probably of little over 100 adult females in most years, is highly vulnerable to stochastic extinction. The only survey of the Pevensey population in 1992 estimated that there were over 3000 adult females. The fen raft spider has been recorded throughout the Palaearctic. Under recording and confusion over identification make assessment of status difficult, but it appears to be declining and often under threat of extinction in western and central-southern Europe whilst remaining well established in Scandinavia and the Baltic States.

1.3 In Great Britain this species is classified as *Endangered*. It is given full protection under Schedule 5 of the Wildlife and Countryside Act 1981.

2. Current factors causing loss or decline

2.1 Water abstraction.

2.2 Inappropriate ditch management.

2.3 Deterioration in water quality.

2.4 Loss of suitable wetland habitat.

3. Current action

3.1 Most of the Pevensey population occurs within the Pevensey Levels NNR/SSSI complex. The population at Redgrave and Lopham Fen occurs within an NNR, which is included within the Waveney and Little Ouse Valley Fens candidate SAC.

3.2 The fen raft spider has been the subject of an EN Species Recovery Programme since 1991.

3.3 Habitat restoration, initiated in 1993 at Redgrave and Lopham Fen by the Suffolk Wildlife Trust, with grant-aid from the EU Life Fund, has involved restoration of the fen's natural hydrology, extensive peat-stripping, scrub clearance and grazing.

4. Action plan objectives and targets

4.1 Achieve a ten-fold increase in the range of the population at Redgrave and Lopham Fen.

4.2 Increase the population density throughout much of the range of Redgrave and Lopham Fen to a mean maximum of *c*15 individuals per pool (the maximum level supported since monitoring began in 1991).

4.3 Maintain the density and range of the fen raft spider on the Pevensey Levels.

4.4 Introduce populations to two suitable new sites by 2010.

5. Proposed action with lead agencies

Priority action for this species should be to ensure appropriate habitat management throughout both existing sites. The most important elements of this are the maintenance of summer water levels, water quality and suitable emergent vegetation. Translocations should be made to new sites to reduce the species' intrinsic vulnerability. Systematic monitoring is vital in assessing progress towards the targets, and in making appropriate adjustments to management.

5.1 Policy and legislation

5.1.1 Where appropriate, include the requirements of the species when revising prescriptions for relevant agri-environment schemes. (ACTION: EN, MAFF)

5.1.2 Address the requirements of this species in the LEAP process and in relevant WLMPs. (ACTION: EA, IDBs, LAs, MAFF)

5.1.3 Take account of the requirements of the species in response to applications for water abstraction licences. (ACTION: EA)

5.2 **Site safeguard and management**

5.2.1 Where possible, ensure that occupied and potential habitat is appropriately managed, including the maintenance of water quality and water levels, by 2005. (ACTION: EA, EN)

5.2.2 Ensure that the species is included in site management documents for all relevant SSSIs. (ACTION: EN)

5.3 **Species management and protection**

5.3.1 Translocate spiders within existing sites where physical isolation prevents recolonisation of suitable habitat. (ACTION: EN)

5.3.2 Introduce to a series of new sites in East Anglian and southern England to establish a new viable population in each region. (ACTION: EN)

5.4 **Advisory**

5.4.1 Advise landowners and managers of the presence of the fen raft spider and the importance of beneficial management for its conservation. (ACTION: EN).

5.5 **Future research and monitoring**

5.5.1 Continue regular monitoring at Redgrave and Lopham Fen, and establish a regular monitoring programme for the species at Pevensey Levels and for newly established populations. (ACTION: EN)

5.5.2 Conduct targeted autecological research to inform habitat management. (ACTION: EN)

5.5.3 Encourage research on the ecology and conservation of this species on an international level, and use the experience gained towards its conservation. (ACTION: EN, JNCC)

5.6 **Communications and publicity**

5.6.1 Promote opportunities for the appreciation of this species and the conservation issues associated with its habitat. This should be achieved through articles within appropriate journals, and by a publicity leaflet, as well as by increasing opportunities for public viewing. (ACTION: EN)

5.7 **Links with other action plans**

5.7.1 Implementation of this action plan could benefit other species of fens and grazing marshes, including the freshwater molluscs *Anisus vorticulus* and *Segmentina nitida*.

5.7.2 This plan should be considered in conjunction with those for coastal and floodplain grazing marsh, and fens.

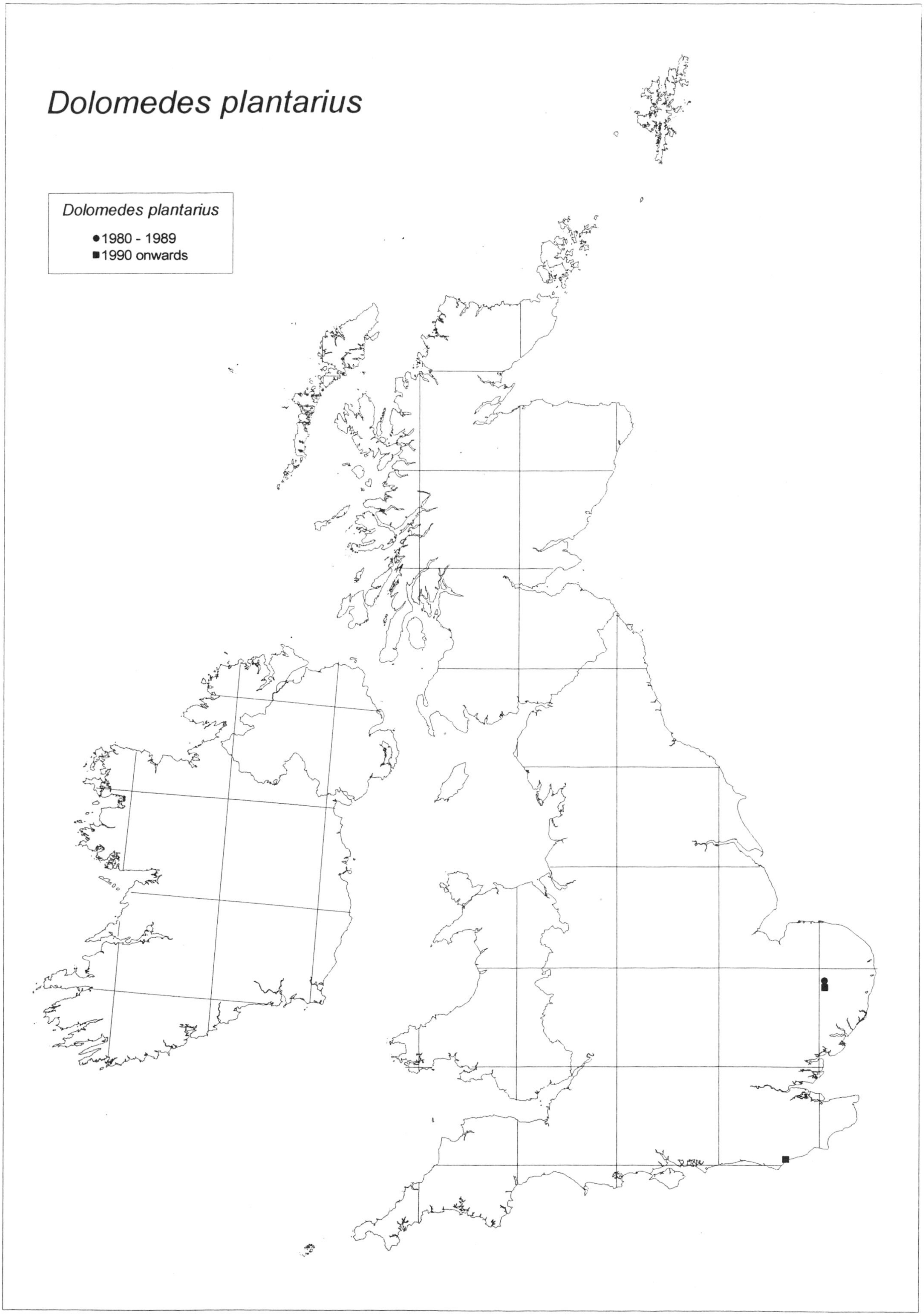

Distribution of Dolomedes plantarius - fen raft spider in Britain, by 10km square.
Source: The British Arachnological Society and English Nature - Invertebrate Site Register.

Ladybird spider (*Eresus sandaliatus = cinnaberinus*) (Order: Araneae) Action Plan

1. Current status

1.1 The ladybird spider is found on dry sandy heaths with bare or lichen covered patches, where it forms burrows in the sandy substrate and is protected from the wind by the surrounding heather. It preys on insects blundering into the external web. Females will only leave their burrows if conditions deteriorate and they have to relocate. Males only leave the burrow to mate, for a period of about two weeks in early summer. Females are able to survive for several years as adults before breeding. This species needs very warm, dry conditions and may not breed in wet years. The species has a long life cycle of up to eight years and may therefore be slow to respond to improved habitat conditions. Until recently this species was considered conspecific with *Eresus cinnaberinus* (*=niger*) but northern and montane European populations, including the British population, have been referred to *E. sandaliatus*.

1.2 Until the late 1920s the species was recorded from several sites in Dorset but it was then thought to have become extinct in Britain. Although was rediscovered in 1979, it is known from only a single site, in Wareham Forest, where the exceedingly small population is less than 300 adults. This is slowly increasing but the population remains vulnerable. There are likely, but unconfirmed records from Kynance Cove in Cornwall, the Undercliffs of the Isle of Wight, and Kirkby Moor in Lincolnshire. It is rare and apparently declining in northern Europe (Denmark, Germany, Netherlands and Sweden) and otherwise occurs only in areas of the Alps and the Pyrenees.

1.3 In Great Britain this species is classified as *Endangered*. It is given full protection under Schedule 5 of the Wildlife and Countryside Act 1981.

2. Current factors causing loss or decline

2.1 Encroachment and shading by *Rhododendron*, pine and bracken.

2.2 Competition from southern wood ants may be a factor.

3. Current action

3.1 The ladybird spider has been the subject of an EN Species Recovery Programme since 1991, under which FE has carried out extensive habitat management and enlargement of the occupied site.

3.2 There has been regular monitoring of the known population and considerable survey for additional sites.

3.3 An experimental captive breeding programme has been established with specimens imported from Denmark. These specimens will not be used for establishment in the UK.

4. Action plan objectives and targets

4.1 Maintain the population size at its known site.

4.2 Enhance the population size at Wareham Forest by 2010.

4.3 Restore populations to two suitable sites within the historic range by 2010.

4.4 Continue to support an *ex-situ* programme to provide material for reintroductions and ecological research.

5. Proposed action with lead agencies

The objectives for the ladybird spider will be achieved by continuing the regular monitoring of the known site so that management action can be immediate if the site is threatened. Other heathland areas within 30 km of the extant site should be surveyed to establish their potential to support populations of the species, and to ensure that the species does not occur elsewhere. If the captive breeding programme is successful, then a similar programme will be established with British specimens and the offspring used to establish further colonies.

5.1 Policy and legislation

5.1.1 None proposed.

5.2 Site safeguard and management

5.2.1 Prevent external activities threatening the existing population. (ACTION: EN, FE)

5.2.2 Remove encroaching pine, *Rhododendron*, bracken and scrub at appropriate intervals to maintain areas of bare ground and to encourage the regeneration of heather. (ACTION: EN, FE)

5.2.3 Where possible, increase the available habitat at the known site and adjacent areas, and attempt to link up existing fragments of habitat. (ACTION: EN, FE)

5.2.4 If new populations are found on any SSSIs, ensure that the species is included in relevant site management documents. (ACTION: EN)

5.2.5 Consider notifying any newly discovered sites for the species as SSSIs. (ACTION: EN).

5.3 Species management and protection

5.3.1 Establish the ladybird spider on at least two additional sites within the former range by 2010. (ACTION: EN)

5.4 Advisory

5.4.1 Advise landowners and managers of sites where the ladybird spider is introduced about the habitat requirements and site management requirements of this species. (ACTION: EN).

5.5 Future research and monitoring

5.5.1 Undertake surveys to determine the status of the species. These should concentrate on heathland areas within a radius of 30 km of the extant site. (ACTION: EN)

5.5.2 Continue monitoring of extant population and initiate monitoring of any establishments. (ACTION: EN)

5.5.3 Consider genetic analysis of the population to identify inbreeding problems. If further colonies are discovered, take advice on the desirability of facilitating gene flow between populations, at least in the origination of new colonies. (ACTION: EN)

5.6 Communications and publicity

5.6.1 Promote opportunities for the appreciation of the species, and the conservation issues associated with its habitat. Continue to use this species as a flagship to inform and popularise the problems faced by heathland invertebrates and spiders in general. (ACTION: EN)

5.7 Links with other action plans

5.7.1 This action plan should be considered in conjunction with that for lowland heathland.

(Map not provided, for site confidentiality.)

Lophopus crystallinus (a freshwater bryozoan) (Order: Bryozoa) Action Plan

1. Current status

1.1 *Lophopus crystallinus* is one of 11 freshwater bryozoans found in the UK, and is the only member of its family in this country. Bryozoans feed on minute organisms suspended in the water column. *L. crystallinus* lives in lakes, ponds, ditches and slow rivers, where it has been found growing on a variety of substrata including water plants, rocks, shells, wood and dead leaves. Bryozoans are hermaphrodites. Sexual reproduction produces a short-lived free-swimming stage. They also reproduce asexually in two ways: by 'budding' from the mature colony; and by producing statoblasts, a seed-like resting stage which is able to withstand environmental extremes and can remain dormant for several years. The characteristic floating statoblasts of *L. crystallinus* are the most likely means of long-distance dispersal.

1.2 Since 1970 *L. crystallinus* has been found at only four sites: Bagmore Pit, Norfolk; Chil Brook, Oxfordshire; Barton Blow Wells, South Humberside; and near Westhoughton, Lancashire. There are older records from: near Port Meadow, Oxfordshire; several of the Norfolk and Suffolk Broads and waterways; Langmere, Norfolk; Hartwell, Buckinghamshire; Little Baddow, Essex; and Chelsea, Middlesex. A record from the River Ravensbourne, Kent, is undated. It is typical for records of this species at any particular site to be for a short period only; this may be a natural aspect of its ecology or because continual occurrences tend not to be reported. *Lophopus crystallinus* has been widely recorded in Europe but its current status outside Britain is not known.

1.3 In Great Britain this species is classified as *Rare*.

2. Current factors causing loss or decline

2.1 Eutrophication of water bodies.

2.2 Water abstraction.

2.3 Over-tidying of waterbodies, especially the removal of fallen wood.

3. Current action

3.1 Barton Blow Wells are within Barton & Barrow Clay Pits SSSI.

4. Action plan objectives and targets

4.1 Maintain all long-term populations of *Lophopus crystallinus*.

4.2 Facilitate natural increase in the number of populations by 2010.

5. Proposed action with lead agencies

The current threats to *L. crystallinus* are identified as pollution, water abstraction and inappropriate site management. The actions therefore aim to improve water quality and ensure adequate water supply at sites where this species occurs, and to promote positive habitat management to benefit the species. The lack of knowledge about *L. crystallinus* needs to be addressed through survey and autecological studies.

5.1 Policy and legislation

5.1.1 Address the requirements of this species in the LEAP process and in relevant WLMPs. (ACTION: EA, IDBs, LAs, MAFF)

5.1.2 Take account of the species' requirements in response to applications for water abstraction licences. (ACTION: EA)

5.2 Site safeguard and management

5.2.1 By 2004, reduce water abstraction from Barton Blow Wells aquifer and Breck aquifers. (ACTION: EA).

5.2.2 Where possible, ensure that all occupied habitat is appropriately managed, including the reduction and elimination of sources of eutrophication or pollution, by 2008. (ACTION: EN).

5.2.3 Ensure that this species is included in site management documents for all relevant SSSIs. (ACTION: EN).

5.2.4 Consider notifying as SSSIs sites holding viable populations of this species, where this is necessary to secure their long-term protection and appropriate management. (ACTION: EN)

5.3 Species management and protection

5.3.1 None proposed.

5.4 Advisory

5.4.1 Advise landowners and managers of the presence of the species and the importance of beneficial management for its conservation. (ACTION: EA, EN)

5.5 Future research and monitoring

5.5.1 By 2004, assess the possibility of surveying for *Lophopus crystallinus* by examining sediments for statoblasts, using pollen concentration techniques. (ACTION: EN).

5.5.2 Conduct targeted autecological research to inform habitat management. (ACTION: EN, EA)

5.5.3 By 2000 start long-term surveillance of one or more populations, possibly using artificial substrata to allow quantitative population studies, in order to study natural fluctuations in population size. (ACTION: EA, EN)

5.5.4 Trawl for unpublished records through appeals in appropriate literature, and undertake surveys to determine the status of this species, by 2004. (ACTION: EN)

5.6 Communications and publicity

5.6.1 Promote opportunities for the appreciation of the species and the conservation issues associated with its habitat. This should be achieved articles within appropriate journals, as well as by a publicity leaflet. (ACTION: EN)

5.7 Links with other action plans

5.7.1 Implementation of this action plan could also benefit *Bidessus unistriatus*.

5.7.2 This plan should be considered in conjunction with those for aquifer-fed fluctuating waterbodies, wet woodlands, and mesotrophic lakes.

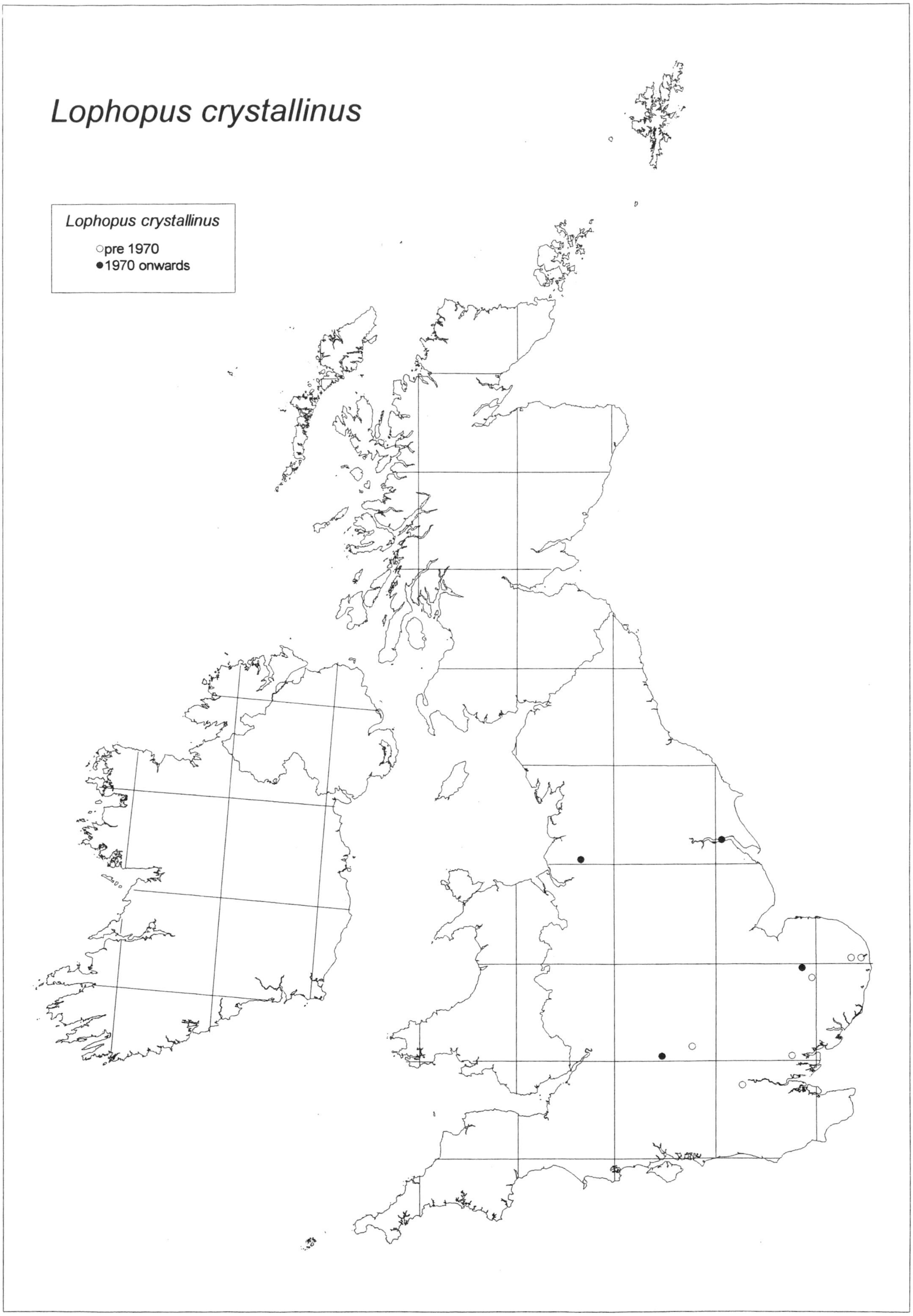

Distribution of Lophopus crystallinus - a freshwater bryozoan in Britain, by 10km square.
Source: English Nature - Invertebrate Site Register.

New Forest cicada (*Cicadetta montana*)
(Order: Hemiptera)
Action Plan

1. Current status

1.1 The New Forest cicada is the only representative of the Cicadidae in the UK. The species occurs on warm, south-facing, open scrub and woodland-edge sites and has an unusually long life cycle. Eggs are laid in woody stems and bracken and hatch during September to November. The tiny nymphs burrow into the ground where they feed on the roots of purple moorgrass *Molinia caerulea* and woody plants. They take 6-8 years to mature. Nymphs build small earthworks ('turrets') in March before emergence as adults in May and June. The winged adults live for about three weeks.

1.2 The New Forest cicada is very rare, known with certainty from only two areas in the New Forest in the last 50 years, although there are some other doubtful records from other areas. Between 1941 and 1962 there were two records, but in 1962 a new site for nymphs and adults was discovered and 100 singing males were counted. The cicada has been monitored here since 1962, but there has been a long slow decline which is probably due to habitat change. There were occasional peak years (eg 30 turrets in 1986), which could relate to an eight-year life cycle. On a second site, singing has been heard occasionally up to 1994 and an adult was collected in 1990. In 1996 and 1997 there was no evidence of the occurrence of cicadas. In nearby European continental areas the species is uncommon, and has declined in alpine sites; it is commoner in parts of Russia and the Caucasus.

1.3 In Great Britain this species is classified as *Endangered*. It is given full protection under Schedule 5 of the Wildlife and Countryside Act 1981.

2. Current factors causing loss or decline

2.1 Natural succession to shaded woodland on ungrazed sites.

2.2 Loss of habitat due to intensive grazing on the common lands preventing bush regeneration.

2.3 Loss of open bush and deciduous tree habitats resulting from conifer forest management.

2.4 Extensive bracken invasion causing shading.

2.5 Trampling damage to turrets and egg nests between March and October.

3. Current action

3.1 The best known site for the New Forest cicada is managed by the FE, EN and the Hampshire Wildlife Trust to provide optimal habitat for the species. Glades were cleared in 1993, 1996 and 1998 by volunteers and FE.

3.2 The best site is monitored for singing males, nymphal turrets, and egg nests in plants.

3.3 Surveys of suitable habitat are organised by EN, to include searches for cicadas near sites with recent records, and in the New Forest generally.

3.4 A species action plan, commissioned by EN, was written in 1995 and has been revised annually since then.

4. Action plan objectives and targets

4.1 Maintain all current populations.

4.2 Enhance the population size at all known sites by 2020.

4.3 Establish populations at two suitable sites within the known range by 2020.

4.4 Establish an *ex-situ* programme for study and to provide material for reintroductions and ecological research

5. Proposed action with lead agencies

The status of this species in the New Forest requires annual surveys of likely areas, with particular attention to the last two known sites, and of adjacent areas where dispersal might have occurred. The management and availability of suitable habitat is important, and involves FE in freeing small areas from forestry operations. Results cannot be achieved quickly because of the 6-8 year life cycle. A better understanding of the habitat is needed and may include studies of extant continental sites. Preparation for possible reintroduction involves testing the methodology for *ex-situ* breeding and, if no native cicadas can be found, this long-term work could begin by using continental stock.

5.1 Policy and legislation

5.1.1 None proposed.

5.2 **Site safeguard and management**

5.2.1 Where possible, ensure that all occupied and potential habitat is appropriately managed, including reduction of trampling by grazing animals between March and October by 1999, and rotational management of woodland margins by 2004. (ACTION: EN, FE)

5.2.2 Ensure that the species is included in site management documents for all relevant SSSIs. (ACTION: EN)

5.3 **Species management and protection**

5.3.1 Strengthen populations by using captive-bred stock if necessary, taking into account the long generation time. (ACTION EN)

5.3.2 Consider (re)introducing the New Forest cicada to a series of sites within the former range, if necessary to establish two new viable populations by 2020. (ACTION: EN)

5.4 **Advisory**

5.4.1 Ensure that all relevant managers and local staff in the New Forest are aware of the species and its conservation requirements. (ACTION: EN, FC)

5.5 **Future research and monitoring**

5.5.1 Attempt to determine the current status by making annual searches for singing males and egg nests in suitable habitat areas in the New Forest, with special attention to the last two known sites and adjacent areas. (ACTION: EN)

5.5.2 Monitor emergence turrets, singing males and egg nests on any extant site. (ACTION: EN)

5.5.3 Encourage research on the ecology and conservation of this species at an international level, and use the experience gained towards its conservation in the UK. (ACTION: EN, JNCC)

5.5.4 Test rearing methodology using stock from continental sites. This is a long-term project as the life cycle is 6-8 years underground. (ACTION: EN)

5.6 **Communication and publicity**

5.6.1 Improve awareness of the song of the male cicada in the New Forest in order to increase the chances of finding small dispersed populations. (ACTION: EN)

5.6.2 Promote opportunities for the appreciation of the species and conservation issues associated with its habitat. This should be achieved through articles within appropriate readership journals, as well as by a publicity leaflet. (ACTION: EN)

5.7 **Links with other action plans**

5.7.1 This plan should be considered in conjunction with that for the lowland wood pastures and parklands.

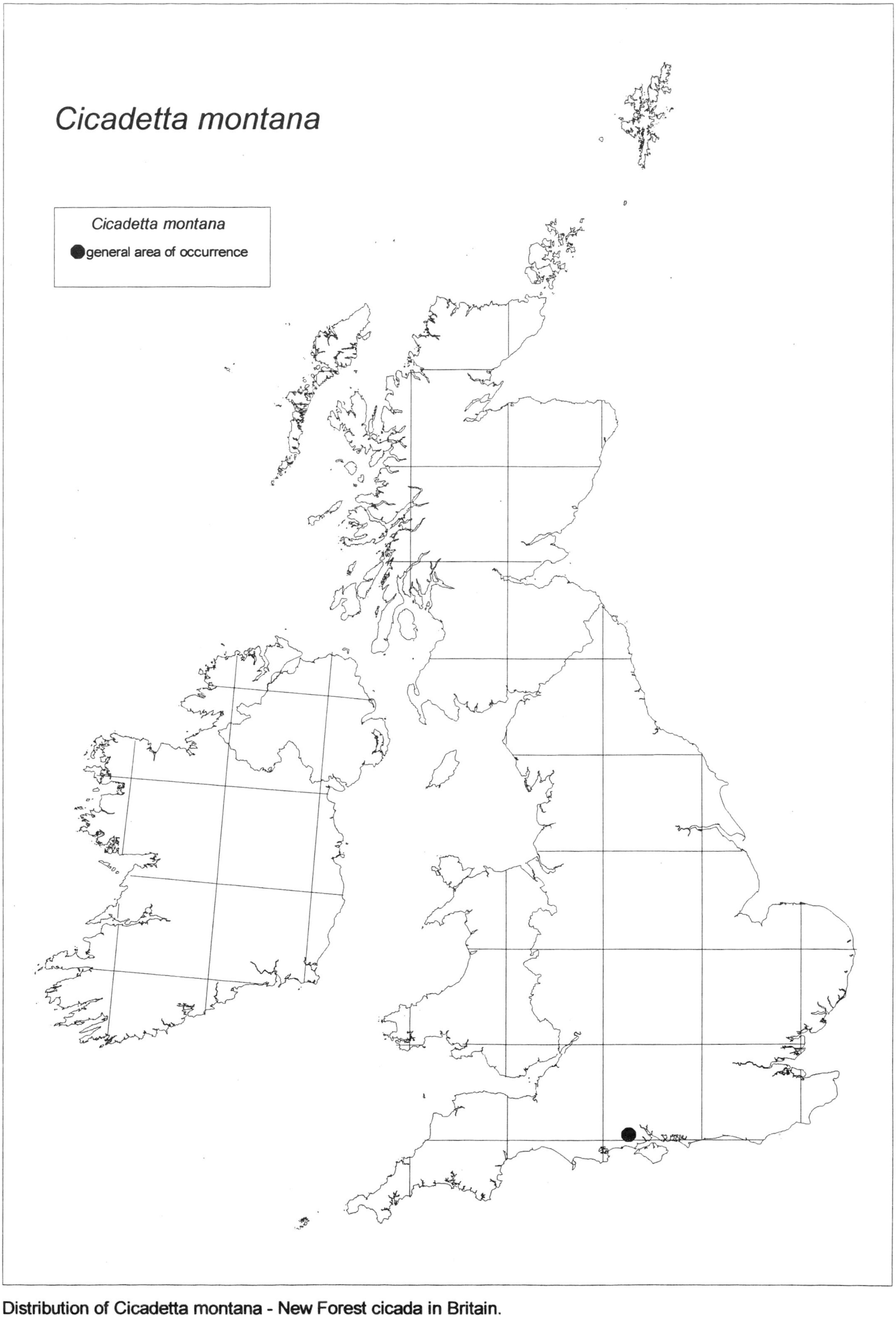

Distribution of Cicadetta montana - New Forest cicada in Britain.
Source: English Nature - Invertebrate Site Register.

Wart-biter (*Decticus verrucivorus*)
(Order: Orthoptera)
Action Plan

1. Current status

1.1 The wart-biter is a species of calcareous grassland, although one extant UK colony occupies a heathland/grassland site. The species requires a finely balanced habitat mosaic: bare ground/short turf, into which eggs are laid; grass tussocks, amongst which older nymphs and adults conceal themselves from predators; and a sward rich in flowering forbs and invertebrates, which provide nutrition. The species is thermophilous, and tends to occur on sites with a southerly aspect. Eggs are laid into the soil and persist underground over two winters, hatching in mid to late April. There are seven nymphal instars, and the adult stage is usually attained in July. Oviposition occurs from August until around early October, when the adults die off. Although regarded as the same species, the wart-biter appears to differ slightly in the UK from individuals found in continental populations.

1.2 Records suggest that the species has been very localised in southern England since at least the early 1800s. Former records exist for Hampshire and the Isle of Wight, and a number of historic colonies have been lost from within the current range. There are currently five populations, two in East Sussex and one each in Dorset, Wiltshire and Kent (the latter arising from a recent reintroduction). Numbers of individuals vary considerably between years, but all extant populations are small. The largest is estimated to contain 2000 adults in peak years, but colonies often contain only 20-50 adults, or fewer in poor years. The species is widespread in central and southern Europe, but appears to be declining in parts of this range.

1.3 In Great Britain this species is classified as *Vulnerable*. It is given full protection under Schedule 5 of the Wildlife and Countryside Act 1981.

2. Current factors causing loss or decline

2.1 Inappropriate grassland management, leading to loss of habitat quality and small population sizes, is the major threat to this species.

2.2 Predation, particularly by birds, is a significant problem at some sites.

3. Current action

3.1 A programme of research on this species and its habitat requirements, on behalf of EN, has been in operation since 1987. This has involved surveys of historical, extant and potential (re)introduction sites, population monitoring, formulation of habitat management recommendations and a (re)introduction programme.

3.2 A captive breeding programme for this species has been operating at the Invertebrate Conservation Centre, London Zoo (on behalf of EN), since 1993/94.

3.3 The sites of the five current populations comprise two NNRs, two SSSIs and one County Trust Nature Reserve.

3.4 A species action plan, commissioned by EN, was completed in 1997.

4. Action plan objectives and targets

4.1 Maintain populations at all known sites.

4.2 Enhance the population size at all known sites by 2005.

4.3 Restore populations of the wart-biter to at least three sites, and attain long-term viable populations at four sites, by 2005.

4.4 Secure the future of the species in England by providing a minimum of 10 populations across its known range by 2010, provided that suitable habitat and (re)introduction stock are available.

5. Proposed action with lead agencies

Action to monitor extant populations and habitat conditions at occupied sites, and to ensure that appropriate site management systems are applied, is required. This should be combined with a continuing programme of surveys to identify and monitor potential sites for (re)introductions, and support for the captive breeding of this species.

5.1 Policy and legislation

5.1.1 Where appropriate, include the requirements of the species when preparing or revising prescriptions for agri-environment schemes. (ACTION: EN, MAFF)

5.2 Site safeguard and management

5.2.1 Where possible, ensure that all occupied and nearby potential habitat is appropriately managed by 2005, for example through SSSI or agri-environment scheme management agreements. (ACTION: EN, MAFF)

5.2.2 Ensure that the habitat requirements of the wart-biter are taken into account in any relevant development policies, plans and proposals. (ACTION: EN, LAs)

5.2.3 Ensure that the species is included in site management documents for all relevant SSSIs. (ACTION: EN).

5.2.4 Consider notifying as SSSIs sites holding key populations of this species, where this is necessary to secure their long-term protection and appropriate management. (ACTION: EN).

5.3 Species management and protection

5.3.1 Monitor, and take relevant action against, competitive and predatory species. (ACTION: EN).

5.3.2 (Re)introduce the wart-biter to sites within the former range of the species, where appropriate habitat and site management are available, in order to restore three populations by 2005, and ensure that there are a minimum of 10 populations by 2010. (ACTION: EN).

5.4 Advisory

5.4.1 Advise landowners and managers of the presence of the species and the importance of beneficial management for its conservation. (ACTION: EN)

5.5 Future research and monitoring

5.5.1 Conduct targeted autecological research to inform habitat management. (ACTION: EN)

5.5.2 Support the continued development of a captive breeding and (re)introduction programme. (ACTION: EN)

5.5.3 Continue to monitor populations and habitat conditions at occupied sites. (ACTION: EN)

5.5.4 Continue a programme of surveys to identify potential sites for (re)introductions. (ACTION: EN)

5.5.5 Pass information gathered during survey and monitoring of this species to a central database for incorporation into national and international databases. (ACTION: EN).

5.6 Communication and publicity

5.6.1 Promote opportunities for the appreciation of this species and the conservation issues associated with its habitat. This should be achieved through articles within appropriate journals, as well as by a publicity leaflet. (ACTION: EN)

5.7 Links with other action plans

5.7.1 This action plan should be considered in conjunction with that for lowland calcareous grassland.

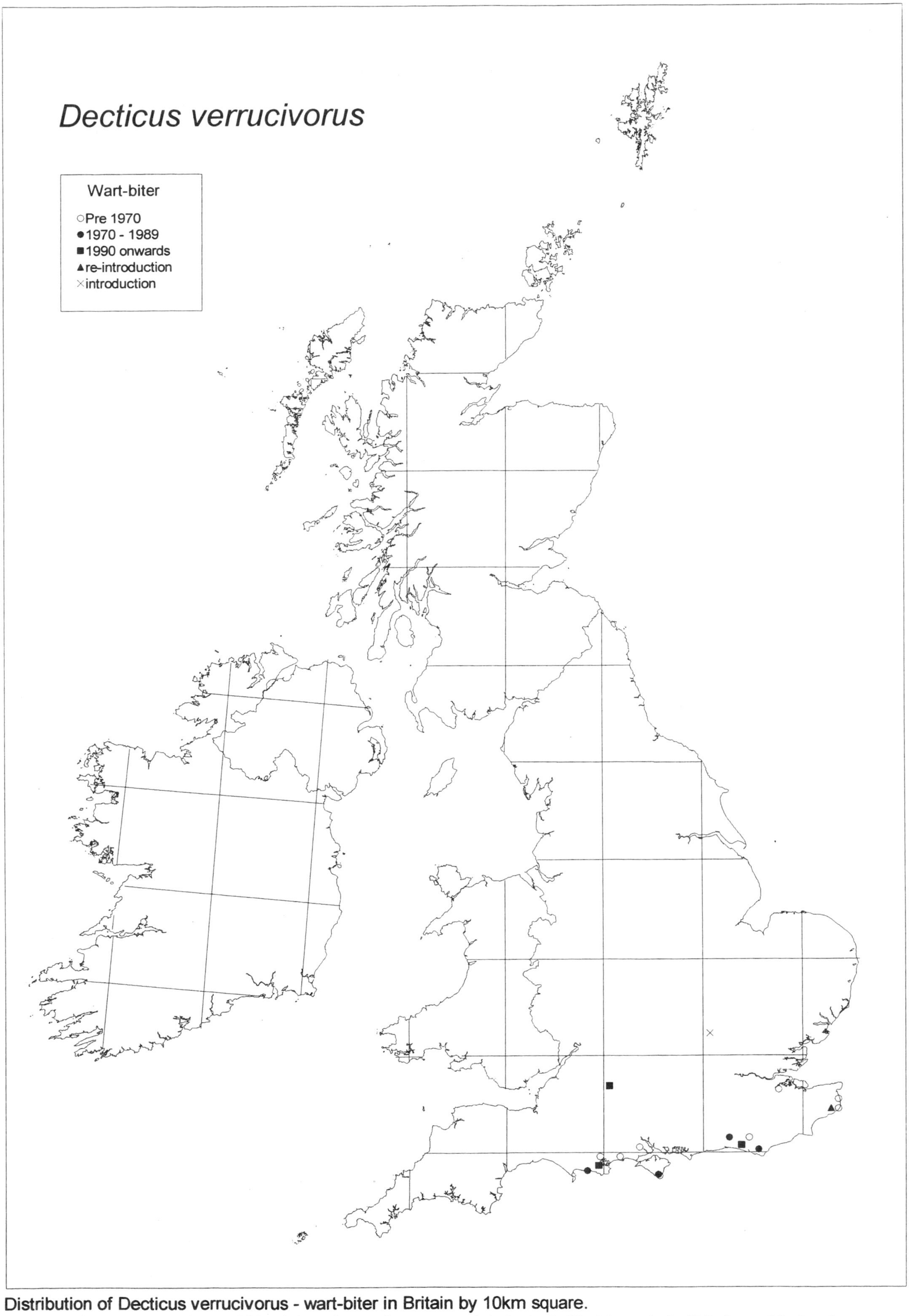

Distribution of Decticus verrucivorus - wart-biter in Britain by 10km square.
Source: Haes and Harding, 1997. Atlas of grasshoppers, crickets and allied insects in Britain and Ireland, Biological Records Centre (ITE)/JNCC and English Nature - Invertebrate Site Register.

Field-cricket (*Gryllus campestris*) (Order: Orthoptera) Action Plan

1. Current status

1.1 The field-cricket is a flightless insect of short, warm, tussocky grasslands which have between 10 and 50% bare ground. Oviposition and early nymphal stages are associated with patches of bare ground. Later development and overwintering occurs within grass tussocks, at the base of which the field-cricket constructs its burrows. As such, it is a species of early- to mid-successional grassland rather than established meadows. This successional component may be naturally extended on steep, south-facing banks. The species' reproductive success is naturally sporadic, with occasional large population increases interspersed with periods of several years when the population naturally decreases. One factor driving this pattern is the weather conditions over each yearly reproductive cycle; another factor is the availability of suitable sunny, bare ground for oviposition.

1.2 The field-cricket is an extremely rare, declining and vulnerable insect which, in the UK, is restricted to one natural population, consisting of three sub-populations, within one square kilometre in West Sussex. Two reintroduced populations have been established, both of which are also in West Sussex. Other reintroductions within its confirmed natural range are planned. This species has always had a very restricted range in England, being bounded (approximately) to the east by the River Arun, to the west by the Solent, to the north by the North Downs and to the south by the Isle of Wight. The majority of records are from sandstone areas, although there are a few from the chalk. Records from outside this area either refer to accidental imports from the Continent or, more often, to misidentifications of the call of the house cricket, *Acheta domesticus*. The field cricket is widespread in southern and central Europe, north to the Netherlands and Germany, although it is in severe decline throughout much of its range. Towards the southern edge of its range it becomes a montane species, being replaced at lower latitudes by *Gryllus bimaculatus*.

1.3 In Great Britain this species is classified as *Endangered*. It is given full protection under Schedule 5 of the Wildlife and Countryside Act 1981.

2. Current factors causing loss or decline

2.1 Inappropriate site management reducing the availability of bare ground areas.

2.2 Unfavourably warm winters followed by wet spring weather. This is a possible scenario under global warming.

2.3 Invasion of acidic grasslands by bracken.

3. Current action

3.1 This species has been part of the EN's Species Recovery Programme since 1991. Under this programme, a species action plan was written in 1995 and has been revised annually since then.

3.2 The last fully native population is, in part, on an SSSI. Both reintroductions are on SSSIs.

4. Action plan objectives and targets

4.1 Maintain populations at all known sites.

4.2 Enhance the population size at all known sites by 2010.

4.3 Restore populations to further suitable sites within the historic range to achieve a total of ten viable populations by 2010.

4.4 Maintain an *ex situ* programme to provide material for reintroductions and ecological research.

5. Proposed action with lead agencies

This action plan builds on the ongoing work for the species under the Species Recovery Programme. The priority is the maintenance of early- to mid-successional grassland habitats in full exposure to the sun on all actual or potential sites. Captive breeding will be necessary to provide material for reintroductions to ensure 10 viable populations are established by 2010.

5.1 Policy and legislation

5.1.1 Where appropriate, include the requirements of the species when preparing or revising prescriptions for agri-environment schemes (ACTION: EN, MAFF)

5.2 Site safeguard and management

5.2.1 Where possible, ensure that all occupied and nearby potential grassland habitat is appropriately managed by 2008. This should be achieved through a rotational programme of ground disturbance, and subsequent appropriate grazing or mechanical management. (ACTION: EN, MAFF)

5.2.2 Ensure that the habitat requirements of the field-cricket are taken into account in relevant development policies, plans and proposals. (ACTION: EN, LAs)

5.2.3 Consider notifying sites supporting viable populations of field-crickets as SSSIs where this is necessary to secure their long-term protection and appropriate management. (ACTION: EN)

5.3 Species management and protection

5.3.1 Maintain and, if necessary, expand the existing captive rearing and release programme until the English populations are considered beyond threat. (ACTION: EN)

5.3.2 Re-introduce the field-cricket to a series of sites to achieve a total of 10 viable populations. (ACTION: EN)

5.4 Advisory

5.4.1 Advise landowners and managers of the presence of the species and the importance of beneficial management for its conservation. (ACTION: EN)

5.5 Future research and monitoring

5.5.1 Conduct further targeted autecological research to inform habitat management. (ACTION: EN)

5.5.2 Establish a regular monitoring programme. (ACTION: EN)

5.5.3 Pass information gathered during survey and monitoring of this species to a central database for incorporation in national and international databases. (ACTION: EN)

5.5.4 Encourage research on the ecology and conservation of this species on an international level and use the experience gained towards its conservation in the UK. (ACTION: EN, JNCC)

5.6 Communications and publicity

5.6.1 Promote opportunities for the appreciation of the species and the conservation issues associated with its habitat. This should be achieved through articles within appropriate journals, as well as by publicity leaflets. (ACTION: EN)

5.7 Links with other action plans

5.7.1 This action plan should be considered in conjunction with that for lowland dry acid grassland.

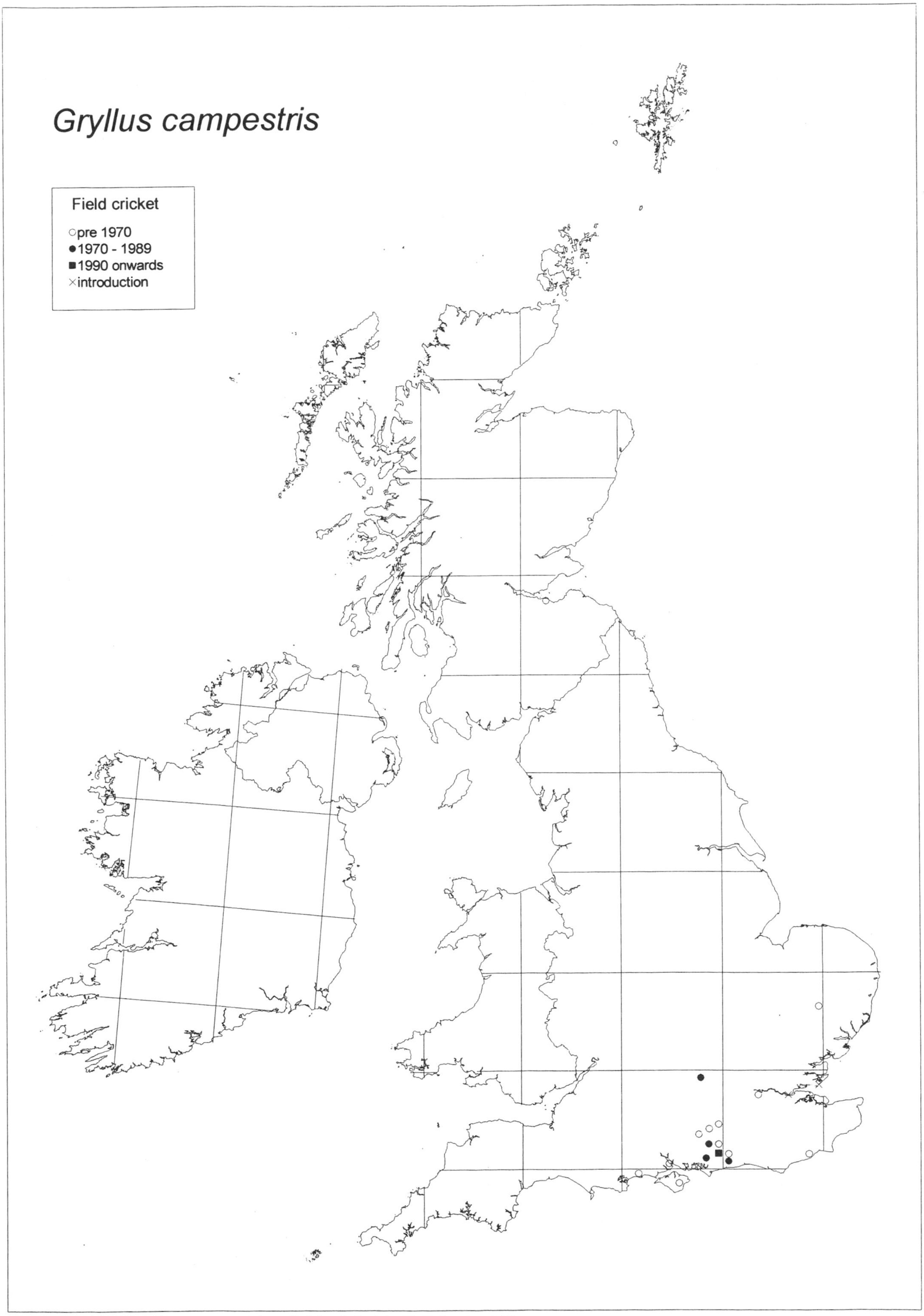

Distribution of Gryllus campestris - field cricket in Britain, by 10km square.
Source: Haes and Harding, 1997. Atlas of grasshoppers, crickets and allied insects in Britain and Ireland, Biological Records Centre (ITE)/JNCC and English Nature - Invertebrate Site Register.

Large marsh grasshopper (*Stethophyma grossum*) (Order: Orthoptera) Action Plan

1. Current status

1.1 The large marsh grasshopper is the UK's largest grasshopper. It is restricted to very wet, marshy areas, commonly quaking acidic bogs, although historically the species also occupied fenland and riverside habitats. The detailed ecology of the species is poorly known. It appears that eggs (in batches of 10-14, in elongated pods) are laid at the bases of grass stems. Four nymphal instars are reported, with the first emerging in May/June; the adult stage is attained by mid July and adults may survive into November in favourable conditions.

1.2 The UK range of the large marsh grasshopper formerly included the Thames Valley (to the mid 19th century) and East Anglia (to the late 1960s). The species has declined severely in the Somerset Levels since around 1960, and its current status in this area is unclear; the last confirmed records are from 1989 at one site and 1995 at a second. Two small, isolated colonies in Surrey (at least one of which arose from an introduction in the late 1960s) have not been confirmed since 1991. There are currently a number of populations in Dorset and the New Forest, but little information on their size is available other than to suggest that most are small. The species is present throughout Europe (except in the extreme south), extending eastwards into the former Soviet Union, but it is vulnerable to habitat loss throughout its range. UK populations represent some of the most northerly colonies of the species.

1.3 In Great Britain this species is classified as *Vulnerable.*

2. Current factors causing loss or decline

2.1 Drainage of wetlands for land reclamation and peat extraction has had a major impact on the large marsh grasshopper.

2.2 Land use on areas adjacent to occupied sites may also affect this species through pollution and impact on local water tables.

2.3 Climate change may adversely affect this species, through the drying-out of suitable habitat.

3. Current action

3.1 Clarification of the current range and status of this species in the UK was the subject of a project under the EN Species Recovery Programme in 1997.

3.2 Recent surveys by the Dorset Environmental Records Centre have contributed to the assessment of the species' status in this county.

3.3 Most known extant populations of the large marsh grasshopper occur in SSSIs and/or NNRs.

3.4 Bristol Zoo is currently investigating a captive breeding strategy for this species.

3.5 A species action plan, commissioned by EN, was written in 1997.

4. Action plan objectives and targets

4.1 Prevent further contraction in range, and decline in population sizes, at known sites.

4.2 Restore populations to five suitable sites within the historic range of the species by 2010.

5. Proposed action with lead agencies

A comprehensive site survey and programme of autecological research will provide baseline information and allow recommendations for appropriate management of wetland habitat for the large marsh grasshopper to be developed. Application of appropriate management should allow further decline of the species to be arrested and, in combination with a survey of potential (re)introduction sites and a captive breeding programme, will provide a basis for increasing the number of colonies in the UK.

5.1 Policy and legislation

5.1.1 Where appropriate, include the requirements of the species when preparing or revising prescriptions for agri-environment schemes. (ACTION: EN, MAFF)

5.1.2 Address the requirements of this species in the LEAP process and in relevant WLMPs. (ACTION: EA, IDBs, LAs, MAFF)

5.1.3 Take account of the species' requirements in response to applications for water abstraction licences. (ACTION: EA)

5.2 Site management and protection

5.2.1 Where possible, ensure that all occupied and potential habitat is appropriately managed by 2010, for example through SSSI or agri-environment scheme management agreements. (ACTION: EN, MAFF)

5.2.2 Ensure that the habitat requirements of the large marsh grasshopper are taken into account in any relevant development policies, plans and proposals. (ACTION: EN, LAs)

5.2.3 Ensure that the species is included in site management documents for all relevant SSSIs. (ACTION: EN)

5.2.4 Consider notifying as SSSIs sites holding key populations of this species, where this is necessary to secure their long-term protection and appropriate management. (ACTION: EN).

5.3 Species management and protection

5.3.1 (Re)introduce the large marsh grasshopper to sites within the former range of the species, where appropriate habitat and site management are available, in order to restore populations to five sites. (ACTION: EN).

5.4 Advisory

5.4.1 Advise landowners and managers of the presence of the species and the importance of beneficial management for its conservation. (ACTION: EN)

5.5 Future research and monitoring

5.5.1 Undertake further surveys to determine the status of this species and to identify potential sites for (re)introductions. (ACTION: EN)

5.5.2 Conduct targeted autecological research to inform habitat management. (ACTION: EN)

5.5.3 Establish a regular monitoring programme for this species. (ACTION: EN)

5.5.4 Support the development of a captive breeding strategy as a component of any (re)introduction programme. (ACTION: EN)

5.5.5 Pass information gathered during survey and monitoring of this species to a central database for incorporation into national and international databases. (ACTION: EN)

5.6 Communication and publicity

5.6.1 Promote opportunities for the appreciation of the species and the conservation issues associated with its habitat. This should be achieved through articles within appropriate journals, as well as by a publicity leaflet. (ACTION: EN).

5.7 Links with other action plans

5.7.1 Implementation of this action plan could benefit other species of lowland mire, including the ground beetle *Pterostichus aterrimus*.

5.7.2 This plan should be considered in conjunction with that for fens.

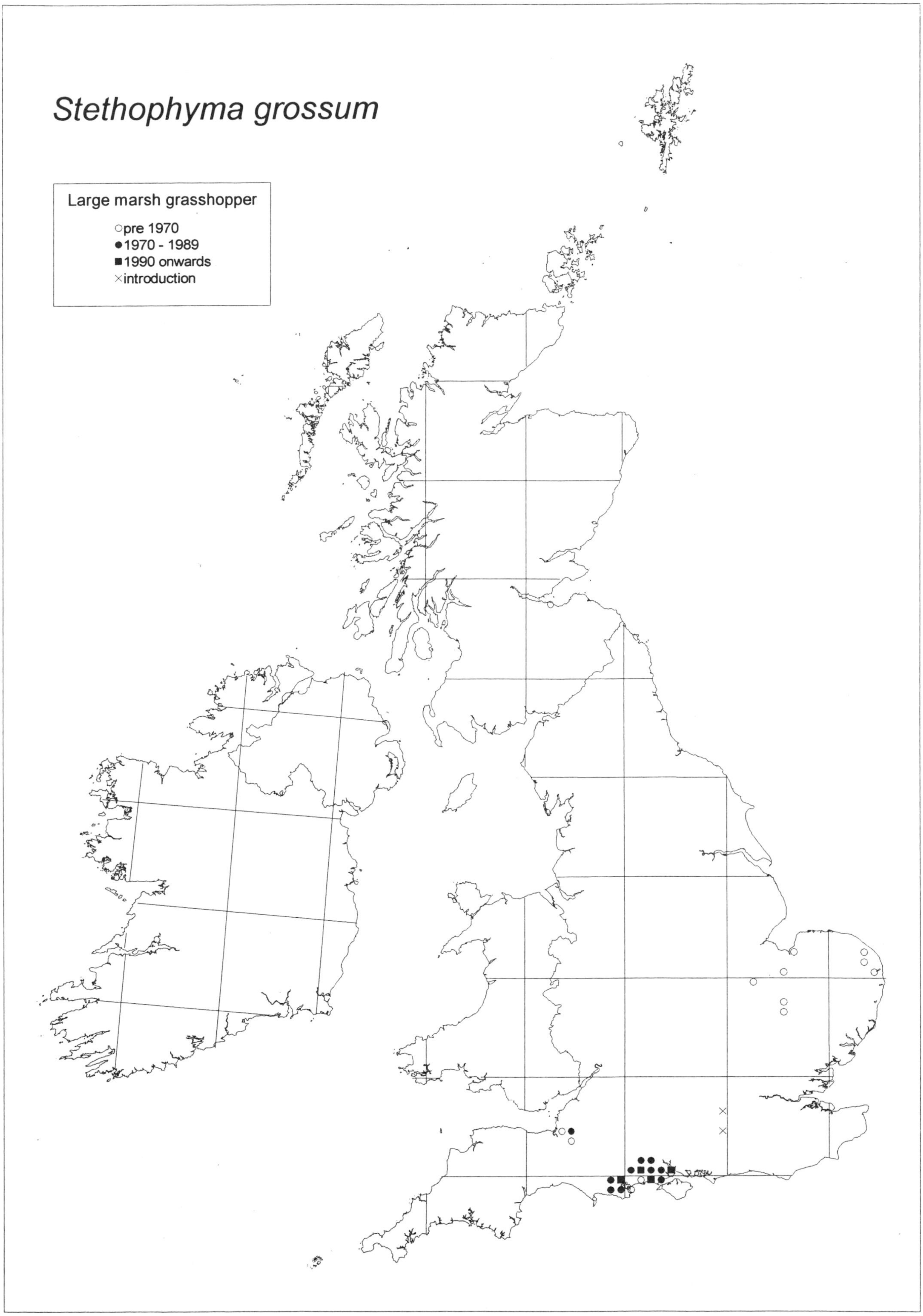

Distribution of Stethophyma grossum - large marsh grasshopper in Britain, by 10km square.
Source: Haes and Harding, 1997. Atlas of grasshoppers, crickets and allied insects in Britain and Ireland, Biological Records Centre (ITE)/JNCC and English Nature - Invertebrate Siste Register.

Clubiona subsultans (a spider)
(Order: Araneae)
Species Statement

1. Current status

1.1 *Clubiona subsultans* is not infrequent in semi-natural pine forests in a few areas of Scotland. It has been found in a range of situations: under bark and stones, in pine litter, amongst moss, on branches, amongst young pines, and in juniper bushes under pines. Adult spiders are present in the summer, with males being recorded as late as September.

1.2 *Clubiona subsultans* was recorded from Abernethy Forest several times between 1945 and 1993. It was also found near Coylumbridge in 1979 and there are sporadic records from the Black Wood of Rannoch between 1913 and 1987. It is thought to be fairly plentiful in Abernethy Forest, but more sparse in the Black Wood of Rannoch. The species is widespread in Scandinavia, central Europe and Russia.

1.3 In Great Britain this species is classified as *Vulnerable*.

2. Current factors causing loss or decline

2.1 Changes in the extent, density and management of native pine woodland may affect this spider.

2.2 Pinewood regeneration should have a beneficial effect by creating new areas of habitat. However, areas of dense regeneration may be as unsuitable as plantation woodland for this species.

3. Current action

3.1 The spider is present in SSSIs and NNRs. It is also in RSPB and FC nature reserves, including the Abernethy Forest Reserve.

4. Objective for the species

4.1 Maintain known populations of *Clubiona subsultans*.

5. Proposed action

5.1 Monitoring only. This species could benefit from the action plans for other species of Scottish pine woods, including the Scottish wood ant *Formica aquilonia* and twinflower *Linnaea borealis*. The requirements of the species should be taken into account in the implementation of the action plan for native pine woodland.

Uloborus walckenaerius (a spider)
(Order: Araneae)
Species Statement

1. Current status

1.1 *Uloborus walckenaerius* inhabits lowland heathland where it spins an almost horizontal orb web about midway between the ground and the top of mature heather plants. Both sexes are adult in June, adult females also occur in July and occasionally in August.

1.2 This spider has been found in large numbers on heathland at a few sites in the south of England: the New Forest (south Hampshire), Chobham Common (Surrey), and Thursley Common (Surrey). It has also been recorded from Crookham Common (north Hampshire), Ambersham Common (West Sussex), Ash Ranges (Surrey), Bloxworth (Surrey) and Wokingham (Berkshire). It has disappeared from several of its former strongholds and is declining as the area of heathland declines, but this has not been quantified. In the UK it is confined to the southern counties of England, but it has a palaearctic distribution and is widespread in central and southern Europe. A related species, *Uloborus plumipes*, has established itself in glasshouses in England.

1.3 In Great Britain this species is classified as *Rare*.

2. Current factors causing loss or decline

2.1 Loss of heathland due to development and afforestation.

2.2 Inappropriate heathland management.

3. Current action

3.1 A number of the known sites for this species are SSSIs or NNRs.

4. Objective for the species

4.1 Maintain known populations of *Uloborus walckenaerius*.

5. Proposed action

5.7.1 Monitoring only. It is likely that this species will benefit from the action plans for other species of lowland heathland, including *Amara famelica, Cicindela sylvatica* and *Pterostichus kugelanni*. The requirements of the species should be taken into account in the implementation of the action plan for lowland heathland.

Lesser water measurer (*Hydrometra gracilenta*)
(Order: Hemiptera)
Species Statement

1. Current status

1.1 Little is known of the biology of the lesser water measurer, but it is probably a predator and scavenger. The habitat of the species appears to be the surface of small water bodies such as dykes or shallow pools with overhanging vegetation. The water bodies are usually situated in mature fen vegetation, although on the Pevensey Levels, East Sussex, the lesser water measurer occurs on a grazing marsh dyke with emergent vegetation. The bug may leave the water at certain times of year and take up residence in nearby vegetation.

1.2 This semi-aquatic bug is locally widespread in northern and central Europe, east to Asian Russia. In Britain the species is known from the Ant Valley in the Norfolk Broads, the Pevensey Levels and the New Forest. The species has been recorded only once in the Pevensey Levels and once in the New Forest. The Pevensey Levels record is recent (1988) while the New Forest record lacks details and is pre 1960. In the Ant Valley it was first recorded in 1938 at Barton Broad, and was recorded irregularly at Barton and Sutton Broads during the 1950s. The only record since then was at Reedham Marsh in 1989. It is possible that the species occurs, undiscovered, elsewhere.

1.3 In Great Britain this species is classified as *Rare*.

2. Current factors causing loss or decline

2.1 Not known.

3. Current action

3.1 All known sites are within SSSIs. All Norfolk sites are in the Ant NNR.

4. Objective for the species

4.1 Maintain existing populations of the lesser water measurer.

5. Proposed action

5.1 Monitoring only. This species could benefit from the action plans for other species of lowland fens and grazing marshes, including: *Dolomedes plantarius*, *Segmentina nitida*, *Anisus vorticulus*, *Najas marina* and *Potamogeton compressus*. The requirements of the species should be taken into account in the delivery of the action plans for fens, and coastal and floodplain grazing marshes.

Prostoma jenningsi (a freshwater nemertean)
(Order: Nemertea)
Species Statement

1. Current status

1.1 This is a small, inconspicuous freshwater species which can only be distinguished from other freshwater nemerteans of the genus by means of detailed histological studies of its internal morphology.

1.2 So far, this species is known from only one locality in the world, a pond at Croston, Lancashire where it was discovered in 1971. At the time of its discovery more than 200 ponds in the Lancashire, Merseyside and Wirral region had been investigated for their freshwater fauna, but no other sites yielded specimens of *Prostoma jenningsi*. The species has not been recorded since 1978, although there have been no specific surveys for this species since 1980, and it is very unlikely that it would be recorded in general aquatic invertebrate surveys.

1.3 In Great Britain this species is classified as *Insufficiently Known*.

2. Current factors causing loss or decline

2.1 The pond at Croston was contaminated by spillage of agricultural fertiliser around 1978 and the species has not been found since.

3. Current action

3.1 None known.

4. Objective for the species

4.1 Maintain any discovered populations.

5. Proposed action

5.1 Search only.

Annex 1. List of abbreviations and acronyms

ASSI	Area of Special Scientific Interest (Northern Ireland)
CC	County Council
CCW	Countryside Council for Wales
DANI	Department of Agriculture for Northern Ireland
DETR	Department of the Environment, Transport and the Regions
EA	Environment Agency
EC	European Community
EH	English Heritage
EHS	Environment and Heritage Service (Northern Ireland)
EN	English Nature
ESA	Environmentally Sensitive Area
FC	Forestry Commission
FE	Forest Enterprise
FWAG	Farming and Wildlife Advisory Group
HA	Highways Agency
IDB	Internal Drainage Board
IUCN	International Union for the Conservation of Nature
JNCC	Joint Nature Conservation Committee
LA	Local Authority
MAFF	Ministry of Agriculture, Fisheries and Food
MoD	Ministry of Defence
NGO	Non-governmental organisation
NNR	National Nature Reserve
NTS	National Trust for Scotland
RSPB	Royal Society for the Protection of Birds
SAC	Special Area of Conservation
SEPA	Scottish Environmental Protection Agency
SNH	Scottish Natural Heritage
SO	The Scottish Office
SOAEFD	Scottish Office Agriculture, Environment and Fisheries Department
SPA	Special Protection Area
SSSI	Site of Special Scientific Interest (Britain)
WGS	Woodland Grant Scheme
WOAD	Welsh Office Agriculture Department

Annex 2. Action plan costings

Summary table showing estimated additional costs in £K per year for the first and second five years of each Species Action Plan

		1st five years	2nd five years
Coleoptera			
Agabus brunneus	a diving beetle	16.4	13.1
Amara famelica	a ground beetle	10.3	9.4
Anisodactylus poeciloides	a ground beetle	12.6	12.2
Anostirus castaneus	a click beetle	16.6	13.1
Bidessus unistriatus	a diving beetle	14.3	6.0
Byctiscus populi	a leaf-rolling weevil	27.5	22.8
Cicindela germanica	a tiger beetle	16.1	13.0
Cicindela hybrida	a tiger beetle	13.2	12.8
Cicindela sylvatica	heath tiger beetle	16.6	13.5
Cryptocephalus nitidulus	a leaf beetle	13.2	11.2
Cryptocephalus primarius	a leaf beetle	10.7	7.5
Cryptocephalus sexpunctatus	a leaf beetle	13.8	12.3
Curimopsis nigrita	mire pill-beetle	12.7	8.1
Donacia aquatica	a reed beetle	14.3	12.8
Donacia bicolora	a reed beetle	17.4	11.3
Ernoporus tiliae	a bark beetle	13.0	3.8
Graphoderus zonatus	spangled water beetle	11.1	3.2
Helophorus laticollis	a water beetle	12.6	11.7
Hydrochara caraboides	lesser silver water beetle	13.1	5.8
Hydroporus rufifrons	a diving beetle	16.7	9.4
Laccophilus poecilus	a diving beetle	8.0	5.6
Malachius aeneus	a false soldier beetle	15.8	11.8
Melanapion minimum	a weevil	10.7	11.9
Melanotus punctolineatus	a click beetle	8.7	6.4
Pachytychius haematocephalus	a weevil	12.1	6.4
Paracymus aeneus	a water beetle	11.5	6.6
Procas granulicollis	a weevil	24.5	10.2
Psylliodes sophiae	a flea beetle	10.2	9.3
Pterostichus aterrimus	a ground beetle	20.3	13.3
Pterostichus kugelanni	a ground beetle	12.2	8.4
Rhynchaenus testaceus	a jumping weevil	9.0	8.7
Diptera			
Blera fallax	a hoverfly	5.9	4.8
Bombylius discolor	dotted bee-fly	21.6	17.4
Bombylius minor	heath bee fly	14.1	6.0
Cliorismia rustica	a stiletto fly	27.2	15.2
Doros profuges	a hoverfly	15.9	6.8
Dorycera graminum	a picture winged fly	18.0	8.8
Eristalis cryptarum	a hoverfly	16.8	15.2
Hammerschmidtia ferruginea	a hoverfly	14.3	18.7
Lipsothrix ecucullata	a cranefly	17.4	7.3

		1st five years	2nd five years
Lipsothrix nervosa	a cranefly	12.8	7.3
Lipsothrix nigristigma	a cranefly	17.1	18.1
Thyridanthrax fenestratus	mottled bee-fly	23.8	14.8
Hymenoptera			
Andrena ferox	a mining bee	17.1	19.5
Andrena gravida	banded mining bee	20.3	22.2
Andrena lathyri	a mining bee	11.4	3.9
Bombus distinguendus	great yellow bumblebee	18.4	8.8
Bombus humilis	a carder bumblebee	23.8	14.7
Bombus ruderatus	large garden bumblebee	15.4	17.6
Bombus subterraneus	short-haired bumblebee	15.4	17.3
Cerceris quadricincta	a solitary wasp	17.6	19.5
Cerceris quinquefasciata	a solitary wasp	21.7	22.5
Chrysis fulgida	a ruby-tailed wasp	12.5	3.3
Colletes floralis	the northern colletes	12.0	6.5
Formica aquilonia	Scottish wood ant	6.4	2.4
Formica rufibarbis	red barbed ant	11.1	10.7
Homonotus sanguinolentus	a spider-hunting wasp	10.0	17.3
Nomada armata	a cuckoo bee	13.3	12.3
Nomada errans	a cuckoo bee	12.0	7.7
Osmia inermis	a mason bee	17.7	9.6
Osmia parietina	a mason bee	22.6	23.2
Osmia uncinata	a mason bee	17.4	9.1
Osmia xanthomelana	a mason bee	17.7	8.2
Pseudopipona herrichii	Purbeck mason wasp	11.4	1.9
Lepidoptera			
Ascometia caliginosa	reddish buff	12.6	24.3
Aspitates gilvaria	straw belle	12.2	12.3
Athetis pallustris	marsh moth	7.9	6.1
Bembecia chrysidiformis	fiery clearwing	17.5	9.4
Carterocephalus palaemon	chequered skipper	23.8	23.9
Catocala promissa	light crimson underwing	12.9	9.4
Catocala sponsa	dark crimson underwing	12.5	7.1
Coleophora tricolor	basil-thyme case-bearer	12.0	18.2
Cosmia diffinis	white-spotted pinion	13.8	10.3
Cucullia lychnitis	striped lynchis	26.1	21.0
Cyclophora pendularia	dingy mocha	16.1	15.7
Dicycla oo	heart moth	12.0	3.9
Epione parallelaria	dark-bordered beauty	14.3	19.0
Heliophobus reticula marginosa	bordered gothic	15.5	15.1
Hemaris tityus	narrow-bordered bee hawk-moth	16.1	22.2
Hypena rostralis	buttoned snout	22.9	20.1
Idaea dilutaria	silky wave	11.5	8.6
Jodia croceago	orange upperwing	11.3	25.2
Lysandra bellargus	Adonis blue	30.5	21.3
Mythimna turca	double line	17.3	15.9
Oria musculosa	Brighton wainscot	16.3	7.2

		1st five years	2nd five years
Pareulype berberata	barberry carpet	18.5	25.8
Pechipogo strigilata	common fan-foot	14.0	15.2
Plebejus argus	silver-studded blue	39.5	27.7
Polia bombycina	pale shining brown	16.1	7.0
Semiothisa carbonaria	netted mountain moth	24.2	15.0
Siona lineata	black-veined moth	12.3	20.1
Tyta luctuosa	four-spotted moth	17.0	20.5
Xylena exsoleta	sword-grass	20.5	11.3
Zygaena loti scotica	slender Scotch burnet	18.8	11.3
Zygaena viciae argyllensis	New Forest burnet	12.5	5.0
Other invertebrates			
Clubonia rosserae	a spider	8.6	1.3
Dolomedes plantarius	fen raft spider	11.8	5.3
Eresus sandaliatus	ladybird spider	14.5	2.5
Lophopus crystallinus	a freshwater bryozoan	23.8	8.3
Cicadetta montana	New Forest cicada	12.0	10.9
Decticus verrucivorus	wart-biter bush cricket	15.0	17.9
Gryllus campestris	field cricket	16.4	26.6
Stethophyma grossum	large marsh grasshopper	23.5	14.7
	Annual total (£K)	1631.0	1283.4
	Total five year cost (£K)	8154.8	6417.0

Costs exclude 10% administration, and the contribution of agri-environment schemes which is being estimated separately.

Annex 3. List of species, with Contact Points and Lead Partners

Table 1, below, lists the Contact Points and Lead Partners for the species action plans published in this volume. Lead Partners for 15 species are still to be determined at the time of going to press. In order to benefit from the geographical/habitat/taxonomic associations of some of the species, a number have been placed in small groups to each of which a contact point and lead partner/joint lead partners have been assigned. These groups are listed in Table 2. A list of Species Statements included in this volume is given in Table 3.

Table 1: Species Action Plans

Species	Contact Point	Lead Partner	Group
Coleoptera			
Agabus brunneus a diving beetle	Environment Agency	to be determined	-
Amara famelica a ground beetle	English Nature	to be determined	-
Anisodactylus poeciloides a ground beetle	Environment Agency	to be determined	-
Anostirus castaneus a click beetle	English Nature	to be determined	-
Bidessus unistriatus a diving beetle	English Nature	to be determined	-
Byctiscus populi a leaf-rolling weevil	English Nature	to be determined	-
Cicindela germanica a tiger beetle	English Nature	English Nature	16
Cicindela hybrida a tiger beetle	English Nature	English Nature	16
Cicindela sylvatica heath tiger beetle	English Nature	English Nature	16
Cryptocephalus nitidulus a leaf beetle	English Nature	Leeds University	15
Cryptocephalus primarius a leaf beetle	English Nature	Leeds University	15
Cryptocephalus sexpunctatus a leaf beetle	English Nature	Leeds University	15
Curimopsis nigrita mire pill-beetle	English Nature	The Wildlife Trusts	-
Donacia aquatica a reed beetle	English Nature	Scottish Natural Heritage	4
Donacia bicolora a reed beetle	English Nature	English Nature	4
Ernoporus tiliae a bark beetle	English Nature	Forest Enterprise	-
Graphoderus zonatus spangled diving beetle	English Nature	English Nature	-
Helophorus laticollis a water beetle	English Nature	Forest Enterprise - New Forset Group	14

Species	Contact Point	Lead Partner	Group
Hydrochara caraboides lesser silver water beetle	English Nature	to be determined	-
Hydroporus rufifrons a diving beetle	English Nature	to be determined	-
Laccophilus poecilus a diving beetle	English Nature	to be determined	-
Malachius aeneus a false soldier beetle	English Nature	English Nature	-
Melanapion minimum a weevil	English Nature	to be determined	-
Melanotus punctolineatus a click beetle	English Nature	to be determined	-
Pachytychius haematocephalus a weevil	English Nature	to be determined	-
Paracymus aeneus a water beetle	English Nature	English Nature	-
Procas granulicollis a weevil	Countryside Council for Wales	Countryside Council for Wales	-
Psylliodes sophiae a flea beetle	English Nature	The Wildlife Trusts	-
Pterostichus aterrimus a ground beetle (N.I.)	Environment and Heritage Service	Environment and Heritage Service	-
Pterostichus aterrimus a ground beetle (England)	English Nature	Forest Enterprise - New Forest Group	14
Pterostichus kugelanni a ground beetle	English Nature	Forest Enterprise - New Forest Group	14
Rhynchaenus testaceus a jumping weevil	English Nature	to be determined	-
Diptera			
Blera fallax a hoverfly	Scottish Natural Heritage	Royal Society for the Protection of Birds	10
Bombylius discolor dotted bee-fly	English Nature	English Nature	-
Bombylius minor heath bee-fly	English Nature	The British Entomological and Natural History Society	3
Cliorismia rustica a stiletto-fly	Environment Agency	Environment Agency - Exposed River Sediments Group	-
Doros profuges a hoverfly	English Nature	to be determined	-
Dorycera graminum a picture-winged fly	English Nature	English Nature	-
Eristalis cryptarum a hoverfly	English Nature	Dartmoor National Park Authority/ English Nature	-
Hammerschmidtia ferruginea a hoverfly	Scottish Natural Heritage	Royal Society for the Protection of Birds	10
Lipsothrix ecucullata a cranefly	English Nature	Scottish Natural Heritage	11

Species	Contact Point	Lead Partner	Group
Lipsothrix nervosa a cranefly	English Nature	Countryside Council for Wales	11
Lipsothrix nigristigma a cranefly	English Nature	English Nature	11
Thyridanthrax fenestratus motted bee-fly	English Nature	The British Entomological and Natural History Society	3
Hymenoptera			
Andrena ferox a mining bee	English Nature	English Nature/Aculeate Conservation Working Group	6
Andrena gravida banded mining bee	English Nature	English Nature/Aculeate Conservation Working Group	6
Andrena lathyri a mining bee	English Nature	English Nature/Aculeate Conservation Working Group	-
Bombus distinguendus great yellow bumblebee	Scottish Natural Heritage	Royal Society for the Protection of Birds/Bombus Working Group	5
Bombus humilis a carder bumblebee	English Nature	English Nature/Bombus Working Group	7
Bombus ruderatus large garden bumblebee	English Nature	English Nature/Bombus Working Group	7
Bombus subterraneus short-haired bumblebee	English Nature	English Nature/Bombus Working Group	7
Cerceris quadricincta a solitary wasp	English Nature	English Nature/Aculeate Conservation Working Group	6
Cerceris quinquefasciata a solitary wasp	English Nature	English Nature/Aculeate Conservation Working Group	6
Chrysis fulgida a ruby-tailed wasp	English Nature	English Nature/Aculeate Conservation Working Group	2
Colletes floralis the northern colletes	Scottish Natural Heritage	Royal Society for the Protection of Birds/Bombus Working Group	5
Formica aquilonia Scottish wood ant	Scottish Natural Heritage	Forestry Commission	-
Formica rufibarbis red-barbed ant	English Nature	English Nature/Aculeate Conservation Working Group	2
Homonotus sanguinolentus a spider-hunting wasp	English Nature	English Nature/Aculeate Conservation Working Group	2
Nomada armata a cuckoo bee	English Nature	English Nature/Aculeate Conservation Working Group	6
Nomada errans a cuckoo bee	English Nature	English Nature/Aculeate Conservation Working Group	-
Osmia inermis a mason bee	Scottish Natural Heritage	Scottish Natural Heritage/ Aculeate Conservation Working Group	-
Osmia parietina a mason bee	English Nature	English Nature/Aculeate Conservation Working Group	-
Osmia uncinata a mason bee	Scottish Natural Heritage	Royal Society for the Protection of Birds	-

Species	Contact Point	Lead Partner	Group
Osmia xanthomelana a mason bee	Countryside Council for Wales	Countryside Council for Wales /Aculeate Conservation Working Group	-
Pseudepipona herrichii Purbeck mason wasp	English Nature	English Nature/Aculeate Conservation Working Group	2
Lepidoptera			
Acosmetia caliginosa reddish buff	English Nature	Butterfly Conservation	1
Aspitates gilvaria straw belle	English Nature	Butterfly Conservation	8
Athetis pallustris marsh moth	English Nature	Butterfly Conservation	-
Bembecia chrysidiformis fiery clearwing	English Nature	Butterfly Conservation/English Nature	-
Carterocephalus palaemon chequered skipper	Scottish Natural Heritage	Butterfly Conservation	-
Catocala promissa light crimson underwing	English Nature	Butterfly Conservation	13
Catocala sponsa dark crimson underwing	English Nature	Butterfly Conservation	13
Coleophora tricolor basil thyme case-bearer	English Nature	Butterfly Conservation	-
Cosmia diffinis white-spotted pinion	English Nature	Butterfly Conservation	-
Cucullia lychnitis striped lychnis	English Nature	Butterfly Conservation	8
Cyclophora pendularia dingy mocha	English Nature	Butterfly Conservation	1
Dicycla oo heart moth	English Nature	Butterfly Conservation	12
Epione parallelaria dark-bordered beauty	Scottish Natural Heritage	Butterfly Conservation/Royal Society for the Protection of Birds	-
Heliophobus reticulata marginosa bordered gothic	English Nature	Butterfly Conservation	8
Hemaris tityus narrow-bordered bee hawk-moth	Countryside Council for Wales	Butterfly Conservation	9
Hypena rostralis buttoned snout	English Nature	Butterfly Conservation	-
Idaea dilutaria silky wave	Countryside Council for Wales	Butterfly Conservation	-
Jodia croceago orange upperwing	English Nature	Butterfly Conservation	12
Lysandra bellargus Adonis blue	English Nature	Butterfly Conservation	-
Mythimna turca double line	Countryside Council for Wales	Butterfly Conservation	9

Species	Contact Point	Lead Partner	Group
Oria musculosa Brighton wainscot	English Nature	Butterfly Conservation	-
Pareulype berberata barberry carpet	English Nature	Butterfly Conservation	-
Pechipogo strigilata common fan-foot	English Nature	Butterfly Conservation	12
Plebejus argus silver-studded blue	English Nature	Butterfly Conservation	-
Polia bombycina pale shining brown	English Nature	Butterfly Conservation	8
Semiothisa carbonaria netted mountain moth	Scottish Natural Heritage	Butterfly Conservation	-
Siona lineata black-veined moth	English Nature	Butterfly Conservation	8
Tyta luctuosa four-spotted moth	English Nature	Butterfly Conservation	8
Xylena exsoleta sword-grass	Scottish Natural Heritage	Butterfly Conservation	-
Zygaena loti scotica slender Scotch burnet	Scottish Natural Heritage	Butterfly Conservation	18
Zygaena viciae argyllensis New Forest burnet	Scottish Natural Heritage	Scottish Natural Heritage	18
Other Invertebrates			
Clubiona rosserae a spider	English Nature	English Nature	-
Dolomedes plantarius fen raft spider	English Nature	English Nature	-
Eresus sandaliatus ladybird spider	English Nature	English Nature	-
Lophopus crystallinus a freshwater bryozoan	Environment Agency	to be determined	-
Cicadetta montana New Forest cicada	English Nature	Forest Enterprise - New Forest Group	14
Decticus verrucivorus wart-biter	English Nature	CABI Bioscience	17
Gryllus campestris field cricket	English Nature	The Natural History Museum/English Nature	-
Stethophyma grossum large marsh grasshopper	English Nature	CABI Bioscience	17

Table 2: Species groupings

Group number	Description	Species
1	Heathland moths	*Cyclophora pendularia* and *Ascosmetia caliginosa*
2	Aculeates of lowland heathlands (open, dry sandy heaths)	*Chrysis fulgida, Formica rufibarbis, Homonotus sanguinolentus* and *Pseudepipona herrichii*
3	Heathland flies (open, dry sandy heaths)	*Thyridanthrax fenestratus* and *Bombylius minor*
4	Margin vegetation of lakes, ponds, tarns and rivers	*Donacia aquactica* and *Donacia bicolora*
5	Scottish herb-rich grasslands	*Bombus distinguendus* and *Colletes floralis*
6	Aculeates of flower-rich grasslands	*Andrena ferox, Andrena gravida, Cerceris quadricincta, Cerceris quinquesfasciata* and *Nomata armata*
7	Bumble-bees of flower-rich grasslands	*Bombus humilis, Bombus ruderatus* and *Bombus subterraneus*
8	Calcareous grassland moths	*Aspitates gilvaria, Cucullia lychnitis, Heliophobus reticulata, Polia bombycina, Siona lineata* and *Tyta luctuosa*
9	Unimproved grassland moths	*Hemaris tityus* and *Mythimna turca*
10	Saproxylic hoverfly group	*Hammerschmidtia ferruginea* and *Blera fallax*
11	Wet seepages in damp woodlands and wooded streams	*Lipsothrix ecucullata, Lipsothrix nervosa*, and *Lipsothrix nigristigma*
12	Open oak woodlands	*Dicycla oo, Jodia croceago* and *Pechipogo strigilata*
13	New Forest oak woods - moths	*Catocala promissa* and *Catocala sponsa*
14	New Forest species	*Cicadetta montana, Pterostichus aterrimus, Pterostichus kugelanni* and *Helophorus laticollis*
15	*Cryptocephalus* species	*Cryptocephalus nitidulus, Cryptocephalus primarius* and *Cryptocephalus sexpunctatus*
16	Tiger beetles	*Cicindela germanica, Cicindela sylvatica* and *Cicindela hybrida*
17	Crickets/grasshoppers	*Stethophyma grossum* and *Decticus verrucivorus*
18	*Zygaena* species - Scotland	*Zygaena loti scotica* and *Zygaena viciae argyllensis*

Table 3: Species Statements

Species name	Common name
Coleoptera	
Badister collaris	a ground beetle
Chrysolina cerealis	rainbow leaf beetle
Dyschirius angustatus	a ground beetle
Hydroporus cantabricus	a diving beetle
Diptera	
Lipsothrix errans	a cranefly
Myolepta potens	a hoverfly
Rhabdomastix laeta	a cranefly
Tipula serrulifera	a cranefly
Hymenoptera	
Chrysura hirsuta	a cuckoo wasp
Evagetes pectinipes	a spider-hunting wasp
Lasioglossum angusticeps	a solitary bee
Nomada ferruginata	a cuckoo bee
Lepidoptera	
Aricia artaxerxes	northern brown argus
Calophasia lunula	toadflax brocade
Hadena albimacula	white-spot
Hydraecia osseola hucherardi	marsh mallow
Minoa murinata	drab looper
Moma alpium	scarce merveille du jour
Paracolax derivalis	clay fan-foot
Paradiarsia sobrina	cousin German
Phyllodesma ilicifolia	small lappet
Polymixis xanthomista	black-banded
Trisateles emortualis	olive cresent
Xestia alpicola alpina	northern dart
Other Invertebrates	
Clubiona subsultans	a spider
Uloborus walckenaerius	a spider
Hydrometra gracilenta	the lesser water measurer
Prostoma jenningsi	a freshwater nemertean